STO

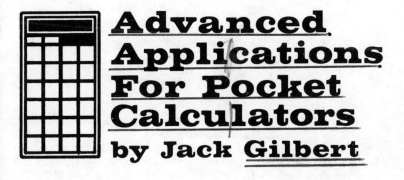

Advanced Applications For Pocket Calculators

by Jack Gilbert

TAB BOOKS

Blue Ridge Summit, Pa. 17214

FIRST EDITION

FIRST PRINTING— JUNE 1975

Copyright ©1975 by TAB BOOKS

Printed in the United States
of America

Hardbound Edition: International Standard Book No. 0-8306-5824-6

Paperbound Edition: International Standard Book No. 0-8306-4824-0

Library of Congress Card Number: 74-33620

Acknowledgments

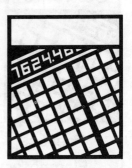

I wish to acknowledge the cooperation and technical assistance of the various manufacturers and distributors whose calculators are described in this book. Firms that contributed descriptive material and operational manuals are listed below:

Bowmar Consumer Products
Casio Electronic Calculators
Commodore Business Machines
DataKing
Hewlett-Packard
Lloyd's Electronics
Melcor Electronics
Monroe, The Calculator Co.
Rockwell International
Sinclair Radionics
Summit International
Texas Instruments

I thank my colleagues and coworkers for their many contributions. In particular, my thanks are due to Eileen Rogers for her suggestions on the organization and content of various chapters, and to Edward Dazzo and Jack Boddy for their reviews and mathematical suggestions.

My apologies to those manufacturers whose products were not included in this book. However, it is not possible to do justice to all pocket calculators on the market in a book of reasonable size.

Contents

Packard's HP-35 Scientific Calculator—Texas Instruments SR-
50—Summit International SI90—Commodore 1400 Slide Rule—
Casio FX-10—Sinclair Scientific

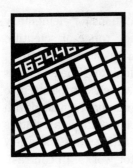

Preface

The recent breakthrough in the design and packaging of electronic pocket calculators has led to a veritable explosion in the sales of these silent, accurate, and incredibly fast devices. Typically, such a calculator is the size of a man's hand, weighs from 6 to 10 ounces, and is capable of performing and displaying arithmetic calculations to 8-digit accuracy. They have been sold by the millions to a public which includes housewives, businessmen, salesmen, accountants, students, teachers, engineers, technicians, and just about anyone with a need to perform occasional arithmetic operations. Anyone owning such a calculator can now perform extensive arithmetic operations with faultless precision for most problems that come his way. But what can the owner do with the calculator after he balances his checkbook or computes his income tax?

It is the purpose of this book to answer that question. The possession of the simple calculator opens up horizons to its owner which far surpass the applications of ordinary arithmetic. This book shows how the ability of the calculator to multiply and divide accurately can be used to calculate square roots, cube roots, powers of numbers, logarithms, and all the trigonometric functions to five or seven places. It also shows how the calculator can help you to solve accurately such problems as quadratic equations, right triangles, compound interest and mortgage problems, and even determine satellite orbits. Armed only with a calculator and a few directions, you will be able to solve these problems to an accuracy well within one part per million. Three convenient tables are provided to aid in these calculations—one for trigonometric functions and one each for common and natural logarithms.

This book describes advanced applications for elementary calculators, plus the operation of a wide range of scientific calculators, special-purpose metric and business calculators, and the latest programmable pocket calculator. The emphasis is on new applications for the reader which can be used to supplement the instruction or operating manual furnished with each calculator. The manuals for the elementary calculators generally offer a description of the operating keys and a few examples to illustrate how the calculator works. In contrast, the approach taken here for each advanced application is both tutorial (why) and mechanistic (how to). For each topic, such as square roots or logarithms, a brief discussion is given on the theory and application of the calculation. Next, simple sequential instructions are given which tell the reader how to do the calculation step by step; this general procedure can be applied to any calculator. Then a specific numerical example of each calculation is shown which identifies the actual keys to be pressed for a typical calculator and what the display should read at each step.

The first chapter describes the various makes of *elementary calculators* and certain special features, including automatic constants and memory functions. It is assumed that these calculators possess at least one memory which can be used for conversions involving a constant or to store and recall an intermediate result during a calculation. Chapters 2−5 discuss how each type of calculator can be used to full advantage and how it can solve advanced problems effectively. Advanced applications for elementary calculators include square root routines; extended precision methods; and simple expansions to generate trigonometric, logarithmic, and exponential functions. These functions can be generated on the simple 4-function calculator, using specified routines given in the book. The second type discussed is the *intermediate calculator*, which can generate simple algebraic functions. These functions include reciprocals $(1/x)$, square roots $(\sqrt{x})$, and squares (x^2). Some of these calculators can compute in scientific notation, which offers advantages in calculations involving very small or very large numbers.

Another chapter addressed to engineering and technical personnel discusses several types of *scientific calculators*. This genre of pocket calculator, which may cost from $70 to $325, combines all the above capabilities, plus many additional algebraic and scientific functions. These functions, available with one or two key strokes, include square roots ($\sqrt{x}$), reciprocals ($1/x$), logarithmic functions (log x, ln$x$), direct trigonometric functions (sin x, cos x, tan x), inverse trigonometric functions (arc functions), and powers of positive numbers (x^y). This type of calculator is often called an *electronic slide rule*, because it has many of the scientific functions which are available on advanced slide rules. Bear in mind, however, that these calculators are truly digital devices and are normally capable of much higher accuracy than an analog slide rule.

Succeeding chapters discuss applications of special-purpose and advanced scientific calculators, including the Hewlett-Packard HP-45. This device has additional capabilities not available in most other models, including two-way rectangular-to-polar conversion, factorial calculations, various statistical functions, and nine storage (memory) registers which can be used for complex calculations.

Advanced-calculator applications are also described that exploit the multiple-memory capability which is available in such calculators. These include iterative solutions of trigonometric, exponential, and cubic equations, as well as the generalized solutions for three (or more) linear simultaneous equations. These chapters pave the way for the treatment of manually and fully programmable pocket calculators discussed in the last chapter.

Chapter 10 describes two types of special-purpose metric conversion calculators—the Rockwell 203 and Summit MCC calculators. These calculators are set up to facilitate length, area, volume, mass, and temperature conversions from customary (English) units of measure to metric units, or vice versa. From 36 to 112 metric conversions are preprogramed in these devices.

The next chapter discusses two leading special-purpose financial calculators—the Hewlett-Packard HP-80 and the Rockwell 204 *Financier*. Each calculator contains a variety of preprogramed functions to facilitate the calculation of such items as present value, future value, compound interest, amount and number of monthly payments, interest rates, bond prices, yield to maturity, sinking-fund payments, depreciation, and other financial quantities. In most cases, it is only necessary to enter the known data and press one or two keys to find the answer.

Finally, there is the top of the line in current pocket calculators, Hewlett-Packard's HP-65, which is discussed in Chapter 12. This is a fully programmable device, which can either automatically execute prerecorded programs or permit you to write and store your own program on small magnetic cards which slip into the machine. This calculator embodies the latest advances in scientific functions and programing capability; it is compressed to the size of an HP-45, runs on batteries, and weighs less than 11 ounces!

Chapter 13 concludes with a commentary on the state-of-the art in pocket calculators and a preview of the new 1975 products. These include the Texas Instruments SR-51, the Rockwell 63R, the Hewlett-Packard HP-21 and HP-55, and the Norris 4510 and 4520.

With this book, you can expand the use of your own calculator for work, fun, or profit. At the same time, it will give you an insight into the mathematics and applications and capabilities of advanced calculators. In any case, it will help you to become more expert and imaginative in the use of any calculator.

Jack Gilbert

Elementary Pocket Calculators

The electronic pocket calculator, with its remarkable ability to perform arithmetic and scientific calculations with instant speed and up to 10-digit accuracy, is revolutionizing many of the habits of both the ordinary public and the professional. It has rendered obsolescent not only the familiar slide rule, with its 3-place accuracy and decimal uncertainty, but also the electromechanical calculator, with its fantastically complicated machinery, slow speed, and noisy operation. Today there are probably 100 models of electronic pocket calculators available, at advertised prices ranging from less than $20 for the cheaper arithmetic calculator, to about $245 for the more advanced scientific calculator, to about $795 for a fully programmable calculator.

INTRODUCTION TO ELEMENTARY CALCULATORS

This book discusses various types of these hand-held *pocket* calculators which can run on self-contained batteries and which feature an electronic display of at least eight digits. As a minimum, these calculators can perform instant addition, subtraction, multiplication, and division with 8-place accuracy.

Many of these calculators now feature a *memory*, or *storage register*, which can retain a constant or an intermediate result to be recalled for later use. Typical models with these operating features are shown in Figs. 1-1 to 1-6. These elementary calculators will be used to illustrate the advanced applications and problems that can be solved using the techniques discussed in the following chapters.

Fig. 1-1. Texas Instruments Datamath.

Fig. 1-2. Elementary calculator with memory and percentage functions—
Lloyd's Accumatic 500.

Fig. 1-3. Bowmar MX 35-1.

This book will enable the reader to expand the use of his calculator to advanced scientific and business applications normally beyond his reach. These advanced applications are generally not covered by the instruction manual furnished with an elementary calculator. This book will show how to generate and use scientific functions, including trigonometric and logarithmic functions, on the simple calculator. You will see that the ability of the calculator to simply add, subtract, multiply, and divide with figure precision can be used to generate advanced functions much more accurately than with the slide rule and with less trouble than with mathematical tables. For example, the sine of an angle can be calculated to four or five decimal places by a simple formula involving a few steps which are easy to memorize. Other trigonometric and logarithmic functions can be calculated using similar routines, with the same accuracy. Your ability to generate and use these scientific functions may exceed your ability to do ordinary arithmetic, once you master the simple simple routines.

For readers who prefer even higher accuracy, I will show how you can use a math table and a few simple calculations to

Fig. 1-4. DataKing LG-800.

obtain accuracy up to seven places, for both trigonometric and logarithmic functions. For example, a trigonometric table lists reference values for sine, cosine, and tangent at 1° intervals up to 45°, to seven places. To calculate a sine function, the user selects the nearest table value and calculates a correction involving multiplication, division, and addition operations for the desired accuracy. The same procedure works for logarithms, except that a separate table lists logarithms to seven places, and the correction procedure is somewhat simpler for 7-place accuracy. Special trigonometric and logarithmic tables are furnished with this book, together with

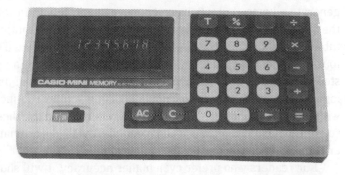

Fig. 1-5. Casio-Mini memory calculator.

the formulas required to calculate the corrections for each of the functions.

To prepare the reader for the advanced applications to be discussed in later chapters, a brief discussion of elementary calculators on the market today is presented first. In general, we will dispense with detailed discussions on how to perform ordinary arithmetic operations on a given calculator; these are well understood and, in any case, are described by the instruction books furnished with each calculator. Instead, our discussions will emphasize the ability of various calculators to solve advanced problems of potential interest to the reader. He can then decide which calculator suits his needs and his means.

Since there are so many makes of calculators, we will discuss the features of only a few representative models. However, as a matter of interest, a partial list of manufacturers in the field of pocket calculators is given in

Fig. 1-6. Rockwell UniCom 201.

Table 1-1. In addition, the desirable operating features and characteristics for the various classes of pocket calculators to be discussed in this book are listed in tables at the end of this chapter. This provides the prospective buyer a convenient checklist to help him decide which type of calculator best suits his needs.

GENERAL DESCRIPTION

The elementary calculator can perform the four conventional operations of arithmetic on 8-digit numbers, with results generally displayed in eight figures. All operations are carried out with electronic speed, and all results are shown with the decimal point positioned in the proper place. Almost all calculators are designed to use *algebraic logic*: that is, operations are performed in the same sequence that you would write, say, $3 \times 4 = 12$ or $10 \div 5 = 2$ when using pencil and

Table 1-1. Manufacturers and Distributors of Pocket Calculators (Partial List).

Manufacturer or Distributor	Location*
Bowmar Consumer Products Div.	Burlington, Mass.
Casio Consumer Products Div.	Doremus and Co., New York, N.Y.
Commodore Business Machines	Palo Alto, Calif.
Columbia Scientific	Santa Monica, Calif.
DataKing	Beverly Hills, Calif.
Hewlett-Packard	Palo Alto, Calif.
Litronix	Cupertino, Calif.
Kingspoint	Jersey City, N.J.
Lloyd's Electronics	East Patterson, N.J.
Melcor Electronics	Farmingdale, N.Y.
Monroe, The Calculator Co.	Orange, N.J. (Los Angeles, Calif.)
Radio Shack	Fort Worth, Tex.
Rockwell International Microelectronics Group	Anaheim, Calif.
Sanyo Electric Trading	Osaka, Japan (Compton, Calif.)
Sears, Roebuck and Co.	Chicago, Ill.
Sharp Electronics	Osaka, Japan (Paramus, N.J.)
Sinclair Radionics	St. Ives, Huntingdonshire, England (New York, N.Y. 10022)
Summit International	Salt Lake City, Utah
Texas Instruments	Dallas, Tex.
Unitrex of America	New York, N.Y.

* Distributor or sales agency address in parentheses.

paper. However, at least two manufacturers, Hewlett-Packard and Sinclair Radionics, use "reverse Polish" notation (*RPN*), wherein the arithmetic operators follow the numbers and the answer appears without the use of an ☐= sign. The above two examples would appear in RPN as follows:

Hewlett-Packard: 3 ☐ENTER ↑ 4 ☐× (12 displayed)
10 ☐ENTER ↑ 5 ☐÷ (2 displayed)

Sinclair: 3 ☐+ 4 ☐× (12 displayed)
10 ☐+ 5 ☐÷ (2 displayed)

It is my opinion that the user can become expert, for all practical purposes, with either type of notation in the same period of time.

The typical calculators shown in Figs. 1-1 through 1-6 are representative of the class of pocket calculators which feature the four functions of arithmetic. In addition, several possess percent (%) capability, and many possess memory capability. These operating features will now be described with reference to a typical calculator, the Rockwell 20R, which has both memory and percent functions (see Fig. 1-7).

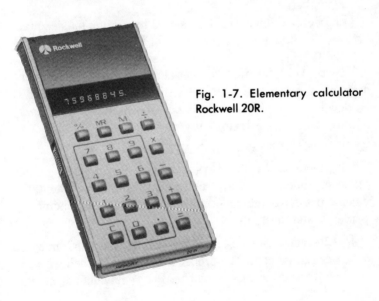

Fig. 1-7. Elementary calculator Rockwell 20R.

KEYBOARD

The keys common to elementary calculators are the following:

+ **Plus.** This key is used to add two numbers, as in a + b = display.

− **Minus.** This key is used to subtract one number from another, as in a − b = display.

× **Multiplication.** This key is used to multiply two numbers, as in a × b = display.

÷ **Divide.** This key is used to divide one number by another, as in a ÷ b = display.

= **Equals.** This key is used to complete a multiplication, division, addition, or subtraction and causes the result to be displayed. This key is also used to terminate a chain or series of calculations, so that the result is available for new calculations.

C **Clear.** This key is used to clear all registers except the memory. It can be used to clear the display. (Some calculators have a dual *clear entry/clear* key.

CE **Clear Entry.** This key is used to clear the *display only* and to remove an incorrect entry from the display.

0 – 9 **Numerals.** These keys are used to enter the numbers.

• **Decimal Point.** This key is used to position the decimal point within the number, as in 3 6 • 7 2, or • 0 0 2 5.

These keys permit the operator to perform the four ordinary functions of arithmetic and to clear the display. However, most of the calculators shown have additional features which are extremely useful.

ADDITIONAL KEYBOARD FEATURES

In addition to the keys required for multiplication, division, addition, and subtraction, many elementary calculators have the following features involving memory, percents, and constants.

% **Percent.** This key is used to multiply a number by a desired percent. The proper answer is obtained without converting the percent number to an equivalent decimal.

[M+] **Memory Add.** This key is used to add the display to memory.

[M −] **Memory Subtract.** This key is used to subtract the display from memory.

[CM] **Clear Memory.** This key is used to clear the memory.

[RM] or [MR] **Memory Recall.** This key is used to recall the contents of memory to the display.

N−A **Accumulate Switch.** In the A (*accumulate*) position, the number in the display is added to memory, if the [=] or [%] key is pressed. When the switch is set to N (*normal*), no accumulation takes place.

F−2 **Floating−Fixed Decimal.** When the switch is in the F position, the full number of digits is displayed. When the switch is in the 2 position, only two decimal digits are displayed.

[K] or CONST **Constant Switch.** In the K position, this switch retains the divisor or multiplier as a constant.

[x⟳y] **Interchange Key** This key interchanges the contents of the x and y registers. It reverses the indicated operation; e.g., x/y becomes y/x.

Most calculators have an automatic overflow or error indication when the result of a calculation exceeds its capacity, generally 10^8 or 99,999,999.

When this overflow signal appears, the calulator must be cleared by use of a special key (normally the *clear* key) before the calculation can proceed.

Percent Key

Several calculators, such as the DataKing 800, Rockwell 20R, and Lloyd's 200 feature a *percent* key, [%]. This permits the operator to enter a percent directly and calculate the product without having to readjust the decimal point. It acts as both a decimal converter and an equal key, [=]. In other words, the calculator positions the decimal point to give the proper answer. For example, to calculate 5% of $500, perform the following four steps:

$$500 \; \boxed{\times} \; 5 \; \boxed{\%} \; ?$$

The calculator will display 25 as the answer.

With most calculators, the percent calculated could be added to or subtracted from the original $500 to get a mark-up or a discount price.

Mark-on $\boxed{500}$ $\boxed{\times}$ 5 $\boxed{\%}$ $\boxed{+}$ $\boxed{=}$ $\boxed{525}$

Discount $\boxed{500}$ $\boxed{\times}$ 5 $\boxed{\%}$ $\boxed{-}$ $\boxed{=}$ $\boxed{475}$

Automatic Constants

Another important feature not covered in the above discussion is the ability of certain calculators to provide selected constants for each of the arithmetic operations. These constant operations require no special key but are provided as an inherent feature of the calculator design. In fact, one can multiply or divide several numbers by a constant without reentering the constant for each calculation. This important feature applies to multiplication, division, subtraction, or addition and is explained with examples later in the chapter. This capability is particularly useful for metric conversions—for example, inches or feet to centimeters, or miles to kilometers—or the conversion of American currency to any foreign currency.

Memory

The availability of at least one addressable memory is the main feature that distinguishes a superior calculator from the run-of-the-mill variety. A memory capability permits the operator to store a given constant or to retain an intermediate result for later use without altering the display. This capability generally involves two memory keys: A *memory enter*, or *store*, key that places the contents of the display into memory, and a *memory recall* key that places the contents of memory into the display. A $\boxed{\text{CM}}$ or *clear memory* key is also provided with some calculators, such as the Rockwell 20R. With most calculators it is necessary to set the memory to zero by storing a zero, which erases the number previously stored in memory. The many applications for memory are further explored in Chapters 2—9.

DESIGN FEATURES

We have seen that additional functions, such as percent and memory, distinguish one calculator from another.

However, of equal importance to the buyer are the packaging and design features that make the calculator convenient to use and operate. Chief among these features are the display, battery recharge capability, keyboard, and packaging.

Display

The display is the most significant feature of the calculator. It shows the numbers as they are entered and it presents the results of intermediate calculations as well as the final answer. It is the only means the operator has to determine what is going on inside the calculator and the only indication of the status of a series of calculations. The calculator should have a bright, well defined display whose numerals can be easily recognized under normal lighting and contrast conditions with absolute clarity. This includes ambient conditions of ordinary office lighting as well as shaded outdoor lighting.

There is almost a two-to-one range in the height of the numerals of the calculators shown in this chapter. (This comparison is illustrated in Fig. 1-8.) If two calculators have comparable functions and price, by all means choose the larger display.

It is advisable to check any calculator you plan to buy to be sure that the figures have sufficient clarity and that each segment of the numerals 8 and 5, or 9 and 6 is distinctly visible and separate from adjoining segments. The decimal point should be prominent and allow sufficient spacing between the integer and decimal parts of the display. Arithmetic results should appear instantly once the ⊟ key is pressed. However, advanced functions such as logarithms and trigonometric functions may take one second or more to appear. Be sure to allow the display to settle completely before entering the next number or pressing the next key.

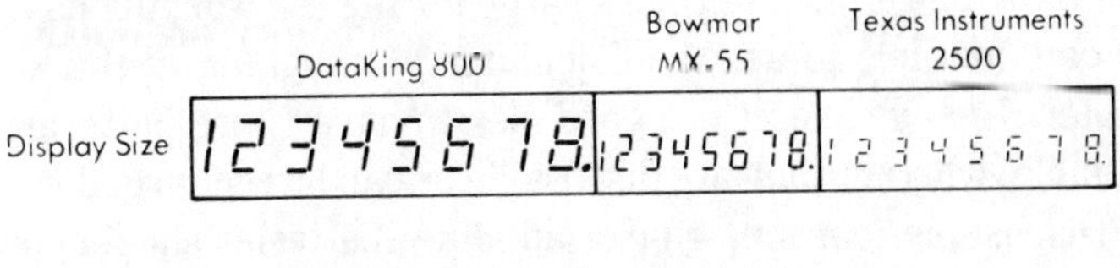

Fig. 1-8. Range of numeral sizes.

The display presents other information about the results of a calculation. Negative quantities, or negative results of a calculation, should be shown with a minus sign $(-)$ preceding the number. Many earlier calculators have a minus light or indicator instead. This may lead to errors of sign omission by the operator, particularly if the minus light or indicator follows the number. Most calculators feature some sort of a warning indication such as the *overflow light* to indicate an illegal or impossible mathematical operation, such as dividing by zero. This sometimes takes the form of a flashing display which can be stopped by pressing the $\boxed{C}$ key.

Some calculators have a *wraparound decimal* capability, which displays the eight most significant digits and a decimal point that is placed eight digits to the left of the actual decimal point. This condition usually locks up the calculator until the overflow condition is cleared. The displayed number must be multiplied by 10^8 for correct results.

Batteries

All pocket calculators run on internal batteries, which require replacement after 3 to 20 hours of operation, depending on the type of display and the size of the batteries used. The DataKing 800 (Fig. 1-4) features a unique display which uses a prism to focus light on the display. Hence, a very little current is required of the batteries. The manufacturer claims the batteries are good for more than *40 hours* of continuous operation. Aside from this exception, it is recommended that you buy a calculator with rechargeable nickel—cadmium batteries together with an ac adapter for charging. These batteries can be recharged from 200 to 500 times. Since the recharging can be done overnight, there is no loss of time on the calculator if you charge the calculator each night after use. Should the batteries lose their charge during the working day, you can continue to use the calculator by plugging in the ac adapter. In any case, it is a good idea to have spare batteries available, whether they are disposable or can be recharged.

Disposable (carbon—zinc or alkaline) batteries should not be used with an ac charger. A continuous charge applied to these batteries will generate heat within the battery and eventually cause swelling—or, in extreme cases, the battery may explode.

Keyboard

Almost all calculators have legible and functionally acceptable keyboards. Examine the printing on and above the keys. It should be clear, well defined, and descriptive of the function or operation it describes. The key should be easy to press with your finger, yet it should give you some mechanical indication that it has completed its travel and made contact. There should be adequate spacing between keys, so that only one key will be pressed at one time. Recent calculators on the market feature keys with two, or even three, functions. These multipurpose keys should be color-coded or otherwise identified, so that the operator can automatically select the alternate functions without undue chance of error.

SPECIAL FEATURES

There are some calculating features and display characteristics that are not evident from inspection of the keyboard. For example, the availability of automatic constants and the ability of the calculator to round the last figure properly are not easily determined by inspection of the keyboard. Therefore, you are encouraged to contact the manufacturer or distributor directly for additional information. The best source of data for each model is the operational manual supplied by the manufacturer with each calculator. A careful study of such a manual will answer most of your questions on calculator operation. The following sections will discuss most of the special features of interest.

Constant Operations

Two terms must be defined: (1) *constant number* and (2) *constant function.*

Constant Number. Any number entered in the display can be used as a constant, which can be used repeatedly. For example, the number 5 is used as a constant.

Key	Display
5	5.
☒	5.
☒	25.
÷	125.
÷	25.
+	5.
+	10.
−	15.
−	10.
−	5.

This example demonstrates the repeat feature.

Constant Function. The functions ÷ and ☒ and sometimes + and − can be set up as constant functions automatically. To do so, the = must be used. The last *number* entered before depression of the = key is maintained as the constant divisor, multiplier, addend, or subtrahend. The last *function* key depressed prior to depression of the = key is established as the constant function. All that is necessary is to enter a new dividend, multiplicand, augend, or minuend and depress the = key for the answer.

AUTOMATIC CONSTANT OPERATION

The *automatic constant* feature of certain calculators, such as the Rockwell 20R and the Lloyd's 500, is a valuable aid to calculation. In the examples that follow, the simple operation will be shown first and then the automatic constant operation is described to enable a direct comparison. The simple operation a ☒ b = *display* is indicated below.

Problem	Keyboard Entry	Display
$15 \times 3 = 45$	15 ☒	15
	3 =	45 (Answer)
2.369×4.8021	2.369 ☒	2.369
$= 11.38$	4.8021 =	11.376174 (Answer)

The answer does not appear until the ⊟ key is pressed.

Automatic Constant Multiplier

It sometimes is necessary to multiply many different numbers by a given constant. For example, one may want to convert several measurements, in feet, to an equivalent number of inches. This can be done with any of the calculators illustrated in Figs. 1-1 to 1-6 as follows: Use the constant factor (12, in this case) as the second multiplier in the first calculation. Then enter the next number of feet—say, 15—and press the ⊟ key immediately. The second conversion for 15 ft follows without reentering the constant 12, as shown below.

Problem	Keyboard Entry	Result
$8 \times 12 = 96$	$\boxed{C}$ 8 $\boxed{\times}$ 12 $\boxed{=}$	96
$15 \times 12 = 180$	15 $\boxed{=}$	180
$10.5 \times 12 = 126$	10.5 $\boxed{=}$	126

It should be noted that the automatic constant feature is not available in many models, nor is the keying procedure the same for all models which have this capability. Generally, the second factor in the multiplication is used as the constant multiplier. In any case, the instruction manual for the calculator will indicate whether the automatic constant feature is available and what sequence should be followed.

Automatic Repeat—Squares and Cubes

Raising a number to a simple power like x^2 or x^3 is a special case of the automatic constant multiplier feature. For example, to get 15^2, the sequence is: 15 $\boxed{\times}$ $\boxed{=}$ 225. For 15^3, the sequence is: 15 $\boxed{\times}$ $\boxed{=}$ $\boxed{=}$ 3375. Clearly, any power like x^5 or x^7 can be obtained by the same procedure, provided the capacity of the machine is not exceeded.

Automatic Constant Divisor

In the division a $\boxed{\div}$ b $\boxed{=}$ *display*, the number b is automatically available as a constant divisor for the next series of divisions. For the next division, c $\boxed{\div}$ b $\boxed{=}$ *display*, enter the next numerator, c, and press $\boxed{=}$ as shown in the examples below. The constant b is replaced by a new constant the next time $\boxed{\times}$ or $\boxed{\div}$ is pressed. In the example shown below, divisor b (2) is the first number entered after the $\boxed{\div}$ key is pressed.

Example (Rockwell 20R):

Problem	Keyboard Entry		Result
		$\boxed{\text{C}}$	0.
25/2 = 12.5	25	$\boxed{\div}$	25.
8/2 = 4	2	$\boxed{=}$	12.5
60.5/2 = 30.25	8	$\boxed{=}$	4.
	60.5	$\boxed{=}$	30.25

Automatic Constant Addition or Subtraction

The addition or subtraction of a constant behaves the same way. The first number entered after the $\boxed{+}$ or $\boxed{-}$ key is pressed prior to the depression of the $\boxed{=}$ key becomes the constant for addition or subtraction.

Chain Calculations

Multiplication and division operations can be performed in a continuous chain just as slide rule operations. For example, the calculation of $^2/_3 \times {}^4/_5 \times 7$ is shown in the example below.

Problem	Keyboard Entry		Result
		$\boxed{\text{C}}$	0.
$^2/_3 \times {}^4/_5 \times 7 = 3.7333324$	2	$\boxed{\div}$	2.
	3	$\boxed{\times}$	0.6666666
	4	$\boxed{\div}$	2.6666664
	5	$\boxed{\times}$	0.5333332
	7	$\boxed{=}$	3.7333324

It is interesting to note that the display registers the result of a given operation only when the new arithmetic function key is pressed. In the example, the result of 2 $\boxed{\div}$ 3 is displayed only when the next key, $\boxed{\times}$, is pressed. The final result, or any intermediate result, will be shown when the $\boxed{=}$ key is pressed.

Accumulation Switch

Certain earlier calculators, such as the Unicom 201, have an *accumulation* switch for adding the contents of the display to memory. It can also be used to store a constant, such as π or $\sqrt{2}$, which is then available for use with any arithmetic key. In the example below, the number 25 is the constant stored in memory. It is then recalled by the RM key as a multiplier (25 × 8 = 200), as a dividend (25/2 = 12.50), and for addition (25 + 37 = 62.) These examples are typical of the way stored constants work in all machines, except that the constant is stored with a K (constant) switch instead of an A (accumulation) switch (see Fig. 1-7).

Constant in Memory (Unicom 201)

Example (decimal setting, 2 places; *accumulation* switch setting, see below):

Problem	Keyboard Entry	Result
	C	0.
	CM	0.
	Accumulation switch setting: A	
	25 =	Set 25 = (Constant)
	Accumulation switch setting: N	
25 × 8 = 200	RM ×	25.
	8 =	200.
25/2 = 12.5	RM ÷	25
	2 =	12.50
25 + 37 = 62	RM +	25.
	37 =	62

Memory—Accumulation of Totals

Problem: $(a \times b) + (c \times d) + (e/f)$. (The decimal setting is 2; *accumulation* switch setting, A.)

Problem	Keyboard Entry	Result
	C	0.
	CM	0.
9 × 8 = 72	9 ×	9.
	8 =	72.
−14 × 3 = −42	14 −	14.0 −*
	×	14.0
	3 =	42. −*
57/3 = 19	57 ÷	57.
	3 =	19.
Total = 49	RM	49.

The *negative* indicator lights up to indicate the minus sign.

The *negative* indicator lights up to indicate the minus sign. Note: When the *accumulation* switch is set to A, the number in the display after ⬜= is pressed will be added to memory.

This example shows that the results of three or more calculations can be continually stored in the memory, and the true algebraic total is recalled by the proper key when the A—N switch is set to A (accumulation). The ⬜CM key is used to clear the memory, and the ⬜RM key is used to recall the final sum or any intermediate sum. Note that the accumulation switch must be set to the A position to use the memory, and that the memory continually adds the results of all previous calculations that have been completed with an equal sign in the A position. Therefore, you must clear the memory before using the A switch to enter a constant, and you must set this switch to N after the constant is entered. Obviously, it is preferable to have a memory which is independently available on command and can be entered or recalled with separate memory keys.

Addressable or Independent Memory

The newer calculators have an addressable memory which is controlled by separate memory keys as shown in Fig. 1-7. The same problem on a calculator with memory, such as the Rockwell 20R, would proceed as shown below.

Problem: $(a \times b) + (c \times d) + (e/f)$

Key—Operation	Display
9 ⬜× 8 ⬜=	72
⬜M ⬜+ 14 ⬜×	14
3 ⬜=	42
⬜M ⬜− 57 ⬜÷	57
3 ⬜= ⬜M ⬜+	19
⬜MR	49

No special switch is needed; the memory is used to record the results of all operations in this example.

CHOOSING YOUR POCKET CALCULATOR

By now, you have a general understanding of elementary pocket calculators and how they operate. The following chapters will describe the capabilities and applications of intermediate slide rule calculators, scientific calculators, and advanced scientific calculators. But your problem may be how to choose the calculator best suited to your needs. There are possibly up to 100 pocket or portable calculators on the market today. At least 10 manufacturers have scientific calculators: Hewlett-Packard, Sears, Bowmar, Keystone, Rockwell, Texas Instruments, Sinclair, Casio, Commodore, and Summit. At the same time, prices are dropping despite general inflationary trends, because of increased demand, the mass-production capability of integrated circuitry, and increasing competition among manufacturers.

The best thing I can do, under the circumstances, is to simplify the problem and offer you some choices. Since you may well be interested in the advanced calculators described later, I have organized data covering the capabilities of four classes of pocket calculators in Tables 1-2 through 1-5. Each table lists both the standard and special features that each class of calculator should have and offers a price range for each class. Armed with these lists, I suggest that you go to the

Table. 1-2. Price Range $20 — $50.

Desirable Features	Notes and Comments
Programmable memory, M	Allows the operator to store or recall constants, or intermediate results from memory. Should be independent of any switch position. Includes store in memory, recall, and, preferably, clear memory keys.
Percent key, %	The operator may enter a percent—say, 5%—directly, and the calculator will correctly position the decimal.
Negative, or minus, sign, −	A dash precedes any negative result or any negative number entry.
Plus — minus key, +/−	Changes the sign of any number in the display.
* Decimal select switch	Selects between F, floating, and 2, fixed decimal.
* Automatic constant	Available in multiplication and division.
* Roundup capability	Properly rounds up the last digit. Example: $2/3 = 0.67$.
* Wraparound decimal	Correctly positions the decimal point in the display when the machine capacity is exceeded. Example: $555,555 \times 555,555 = 3086.4135 \times 10^8$. (Calculator positions decimal; operator supplies 10^8.)
Dimensions: $6 \times 3.5 \times 1\frac{1}{2}$ in. (maximum) Weight: 12 oz. (maximum) Batteries: Rechargeable (Ni − Cad) Numeral Height: $\frac{3}{8}$ in.	

* Useful but not necessary.

Table 1-3. Price Range $40 — $70.

Desirable Features	Notes and Comments
Square root function, $\boxed{\sqrt{x}}$	Provides square root of number in the display with one key stroke. Correctly positions the decimal.
Square function, $\boxed{x^2}$	Squares the number in the display with one key stroke (This capability is available with automatic constants.)
Reciprocal function, $\boxed{1/x}$	Divides the number in the display into unity. Permits any number in the display to act as a divisor.
Scientific notation, 10^{-99} to 10^{+99} E.g. : 2.345×10^{-3}, $3.5678 \times 10^{+6}$ Includes enter exp key $\boxed{EEX}$	Operator may enter very large or very small numbers and retain at least seven significant figures. The display generally reverts to scientific notation whenever the calculation exceeds the machine capacity (10^8).

Note: If these features cannot be found in a calculator under $100, then go to the next class of calculator, in Table 1-4.

nearest distributor and ask to see the models which have the capabilities of interest to you. Try out at least two different models of similar capabilities. Check out the display, availability an of ac adapter and rechargeable batteries, and, of course, the price. You may want to try several calculators and several distributors for price and guarantee. You will probably find that you want a calculator somewhat above your initial budget. That will be your first problem to solve.

Table 1-4. Price Range $60 — $150.

Desirable Features	Notes and Comments
Trigonometric functions	Sin, cos, tan of x in degrees or radians.
Inverse trigonometric functions	Angle in degrees or radians; sin $^{-1}$, cos $^{-1}$, tan $^{-1}$.
Power function $\boxed{x^y}$ or $\boxed{a^x}$	Base must be positive; power can be negative.
Common logarithm $\boxed{\log x}$ and antilog $\boxed{10^x}$	Must be accurate to at least six significant figures.
Natural logarithms $\boxed{\ln x}$ and antilin $\boxed{e^x}$	Must be accurate to at least six significant figures.
Scientific notation	Range 10^{-99} to 10^{99}.
Adressable memories	Must have one; should have 2 to 4 (HP-45 has 9).
Two-level parentheses $\boxed{(\ )}$	Simplifies equation solving and formula reduction.
Working registers	Two minimum, three desirable, four quite useful.
Register exchange $\boxed{x \leftrightarrows y}$	Facilitates use of intermediate results, greater flexibility in equation solving.
Function constants $\boxed{\pi}$	Constant π is a must. Metric constants are also useful.
* Rounding and decimal select (zero to full decimals)	Desirable, but currently available only in HP-45 and Compucorp 322 and 324.
* Hyperbolic functions	Not generally available; easily computed.

* Useful but not necessary.

30

Table 1-5. Price Range $100—$245.

Desirable Features	Notes and Comments
Rectangular-to-polar conversion	Requires two outputs, magnitude and angle.
Polar-to-rectangular conversion	Requires two outputs, x and y components.
Statistical mean and variance	Requires two outputs from a series of numbers.
Summing $\boxed{\Sigma}$ registers	Useful for summing and statistics applications.
Addressable registers	Nine to sixteen registers required for advanced problems.
Factorials $\boxed{x!}$	Useful for statistics and probability problems.
* Hyperbolic functions	Not generally available; easily computed.
* Last entry or X	Permits recall or correction of last number in x register.
Degree — Radian — grad modes	Permits angle or function calculations in three modes.
* Metric constants	Three or more fundamental conversions are useful.
Rolldown or Rollup keys	Permits operator to examine or use other registers.
*Rounding-up and decimal select	Permits operator to select number of decimals from zero to full decimals. Displays accurate last digit.
Degrees to rad or grad conversion	Operator can enter angles in one unit and convert to the other unit: angles in degrees, radians, or grads (0.01).
* Programmability	Operator can enter programs manually or by magnetic tape and execute the program automatically. (See Chapter 12.)

* Useful but not necessary.
** Separate Class of Calculator, See Chapters 12 and 13.

Chapter 2

Finding Roots by Division and Addition

The elementary calculator is basically desired to perform the four arithmetic functions of addition, subtraction, multiplication, and division. As discussed previously, these simple functions cover the vast majority of everyday applications. But other functions are sometimes required; chief among these are *squares* and *square roots*.

SQUARE ROOTS

The square of a number, a, is written a^2, and is equal to the number a multiplied by itself:

$$a \times a = a^2$$

Squaring a number is very straightforward—just multiply the number by itself. But suppose we now ask: "What number, multiplied by itself, is equal to the given number, a?" This unknown number is called the *square root* of a, and is written $\sqrt{a}$. By definition, then,

$$\sqrt{a} \times \sqrt{a} = a$$

which reads: "The square root of a times the square root of a equals a." For example, $\sqrt{16} = 4$, because $4 \times 4 = 16$. Therefore, $\sqrt{16} \times \sqrt{16} = 16$. But what is the square root of a number *between* 16 and 25, say, 19? Actually, the $\sqrt{19}$ is neither an integer (whole number) nor a simple fraction. It turns out that $\sqrt{19}$ equals 4, followed by an infinite string of decimals. It is correct to say that $\sqrt{19} = 4.3589$, with accuracy to four decimal places; or $\sqrt{19} = 4.3588989$, with accuracy to seven decimal places. The desired number of decimal places depends on the application.

There are many uses for the square root in algebra, geometry, and physics. For example, the length of the longest side of a right triangle, the hypotenuse, is equal to the square root of the sum of the squares of the other two sides. This is the famous *Pythagorean theorem,* or *law of right triangles.*

Symbolically, $c = \sqrt{a^2 + b^2}$

where c is the hypotenuse and a and b are the other sides, as shown in the figure.

If the two sides are 3 and 4 units in length, then the hypotenuse is

$C = \sqrt{3^2 + 4^2}$

$C = 5$ units long

This results in the familiar 3, 4, 5 right triangle.

Square Root Process

With its basic ability to divide and add accurately, the pocket calculator can find the square root of any number to as many as seven significant figures. It only requires the operator to start the process with an initial estimate or guess for the square root. The machine does all the difficult arithmetic.

Suppose you were asked to find the hypotenuse of a right triangle whose sides are 2 and 4 units long. Then the hypotenuse $= \sqrt{2^2 + 4^2} = \sqrt{20}$. The square root can be calculated by the following iterative process, which consists of several cycles of estimating, checking, and averaging for a new estimate. This process will be used to find $\sqrt{20}$.

Step 1. Estimate $\sqrt{20}$ mentally. Since $4^2 = 16$ and $5^2 = 25$, $\sqrt{20}$ lies between 4 and 5. Use the average of 4 and 5 (4.5)

$$E_1 \text{ (first estimate)} = 4.5$$

Step 2. Divide 20 by 4.5 to get a check on the first estimate.

$$C_1 \text{ (first check)} = \frac{20}{4.5} = 4.4444444$$

Step 3. Use the average of the first estimate and the first check for the second estimate.

$$E_2 \text{ (second estimate)} = 4.5 + \frac{4.4444444}{2}$$

$$E_2 = 4.4722222$$

Step 4. Divide by the second estimate to get the second check.

$$C_2 \text{ (second check)} = \frac{20}{4.4722222} = 4.4720497$$

Step 5. Use the average of the second estimate and the second check for the third and last estimate.

$$E_3 \text{ (third estimate)} = \frac{4.4720497 + 4.4722222}{2} = 4.4721360$$

Step 6. Divide 20 by the third estimate for the third check.

$$C_3 \text{ (third check)} = \frac{20}{4.4721360} = 4.4721360 \text{ (final answer)}$$

The third check is the final answer because it is the same as the third estimate. The number 4.4721360 is $\sqrt{20}$ to eight significant figures, or seven decimal places. If the square root were needed to only three decimals, the *second check* = 4.472 would be the answer, because it equals the second estimate to three decimals and because 4.472 is followed by a digit less than 5. We will see later that the third estimate, E_3, can often be used without performing a third check. (See examples 2-1 and 2.2 to follow.)

It is desirable to make the first estimate a good one, not only to lessen the operator work, but also to arrive at more accurate answers sooner. In fact, a 5- or 6-figure square root can be found in one cycle of calculation if either a slide rule or small table of square roots is used for the first estimate (see Table 2-1).

Notice that the square root process described is self-checking. Each estimate in steps 2, 4, and 6 is divided into the given number, N, for an automatic check. When the check is equal to the estimate, we have found the square root to a given number of places. For example, if three or four numbers or digits in the estimate and check are identical, then we are sure that the square root is correct to the same number of places, unless the last digit should be rounded up. In our example, $\sqrt{20} = 4.472$ is correct to three decimals, since the fourth decimal is a digit less than 5. This can be seen by inspection of the second estimate and the second check.

Square Roots Using the Elementary Calculator

Now we are able to develop a fixed sequence of machine operations, or program steps, for use with the calculator. This

Table 2-1. Table of Square Roots.

No.	Square	Square Root	No.	Square	Square Root
1	1	1.00	76	5,776	8.72
2	4	1.41	77	5,929	8.77
3	9	1.73	78	6,084	8.83
4	16	2.	79	6,241	8.89
5	25	2.24	80	6,400	8.94
6	36	2.45	81	6,561	9.
7	49	2.65	82	6,724	9.06
8	64	2.83	83	6,889	9.11
9	81	3.	84	7,056	9.17
10	100	3.16	85	7,225	9.22
11	121	3.32	86	7,396	9.27
12	144	3.46	87	7,569	9.33
13	169	3.61	88	7,744	9.38
14	196	3.74	89	7,921	9.43
15	225	3.87	90	8,100	9.49
16	256	4.	91	8,281	9.54
17	289	4.12	92	8,464	9.59
18	324	4.24	93	8,649	9.64
19	361	4.36	94	8,836	9.70
20	400	4.47	95	9,025	9.75
21	441	4.58	96	9,216	9.80
22	484	4.69	97	9,409	9.85
23	529	4.80	98	9,604	9.90
24	576	4.90	99	9,801	9.95
25	625	5.	100	10,000	10.
26	676	5.10	101	10,201	10.05
27	729	5.20	102	10,404	10.10
28	784	5.29	103	10,609	10.15
29	841	5.39	104	10,816	10.20
30	900	5.48	105	11,025	10.25
31	961	5.57	106	11,236	10.30
32	1,024	5.66	107	11,449	10.34
33	1,089	5.74	108	11,664	10.39
34	1,156	5.83	109	11,881	10.44
35	1,225	5.92	110	12,100	10.49
36	1,296	6.	111	12,321	10.54
37	1,369	6.08	112	12,544	10.58
38	1,444	6.16	113	12,769	10.63
39	1,521	6.24	114	12,996	10.68
40	1,600	6.32	115	13,225	10.72
41	1,681	6.40	116	13,456	10.77
42	1,764	6.48	117	13,689	10.82
43	1,849	6.56	118	13,924	10.86
44	1,936	6.63	119	14,161	10.91
45	2,025	6.71	120	14,400	10.95
46	2,116	6.78	121	14,641	11.
47	2,209	6.86	122	14,884	11.05
48	2,304	6.93	123	15,129	11.09
49	2,401	7.	124	15,376	11.14
50	2,500	7.07	125	15,625	11.18
51	2,601	7.14	126	15,876	11.22
52	2,704	7.21	127	16,129	11.27
53	2,809	7.28	128	16,384	11.31
54	2,916	7.35	129	16,641	11.36
55	3,025	7.42	130	16,900	11.40
56	3,136	7.48	131	17,161	11.45
57	3,249	7.55	132	17,424	11.49
58	3,364	7.62	133	17,689	11.53
59	3,481	7.68	134	17,956	11.58
60	3,600	7.75	135	18,225	11.62
61	3,721	7.81	136	18,496	11.66
62	3,844	7.87	137	18,769	11.70
63	3,969	7.94	138	19,044	11.75
64	4,096	8.	139	19,321	11.79
65	4,225	8.06	140	19,600	11.83
66	4,356	8.12	141	19,881	11.87
67	4,489	8.19	142	20,164	11.92
68	4,624	8.25	143	20,449	11.96
69	4,761	8.31	144	20,736	12.
70	4,900	8.37	145	21,025	12.04
71	5,041	8.43	146	21,316	12.08
72	5,184	8.49	147	21,609	12.12
73	5,329	8.54	148	21,904	12.17
74	5,476	8.60	149	22,201	12.21
75	5,625	8.66	150	22,500	12.25

permits the operator to extract the square root of any number with less than eight digits to a precision of up to seven significant figures. The steps explained in the previous example will be generalized for use with any number (N). Example 2-1 shows the sequence of square root operations, the machine operations, and the numerical result for each step. A specific calculator will not be identified for the first few examples, so that the reader can focus on the steps in the process rather than on the mechanics of the calculator.

Example 2-1. This example shows the square root sequence of operations for $\sqrt{20}$.

Sequence of Square Root Steps	Calculator Operations	Desired Numerical Result
1a. First estimate. $E_1 = 4.5$	Operator guess	4.5
1b. First check. $C_1 = \dfrac{N}{E_1} = \dfrac{20}{4.5}$	Enter 20. $\div$ by 4.5.	4.4444444
2a. Second estimate. $E_2 = \dfrac{E + C_1}{2}$	+ 4.5 $\div$ by 2	4.4722222
2b. Second check. $C_2 = \dfrac{N}{E_2} = \dfrac{20}{E_2}$	Enter 20. $\div$ by 4.4722222.	4.4720497
3a. Third estimate. $E3 = \dfrac{E_2 + C_2}{2}$	+ 4.4722222 $\div$ by 2	4.4721360
3b. Third check. $C_3 = \dfrac{N}{E_3} = \dfrac{20}{E_3}$	Enter 20. $\div$ by 4.4721360.	4.4721360

Under the column marked *Calculator Operations*, the operator must choose the first estimate and enter the second and third estimates, E_2 and E_3, which are used in steps 2a and 3a. Notice that the last estimate in step 3b is accurate to eight significant figures. Four-place accuracy or three-decimal accuracy is available in step 2a.

If the calculator has a constant storage or a separate memory register, then the constant numerator (or given number, *20*) could be stored in the machine and recalled by the operator for each division. Such a capability is useful for the square root process. This is especially desirable if the given number has many digits. Remember, the square root should be carried out only to the desired number of places. For most applications, only the first two cycles shown should be necessary for 4-figure precision. The reason for this statement is that the last check can always be averaged with the last estimate mentally to produce an additional significant figure or two without the use of the machine. This is done in the second and third estimates of example 2-4.

To further illustrate these points, let us calculate $\sqrt{52}$. Since $7^2 = 49$ and $8^2 = 64$, the $\sqrt{52}$ must lie between 7 and 8 but is closer to 8. Assume $\sqrt{52}$ is about 7.3. This will be used as the first estimate for machine calculation.

Example 2-2. Find $\sqrt{52}$. Use a mental approximation for first estimate.

Sequence of Operations	Comments
First estimate $= 7.3$	Could have been 7.2
First check $= \dfrac{52}{7.3} = 7.123$	Use only three decimal places.
Second estimate $= 7 + \dfrac{0.3 + 0.123}{2}$	Same result as $\dfrac{7.3 + 7.123}{2}$.
$\qquad = 7.2115$	
Second check $= \dfrac{52}{7.211} = 7.211205$	Drop the last decimal in the second estimate to obtain the second check.
Third estimate $= 7.211 + \dfrac{0.000205}{2} = 7.211102$	Just divide the last three decimals of 7.211205 by 2 and tack on to 7.211.
Third check (machine) $= \dfrac{52}{7.211102} = 7.211103$	The true answer is probably 7.2111025; therefore use 7.211103.

We will find that a final check is generally unnecessary when the difference between the last two estimates is less than 0.001, even if 7-decimal accuracy is desired. The error for any step in the square root process is discussed at the end of the chapter. It is shown that the theoretical error in the square root for this example is less than 10^{-7}, or less than 1 in the seventh decimal.

If the first estimate was chosen to be 7.2, then more accurate results would be obtained for the second estimate. In fact, it is a good idea to use a slide rule or a table of square roots to make the first estimate. This possibility is shown in the next example.

Example 2-3. Find $\sqrt{52}$, using a table or slide rule for the first estimate.

Sequence of Operations	Comments
First estimate = 7.21	Table 2-1 shows $\sqrt{52} = 7.21$
First check = $\dfrac{52}{7.21} = 7.2122052$	
Second estimate = $\dfrac{7.21 + 7.2122052}{2}$ = 7.2111026	The difference between the first and second estimates is less than 0.001.
Second check = $\dfrac{52}{7.2111026}$ = 7.2111025	Differs from the second estimate by about 10^{-7}.

The final answer is $\sqrt{52} = 7.211103$. As before, but it now requires only two cycles of calculations by machine for the final answer.

The operator should now start to rely on a good mental approximation for the first estimate as shown in the next example.

Example 2-4. Find $\sqrt{150}$, using a first mental estimate.

Assume 10 as the first mental guess. Then, 15 is the first mental check 150/10 ; hence

$$12.5 = \frac{10 + 15}{2}$$

is the first estimate for the machine.

Sequence of Operations	Comments
First estimate = 12.5	Mental.
First check = $\dfrac{150}{12.5} = 12.000$	By calculator.
Second estimate = $\dfrac{12 + 12.500}{2} = 12.250$	Correct to three places.
Second check = $\dfrac{150}{12.250} = 12.244898$	

Third estimate $= \dfrac{12.25 + 12.244898}{2} = 12.247449$ Correct to eight places.

Third check $= \dfrac{150}{12.247449} = 12.247448$

Once more the square root is available to eight significant figures. The true square root is rounded up as 12.247449, if your calculator does not have rounding capability. In any case, the square root, correct to seven significant figures, is certainly 12.24745.

The example below shows how a square root calculation might be performed on an elementary calculator such as the Texas Instruments 2500 without memory. It would be necessary to record the intermediate steps as shown below.

Example 2-5. Final $\sqrt{377}$, using any elementary calculator.

Step	Machine Operations	Desired Result	Comments
1.	377	377	Record, if many digits.
2.	÷ 20 +	18.85	First check. $C_1 = 377/20$.
3.	20 ÷ 2 =	19.425	Second estimate. E_2. Record
4.	377	377	for use in steps 5 and 6.
5.	÷ 19.425 +	19.407979	Second check. C_2.
6.	19.425 ÷ 2 =	19.416489	Third estimate. E_3. Record
7.	377	377	for use in step 8.
8.	÷ 19.416489 =	19.416486	Third check. C_3. Stop here for 7-place accuracy.

The answer, correct to seven places, or five decimals, is 19.41649. To estimate the sixth decimal, average the last digits in E_3 and C_3 (6 and 9) and round up the result. Since $(6 + 9)/2 = 7.5$, the last figure rounds up to 8. Then the $\sqrt{377}$, correct to eight places or six decimals, is 19.416488. It can be seen that three cycles of estimate and check will generally suffice for the desired accuracy.

Placing the Decimal Point

A number can have the same significant figures and still have different square roots. For example, $\sqrt{10.0} = 3.16$, while $\sqrt{100} = 10$. The difference in the square root depends on whether the number of figures before the decimal point is even or odd. If this number is odd, then the first one (or three) figures control the square root. If this number is even, then the first two (or four) figures control the square root. Consider the following examples, where each number has the same significant figures.

Number	Pairs	Square Root First Estimate	Second Estimate
34.567	34	5 to 6	5.5
345.67	3 45	10 to 20	15
3456.7	34 56	50 to 60	55
34.567	3 45 67	100 to 200	150

The first estimate is obtained by guessing the lower and upper limits for the square root of the first "pair" and adding zeros for each successive pair. Thus, the first estimate for $\sqrt{34}$ is 5 to 6, with no zero following; and the first estimate for $\sqrt{3\ 45}$ is 1 to 2, with one zero following (10 to 20).

The second estimate is found by averaging the lower and upper limits from the first estimate. In all cases, the number of digits before the decimal point in the square root is always equal to the number of pairs in the original number.

For simplicity, one could use the lower limit of the first estimate directly. This would give an estimate of 10 for $\sqrt{345}$, 50 for $\sqrt{3456}$, and 100 for $\sqrt{34,566}$. The use of these first estimates for the desired square root would eventually give the correct answer in our square root process, but they might require an additional cycle of estimate and check, compared to a better estimate.

The next example shows how the second estimate (150) is used to find $\sqrt{34,566}$.

Example 2-6. Find $\sqrt{34,567}$, using 150 as first estimate.

Calculator Operations	Desired Result	Comment
34567 ÷ 150 =	230.44666	First check.
+ 150 ÷ 2 =	190.22333	Second estimate.
34567 ÷ 190.2233 =	181.71798	Second check.
+ 181.71798 ÷ 2 =	185.97065	Third estimate.
34567 ÷ 185.97065 =	185.87341	Third check.
+ 185.97065 ÷ 2 =	185.92203	Fourth estimate.

The value of $\sqrt{34567}$ correct to eight places is 185.92203. Therefore, the third estimate is high by less than 0.05, and the fourth estimate is correct to all places shown.

The next example shows how an elementary calculator with memory, such as the Rockwell 20R, can be used to extract the square root of a number such as 34567. This number will be used so that the specified calculations can be compared to the mathematical operations described previously.

Example 2-7. Find $\sqrt{34567}$, using any calculator with memory (e.g., Rockwell 20R).

Key – Operation	Display	Comment
34567 $\div$ 150 $+$ $\div$ 2 $=$	190.22333	Second estimate
M C M $+$	190.22333	Estimate in memory
34567 $\div$ MR $+$ $\div$ 2 $=$	185.97065	Third estimate
M C M $+$	185.97065	Estimate in memory
34567 $\div$ MR $+$ $\div$ 2 $=$	185.92203	Last estimate. answer

The answer is correct to every place shown. If a better first estimate were chosen,from Table 2-1(e.g.,180 or 190)then only two cycles of iteration would have given the same accuracy. store these numbers. In fact, it is not even necessary to reenter the original number, 34567, since the M $+$ $=$ sequence restores this number each time it is needed. Nowadays most elementary calculators feature a memory, so that the above routine can be used with any equivalent calculator. (DataKing 800, Bowmar MX 35-1, Casio-Mini *Memory*, etc.).

Square Root of Decimal Numbers

You should now be able to extract the square root of any whole number. However, some hints for finding square roots of decimals are in order. There is no change to the previous procedure if the decimals follow the integer, or whole number part. However, if the given number is a pure decimal (e.g., a number like 0.012344), then there are two choices: Follow a similar pairing procedure, or use scientific notation, making sure that the power of 10 is even.

The first procedure is to arrange the digits of the decimal in pairs, starting at the right of the decimal point. Then line up the decimal points and estimate the square root of each pair as before.

$$\sqrt{.01234} = \overset{.\ 1\ 0\ 0}{\sqrt{.01\ 23\ 40}} = .100 \text{ (first estimate)}$$

$$\sqrt{.12340} = \overset{.\ 3\ 0\ 0}{\sqrt{.12\ 34\ 00}} = .300 \text{ (first estimate)}$$

$$\sqrt{.00123} = \overset{.\ 0\ 3\ 0}{\sqrt{.00\ 12\ 30}} = .030 \text{ (first estimate)}$$

This method is quite simple and easy to use.

The second method would use scientific notation for the first estimate as follows:

Number		Scientific Notation		First Estimate
$\sqrt{0.01234}$	$=$	$\sqrt{1.234 \times 10^{-2}}$	$=$	$1 \times 10^{-1} = 10.$
$\sqrt{0.1234}$	$=$	$\sqrt{12.34 \times 10^{-2}}$	$=$	$3 \times 10^{-1} = 0.30$
$\sqrt{0.00123}$	$=$	$\sqrt{12.3 \times 10^{-4}}$	$=$	$3 \times 10^{-2} = 0.03$

The trick is to make sure that you choose even powers of 10 (10^{-2}, 10^{-4}, etc.) to express the original number before taking the square root.

CUBE ROOTS BY DIVISION

The cube roots of a number N is written $\sqrt[3]{N}$ and is defined by the relation

$$\sqrt[3]{N} \times \sqrt[3]{N} \times \sqrt[3]{N} = N$$

or

$$\sqrt[3]{N} = \frac{N}{(\sqrt[3]{N})^2}$$

This relation leads us to a process for finding the cube root of a number which is similar to the process for the square root just described.

Process for $3\sqrt{N}$	Comments
Estimate the cube root ($= E_1$).	First estimate.
Square the estimate (E_1^2).	
Calculate $\dfrac{N}{E_1^2} = C_1$	First check.
Calculate $\dfrac{(2 \times E_1) + C_1}{3} = E_2$	Second estimate.
Calculate E_2^2.	
Calculate $\dfrac{N}{E_2^2} = C_2$.	Second check.
Calculate $\dfrac{(2 \times E_2) + C_2}{3} = E_3$.	Third estimate.

Repeat process until $E_3 = E_2$, or until $\dfrac{(E_3 - E_2)}{E_3}$ is less than a desired amount.

There is no doubt that this method is more difficult than the similar process for finding the square root of a number. But the concept of a cube root is inherently more complicated than a square root and will require more calculation no matter what method is used. In any case, the method shown is quite practical for use on an elementary calculator.

Now suppose we want to find $\sqrt[3]{10}$ by this method. Let the first estimate, E_1, equal 2, since $2^3 = 8$, which is reasonably close to 10.

Example 2-8. Find $\sqrt[3]{10}$ by division method.

Sequence of Operations	Desired Result
$E_1 = 2$	2
$E_1^2 = 2^2$	4
$C_1 = \dfrac{10}{4}$	2.5
$E_2 = \dfrac{2 \times E_1 + C_1}{3} = \dfrac{(2 \times 2) + 2.5}{3}$	2.1666666
$E_2^2 = 2.1666666^2$	4.6944441
$C_2 = \dfrac{10}{4.6944441}$	2.1301776
$E3 = \dfrac{2 \times 2.1666666 + 2.1301776}{3}$	2.1545036
$E_3^2 = 2.1545036^2$	4.6418857
$C_3 = \dfrac{10}{4.6418857}$	2.1542969
$E_4 = \dfrac{2 \times 2.1545036 + 2.1542969}{3}$	2.1544347

The third estimate, $E_3 = 2.15450$, was in error by about 0.00007, or less than 0.0001. The estimate $E_3 = 2.1545$, then, represents a sufficiently good approximation for most practical purposes. Formulas are derived later in this section which can be used to predict the error at each step. The final answer, E_4, is correct to every place shown. However, it took three full cycles of calculation, plus a fourth estimate, to get this result. Furthermore, it is possible that rounding errors in the seventh decimal can cause the last figure to be in error.

Suppose we now try finding $\sqrt[3]{10}$ using a calculator with memory. The sequence in example 2-9 indicates the calculator sequence of operations and the desired result for each operation. The *Comment* column indicates which results must be recorded or retained for a following calculation, and also identifies the symbol used in the cube root process.

Example 2-9. Find $\sqrt[3]{10}$ by division, using an elementary calculator with memory.

Key — Operation	Display	Comment
10 ÷ 2 M + + 2 M ÷	2	First estimate = 2
= M ÷	2.5	First check = 2.5
3 M ÷	3	Second estimate in memory
10 ÷ MR ÷ MR M ÷	2.1666666	Second estimate, E_2
= M ÷ (Iteration Cycle)	2.1301776	Second check, C_2
3 M ÷	3	Third estimate in memory
10 ÷ MR ÷ MR M ÷	2.1545036	Third estimate, E_3
= M ÷	2.1542968	Third check, C_3
3 M ÷	3	Last estimate in memory
MR	2.1544346	Last estimate = answer

The third estimate, 2.1545036 is the same as E_3 in example 2-8 and the answer, 2.1544346 differs from E_4 only by the rounding error in the calculator. It can be seen that the cube root process requires about 42 steps for three cycles of estimate and check while the square root routine of example 2-7 took 29 steps, including four steps to clear memory, and four steps to store estimates into memory.

ERROR ESTIMATES—SQUARE ROOTS

It is of practical interest to know when the error remaining after each estimate is within desired limits. A good approximation for the error for the second estimate, E_2, is given by

$$\text{Error} = -\Delta^2/2X$$

where

$$\Delta = (\text{first estimate} - \text{first check})/2$$
$$x = (\text{first estimate} + \text{first check})/2$$

The error for the third estimate is given by the same formula, except that Δ and x are defined by the second estimate and check.

The operator can use the formulas to predict the errors for each estimate, if he desires, and terminate the calculation when the error is within acceptable limits.

Derivation

The derivation of the error formula is given below.

$$\text{Let } x = \sqrt{N} \text{ and } x^2 = N \qquad (2\text{-}1)$$

Let the first estimate, E_1, equal $x + \Delta$, where Δ is the error in the first estimate.

Then the first check is

$$C_1 = \frac{N}{x + \Delta} = \frac{x^2}{x + \Delta} \qquad (2\text{-}2)$$

By direct division, it can be shown that

$$C_1 = x - \Delta + \Delta^2/x \text{ approximately} \qquad (2\text{-}3)$$

The second estimate is

$$E_2 = \tfrac{1}{2}(\text{first estimate} + \text{first check})$$
$$- \tfrac{1}{2}[(x + \Delta) + (x - \Delta + \Delta^2/x)]$$
$$= x + \Delta^2/2x \qquad (2\text{-}4)$$

The error in the second estimate is:

$$\text{error} = x - E_2 = x - (x + \Delta^2/2x) \qquad (2\text{-}5)$$

$$\text{error} = -\,\Delta^2/2x \qquad (2\text{-}6)$$

Now we know that

$$E_1 - E_2 = x + \Delta \;-\; (x + \Delta^2/2x)$$
$$= \Delta - \Delta^2/2x \qquad (2\text{-}7)$$

Assuming that $\Delta^2/2x$ is small compared to Δ, then

$$E_1 - E_2 = \Delta \qquad (2\text{-}8)$$

Substituting Eq. 2-8 into Eq. 2-6, we have:

$$\text{error} = -\,\frac{\Delta^2}{2\,x} \qquad (2\text{-}9)$$

where

$$\Delta = E_1 - E_2 \text{ and } x = \sqrt{N}$$

For practical purposes, x can be replaced by E_2, therefore:

$$\text{error} = -\,\frac{(E_1 - E_2)^2}{2E_2} \qquad (2\text{-}10)$$

If its is desired to correct the estimate by the error, then

$$x = E_2 + \text{error} = E_2 - \frac{(E_1 - E_2)^2}{2E_2} \qquad (2\text{-}11\text{a})$$

Notice that the second estimate, E_2, will always be reduced by the magnitude of the error, whether Δ itself is plus or minus. The error formula, Eq. 2-10, also applies to the error in E_3 or E_4. It is only necessary to change subscripts. For example, the error in E_3 is given by

$$\text{error in } E_3 = -\,\frac{(E_1 - E_2)^2}{2E_3} \qquad (2\text{-}11\text{b})$$

ERROR FORMULAS—CUBE ROOTS

Let

$$x = \sqrt[3]{N} \text{ or } x^3 = N$$

and

$$E_1 = x + \Delta \; = \text{first estimate for } x \qquad (2\text{-}12)$$

where

$$x = \text{true cube root of } N$$
$$\Delta = \text{error in } E_1$$

Then $E_1{}^2 = (x + \Delta)^2 = (x^2 + 2\Delta\,x + \Delta^2) \qquad (2\text{-}13)$

For the first check

$$C_1 = N/E_1^2 = x^3/\ x^2 + 2\,\Delta\,x + \Delta^2$$

By direct division

$$C_1 = x - 2\Delta + 3\Delta^2/x \qquad (2\text{-}14)$$

For the second estimate

$$
\begin{aligned}
E_2 &= 2E_1 + C_1/3 && (2\text{-}15)\\
&= 2\,(x + \Delta) + (x - 2\Delta + 3\Delta^2/x)\,/3\\
&= 3x + 3\Delta^2/x\,/3 = x + \Delta^2/x && (2\text{-}16)
\end{aligned}
$$

The error in E_2 is

$$
\begin{aligned}
\text{error} &= x - E_2\\
&= x - x + \Delta^2/x = -\Delta^2/x && (2\text{-}17)
\end{aligned}
$$

Now

$$
\begin{aligned}
E_1 - E_2 &= x + \Delta - x + \Delta^2/x\\
&= \Delta - \Delta^2/x \simeq \Delta && (2\text{-}18)
\end{aligned}
$$

For practical purposes, x can be replaced by E_2. Substituting Eq. 2-18 in Eq. 2-17, we have:

$$\text{error} = -(E_1 - E_2)^2/E_2 \qquad (2\text{-}19)$$

Chapter 3

Trigonometric Functions Using Elementary Calculators

The ability of the elementary calculator to multiply and divide accurately can be used to calculate advanced functions such as sines, cosines, tangents, and logarithms. This chapter describes how trigonometric functions, and the inverse angles, can be calculated to an equivalent error of one second of arc for the largest angle, 45°. It only requires simple routines which are easy to master and can be evaluated on the elementary calculator. Two types of formulas will be discussed; accurate series expansions for any angle, x, and simple interpolation formulas which calculate a correction to an initial value selected from a table. A discussion of approximation errors is included for each formula.

The series expansions for $sin\ x$, $cos\ x$, and $tan\ x$ define the values of these functions in terms of the angle, x, where x must be expressed in radians. The conversion from degrees to radians is

$$x(\text{rad}) = \frac{x^0}{57.29578} \qquad (3\text{-}1)$$

In Table 3-1, three versions of the same series expansion are shown for $sin\ x$. The equations contain more terms as the desired angle increases, in order to maintain an accuracy of better than one second of arc. Although Eq. 3-4 is the most accurate, Eq. 3-3 is simpler and sufficiently accurate for most applications. In fact, Eq. 3-3 is the same as Eq. 3-4, except that the last term, $1 - x^2/42$, is omitted. The first example uses Eq. 3-3 to calculate $sin\ 30°$.

Table. 3-1. Equations for sin x, (x ≤ 45°).

Equation	Formulas for sin x	Recommended Angle Range	Max Error in sin x
3-2	$\sin x = x\left(1 - \dfrac{x^2}{6}\right)$	0-12° 0-30°	3.4×10^{-6} 3.3×10^{-4}
3-3	$\sin x = x\left[1 - \dfrac{x^2}{6}\left(1 - \dfrac{x^2}{20}\right)\right]$	0-30° 0-45°	2×10^{-6} 5×10^{-5}
3-4	$\sin x = x\left\{1 - \dfrac{x^2}{6}\left[1 - \dfrac{x^2}{20}\left(1 - \dfrac{x^2}{42}\right)\right]\right\}$	0-45°	2.5×10^{-7}

For sine functions of angles between 45° and 90°, see equations 3-6 and 3-7.

SINE CALCULATIONS (ELEMENTARY CALCULATOR)

Instructions are given in example 3-1 that illustrate the manner in which an elementary calculator can generate the sine functions, using Eq. 3-3. These instructions are easily converted into machine operations, as shown later.

Example 3-1. Calculate *sin 30°*, using Eq. 3-3.

Sequence of Operations	Desired Result	Comment
1. Enter 30.	30	Given angle.
2. Divide by 57.29578.	0.5235987	Value of n in radians.
3. Record result for use in step 11.		Write x.
4. Square last result (x).	0.2741555	
5. Record this number for later use.		Write x^2.
6. Divide by −20.	−0.0137077	Note negative sign.
7. Add 1.	0.9862923	
8. Multiply by −0.2741555.	−0.2703974	$-x^2$, from step 5.
9. Divide by 6.	−0.0450662	
10. Add 1.	0.9549338	
11. Multiply by x (0.5235987).	0.5000021	Answer: sin x.

The correct value of *sin 30°* is 0.50000000. Therefore, the error is about 2×10^{-6} in the sine function, which is about 0.5 sec of error in the equivalent angle (see error analysis at the end of the chapter). Naturally, this error will decrease markedly when the smaller angles are used with Eq. 3-3. Note that two results must be written or stored for later use; namely, x from step 2, and x^2, from step 4.

Equation 3-3 is recommended for general use; however, for angles below 12° (about 0.2 radian), Eq. 3-2 gives accurate

results, and, of course, it is simpler to use. For angles from 30°
to 45°, Eq. 3-4 may be used for greater accuracy. In the worst
case, *sin* 45°, the maximum error using Eq. 3-4 is about
3×10^{-7} or about 116 times less than Eq. 3-3.

You may want to memorize the formula, or the routines,
for calculating *sin x*. It is easier than one might think. Aside
from the quantities x, x^2, and unity, there are only three
constants to remember for Eq. 3-4. Briefly, the steps to solve
Eq. 3-4 are as follows:

1. Divide x^2 by -42; add 1 (remember 42).
2. Multiply by x^2; divide by -20; add 1 (remember 20).
3. Multiply by x^2; divide by -6; add 1 (remember 6).
4. Multiply by x to get *sin x*.

The three constants to remember are

$$6 = 2 \times 3, \quad 20 = 4 \times 5, \quad 42 = 6 \times 7$$

These constants form a regular progression, and the largest
constant, 42, is used first in the calculation. For less accuracy,
the expression $1 - x^2/42$ can be omitted. The resulting
formula, Eq. 3-3, becomes quite easy to use, since only two
constants, 6 and 20, are required.

For angles between 45° and 90°, Eq. 3-5 is used for
sin x, which means that *cos* $(90° - x)$ is actually calculated
instead of *sin x*.

$$\sin x = \cos (90° - x) \tag{3-5}$$

where x is in degrees.
For example

$$\sin 60° = \cos (90° - 60°) = \cos 30°$$
and
$$\sin 75° = \cos (90° - 75°) = \cos 15°$$

The method for calculating *cos x* is discussed later.

Sine with Typical Calculator

The preceding directions are general and apply to any
calculator. Example 3-2a shows how the keys on a Texas
Instruments *Datamath* calculator are used to calculate *sin x*.
The equal key, $\boxed{=}$, is used to show the numerical result for
each step of the calculation.

To make the most efficient use of the machine and the $\boxed{-}$ operations, the equation is rewritten as follows:

$$\sin x = x \left[-1 + \frac{x^2}{6} \left(-1 + \frac{x^2}{20} \right) \right] \qquad (3\text{-}3a)$$

A *change sign* key could be used to better advantage, but it is not available on simple calculators. Note that these equations can be written with different signs for individual terms and still give the correct result.

Comparing Eq. 3-3 with Eq. 3-3a,

$$\sin x = x \left[1 - \frac{x^2}{6} \left(1 - \frac{x^2}{20} \right) \right] \qquad (3\text{-}3)$$

$$= x \left[1 + \frac{x^2}{6} \left(-1 + \frac{x^2}{20} \right) \right] \qquad (3\text{-}3a)$$

The two equations can be shown to be equivalent. If we multiply the terms in the brackets, [ ], for each equation, we get the same result, Eq. 3-3b, in either case.

$$\sin x = x \left[1 - \frac{x^2}{6} + \frac{x^4}{120} \right] \qquad (3\text{-}3b)$$

In calculating sine functions you will want to use a calculator with memory to avoid writing intermediate results and reentering them later. Example 3-2 first shows the sequence required for any calculator, then example 3-3 shows how a typical calculator with memory can be used to get the same result without manually reentering any intermediate result.

Example 3-2. Calculate *sin 30°* using an elementary calculator without memory.

Step	Key–Operation	Display	Comments
Start	Enter 30.	30	x (degrees)
1	$\boxed{\div}$	30	
2	Enter 57.29578. $\boxed{=}$.	0.5235987	x (radians)
3	Write this result down.		Write x.

Step	Key—Operation	Display	Comments
4	$\boxed{\times}$ (Multiply.)	Same	
5	$\boxed{=}$	0.2741555	x^2 (radians^2)
6	Write this result down.		Write x^2.
7	$\boxed{\div}$ (Divide.)	Same	
8	Enter 20.	20	
9	$\boxed{-}$	0.0127077	
10	1	−1	
11	$\boxed{\times}$ (Multiply.)	−0.9862923	
12	Enter 0.2741555.	0.2741555	From step 5.
13	$\boxed{\div}$ (Divide.)	−0.2703974	
14	6	6	
15	$\boxed{+}$ (Add.)	−0.0450662	
16	1	1	
17	$\boxed{\times}$ (Multiply.)	0.9549338	
18	Enter 0.5235987.	0.5235987	From step 3.
19	$\boxed{=}$	0.5000020	Sin 30°

Example 3-3. Compute *sin 30°* with an elementary calculator with memory (Rockwell 20R, or Lloyd's Accumatic 40).

Key—Operation	Display	Comment
30 $\boxed{\div}$ 57.29528 $\boxed{=}$	0.5235987	x (radians)
$\boxed{M}$ $\boxed{C}$ $\boxed{M}$ $\boxed{+}$ $\boxed{\times}$	0.2741555	x^2 (in memory)
$\boxed{\div}$ 20 $\boxed{-}$	0.0137077	
1 $\boxed{\times}$	−0.9862923	
$\boxed{MR}$ $\boxed{\times}$ $\boxed{\div}$	+0.2703975	
6 $\boxed{+}$	−0.0450662	
1 $\boxed{\times}$	0.9549338	
$\boxed{MR}$ $\boxed{=}$	0.5000020	sin 30°

It is instructive to analyze the machine displays that result after each step in example 3-2. A few observations are in order. First, the machine immediately displays any number entered directly if it does not follow a mathematical operation. For example, 30 is displayed at the start of the calculation. Also, the result of the previous operation is displayed whenever the $\boxed{=}$ key is pressed. For example, the result of 30 $\boxed{\div}$ 57.29578 = 0.5235987 in step 2 is displayed after the $\boxed{=}$ is pressed.

The result of a previous operation is also displayed when the next operator key is pressed. For example, the result of 0.2741555 $\boxed{\div}$ 20 (steps 7 and 8) is displayed in step 9 as 0.0127077 after the $\boxed{-}$ key is pressed. Again, the result of −0.9862923 $\boxed{\times}$0.2741555 from steps 11 and 12 is displayed as −0.2703974 in step 13 when the $\boxed{\div}$ key is pressed. Finally, the last result of all operations is displayed in step 19 when the $\boxed{=}$ key is pressed. Pressing the $\boxed{=}$ key will always give the last result after any mathematical operation.

Each calculator will have its own individual characteristics. Hence I prefer to show the calculations as in example 3-1, where the desired result is indicated rather than the actual machine display. In this way the reader can always determine what the result of the operation is intended to be independent of a given machine's logical peculiarities.

These calculations are greatly simplified if an *intermediate* calculator is available, which has an addressable memory, and $\sqrt{x}$ and x^2 keys, as discussed in example 3-4. Here the number $x^2 = 0.2741555$ is entered into memory in step 6 and recalled for use in step 12 without either writing or reentering the number. Similarly, $x = 0.5235987$ could be recalled in step 18 as $\sqrt{x^2} = x$.

Example 3-4. Calculate *sin 30°*, using memory, $\sqrt{x}$, and x^2 functions.

Step	Key—Operation	Desired Result	Comments
Start	Enter 30.	30	x (degrees)
1	$\boxed{\div}$	30	
2	Enter 57.29578. $\boxed{=}$.	0.5235987	x (radians)
3	Omit.		
4	Omit.		
5	$\boxed{x^2}$	0.2741555	x^2 (radians^2)
6	$\boxed{x \rightarrow M}$		Store x^2 in memory.
7	$\boxed{\div}$ (Divide.)	Same	
8	Enter 20.	20	
9	$\boxed{-}$	0.0137077	
10	1	-1	
11	$\boxed{\times}$ (Multiply.)	-0.9862923	
12	$\boxed{M \rightarrow x}$ (Memory to display.)	0.2741555	x^2 to display.
13	$\boxed{\div}$ (Divide.)	-0.2703974	
14	6	6	
15	$\boxed{+}$ (Add.)	-0.0450662	
16	1	1	
17	$\boxed{\times}$ (Multiply.)	0.9549338	
18	$\boxed{M \rightarrow x}$, $\boxed{\sqrt{x}}$	0.5235987	$\sqrt{\text{memory}} = x$
19	$\boxed{=}$	0.5000020	sin 30°

You should test your mastery of these formulas and routines by calculating the following values for *sin x* and checking against the values below. Are your answers within the error limits listed in Table 3-1?

Calculate	Table Values
sin 10° (using Eq. 3-2)	0.1736482
sin 20° (using Eq. 3-3)	0.3420201
sin 40° (using Eq. 3-4)	0.6427876
sin 70° (using Eq. 3-5)	0.9396926

Remember to use the minus key in the sequence shown in the examples.

Cosine Calculations

In most applications, such as resolving vectors into components, $cos\ x$ calculations occur as frequently as $sin\ x$ calculations. The formula and routines for $cos\ x$ are quite similar to those for $sin\ x$. In fact, $cos\ x$ is often easier to calculate than $sin\ x$. Only the value for x^2 is required in the formula for $cos\ x$ and must be stored or recorded. Once more, there are three simple constants to remember for the most accurate formula (Eq. 3-7).

$$2 = 1 \times 2, \qquad 12 = 3 \times 4, \qquad 30 = 5 \times 6$$

Again, these constants from a regular progression, which makes them easy to remember. (See Table 3-2.)

Table 3-2. Formulas for cos x, x ≤ 90°.

Equation	Formula for cos x	Angle Range	Maximum Error
3-6	$cos\ x = 1 + \dfrac{x^2}{2}\left(-1 + \dfrac{x^2}{12}\right)$	0-20°	2.5×10^{-6}
3-7	$cos\ x = 1 + \dfrac{x^2}{2}\left[-1 + \dfrac{x^2}{12}\left(1 + \dfrac{x^2}{-30}\right)\right]$	0-45°	3.6×10^{-6}
3-8	$cos\ x = sin\ (90° - x)$	45°-90°	Same as for sin x.

The value of $cos\ 45°$ will be calculated in a manner similar to $sin\ x$, using Eq. 3-7 from Table 3-2. Once more the usual formula for $cos\ x$ is rewritten for efficient use of the calculator. This is the most accurate formula and gives better than 1 sec accuracy for $cos\ 45°$. Again, Eq. 3-6 is a special form of Eq. 3-7 with the expression $(1 - x^2/30)$ being omitted.

The maximum error occurs at *cos 45°*. For this worst case, the value, correct to seven places, is 0.7071067. Therefore, the maximum error is 3.6×10^{-6} in *cos x*, which is equivalent to about 1 sec in angle.

Example 3-5. Calculate *cos 45°* using Eq. 3-6.

Step or Instruction	Desired Result	Comment
1. Enter 45.	45	x (degrees)
2. Divide by 57.29578.	0.7853981	x (radians)
3. Multiply by itself.	0.6168501	x^2
4. Write this result down.		Write x^2.
5. Divide by −30.	−0.0205616	
6. Add 1.	0.9794384	
7. Multiply by $x^2 = 0.6168501$.	0.604166	From step 4.
8. Divide by 12.	0.0503472	
9. Subtract 1.	−0.9496528	
10. Multiply by $x^2 = 0.6168501$.	−0.5857934	From step 4.
11. Divide by 2.	−0.2928967	
12. Add 1.	0.7071033	cos 45°

It should be pointed out that the numbers in the *Desired Result* column are those produced when the $\boxed{=}$ button on the computer is pressed after each arithmetic operation ($\boxed{\times}$, $\boxed{-}$, $\boxed{\div}$, $\boxed{+}$). On most calculators, pressing the $\boxed{=}$ key is not necessary in a chain calculation until the final result is needed.

For angles larger than 90°, the following formulas can be applied. It can be seen, in all cases that the angle *x* actually used in the calculation is 45° or less (0.7854 rad or less):

For $90° \leqslant x \leqslant 135°$:
$$\sin x = \cos (x - 90°) \text{ and } \cos x = -\sin (x - 90°) \quad (3\text{-}9)$$

For $135° \leqslant x \leqslant 180°$:
$$\sin x = \sin (180° - x) \text{ and } \cos x = -\cos (180° - x) \quad (3\text{-}10)$$

You should now calculate some values of *cos x* using these formulas to make sure you understand the routines. The table values for each example are given below.

Cos x calculations	Table Values
Calculate cos 40° (using equation 3-7).	0.7660444
Calculate cos 15° (using equation 3-6).	0.9659258
Calculate cos 70° (using equations 3-6 and 3-8).	0.3420201
Calculate cos 160°. What formula should you use?	0.9396926

CALCULATING TANGENT FUNCTIONS

The tangent function is given by

$$\tan x = \frac{\sin x}{\cos x}$$

However, it would be too laborious to separately calculate *sin x* and *cos x*, and then divide. Unfortunately, the usual series expansion for the tangent of an angle converges quite slowly and would require too many terms to achieve even 4-place accuracy. We will use instead the first few terms of the continued fraction expansion to be explained below. This equation results in a reasonably simple expression with an accuracy of 1 sec arc.

The three equations shown in Table 3-3 give the values of the tangent function for three ranges of the angle: $0-10°$, $0-30°$, and $0-45°$. These ranges are chosen to keep the equivalent angle error to within 1 sec of arc. The maximum errors in the function or the angle are also given in Table 3-3.

Table 3-3. Formulas for tan x. ($x \leqslant 45°$).

Equation	Formula	Angle Range	Max Error in Tan x
3-11	$\tan x = \dfrac{3x}{3-x^2}$	0°-10° 0°-20° 0°-25°	3.7×10^{-6} 1.3×10^{-6} 4.0×10^{-4}
3-12	$\tan x = \dfrac{x(15-x^2)}{15-6\,x^2}$	0°-25° 0°-45°	2.3×10^{-6} 2.1×10^{-4}
3-13	$\tan x = \dfrac{x(105-10\,x^2)}{x^2(x^2-45)+105}$	0°-45°	2.3×10^{-6}

These formulas are derived from Eq. 3-14, the continued-fraction expansion form of *tan x*. For example, Eq. 3-11 is derived from the first two terms of Eq. 3-14. These formulas are accurate and easy to use if your calculator has $1/x$, $\sqrt{x}$, x^2, and memory—recall functions.

$$\tan x = \cfrac{x}{1 - \cfrac{x^2}{3 - \cfrac{x^2}{5 - \cfrac{x^2}{7 - }}}} \qquad \begin{matrix}\text{Continued fraction}\\ \text{expansion for } \tan x\end{matrix} \quad (3\text{-}14)$$

Suppose now we wanted to calculate *tan 30°*, using Eq. 3-14. For illustration purposes, only the first three terms of Eq. 3-14 will be used to demonstrate the method. This is equivalent to Eq. 3-12.

Example 3-6A. Calculate $tan\ 30°$, using three terms of Eq. 3-14.

Key or Instruction	Desired Result	Comment
Enter 30.	30	x (degrees)
Divide by 57.29578.	0.52359876	x (radians)
Square x.	0.27415567	x^2
Store in memory (STO).		
Divide by −5.	−0.05483113	$-x^2/5$
Add 3.	2.9451688	
Take reciprocal (1/x).	0.33953910	
Recall from memory (RCL).	−0.27415567	$-x^2$
Multiply by $-x^2$.	−0.09308657	
Add +1.	0.90691342	
Take reciprocal (1/x).	1.1026410	
Recall from memory.	0.27415567	x^2
Take square root ($\sqrt{x}$).	0.52359876	x
Multiply.	0.57734150	tan 30

The correct value of $tan\ 30°$ is 0.5773503; therefore, the maximum error in the calculation is 8.8×10^{-6}, and the equivalent error in angle is −1.4 sec of arc. These errors in $tan\ x$ reduce rapidly for smaller angles. For example, the error in $tan\ 20°$ is about 4.5×10^{-7} in function, or only about −0.08 sec in angle.

The procedure shown in example 3-6 appears to require a calculator with square root and square functions, as well as a change sign key. But these functions are not necessary, as shown in example 3-7. Using the Lloyd's *Accumatic 40*, the Sears 8M, or the Rockwell 20R, $tan\ 30°$ can be found by the following procedure.

Example 3-6B. Find $tan\ 30°$, using an elementary calculator (Rockwell 20R, Sears 8M, etc.).

Key−Operation	Display
30 ÷ 57.29578 = M +	0.5235987 (radians)
9 ÷ ÷ × MR × − 7 =	−6.9695383
÷ ÷ × MR × + 5 =	4.9606638
÷ ÷ × MR × − 3 =	−2.9447342
÷ ÷ × MR × + 1 =	0.9068998
÷ ÷ × MR =	0.5773500

The true value of *tan 30°* is 0.5773503. Similarly, *tan 45°* = 0.9999997, and *tan 65°* = 2.1445038.

For calculators without the additional functions (reciprocals, memory, recall, etc.), Eqs. 3-12 and 3-13 can be used for *tan x* and will give the identical result. To illustrate the use of these equations, *tan 45°* will be calculated using Eq. 3-13, which is equivalent to all terms of Eq. 3-14.

Example 3-7. Calculate *tan 45°*, using Eq. 3-13.

Key or Instruction	Desired Result	Comment
1. Enter 45.	45	x (degrees)
2. Divide by 57.29578	0.7853981	x (radians)
3. Write down result.		Write x.
4. Square x.	0.6168501	x^2
5. Subtract 45.	−44.383159	$x^2 - 45$
6. Multiply by 0.6168501.	0.6168501	x^2 (From step 4.)
7. Press $=$.	−27.37775	$x^2 (x^2 - 45)$
8. Add 105.	105	
9. Press $=$	77.62225	Denominator of equation 6.13.
10. Write this result down for step 18.		
11. Enter 0.6168501.		x^2 (From step 4.)
12. Multiply by −10.	−10	
13. Press $=$.	−6.168501	$-10x^2$
14. Add 105.	98.8315	$105 - 10x^2$
15. Multiply by 0.7853984.		From step 3.
16. Press $=$.	77.622072	$x (105 - 10x^2)$
17. Divide by 77.62225.		From step 8.
18. Press $=$.	0.9999977	tan 45°.

Note: The $=$ operation may be omitted in steps. 9. 13. and 16.

The correct result is 1.000000 for *tan 45°*, the worst case. Therefore the maximum error in the tangent function is −2.3 × 10^6, or about −0.24 sec in angle. Clearly, *tan x* for smaller angles coverges more rapidly. For example, *tan 35°* is found to be 0.70020736, and the error in angle is only −0.02 sec. Note that the error in function is less than one-tenth the previous error.

The simpler formula, Eq. 3-12, can be used for calculating the tangent of angles less than 30° as shown on next page. Note that the error for *tan 30°* is about 1.4 sec in the equivalent angle.

Example 3-8. Calculate *tan 30°* using Eq. 3-12.

Key or Instruction	Desired Result	Comment
1. Enter 30.	30	x (degrees)
2. Divide by 57.29578.	0.52359877	x (radians)
3. Write down result.		Write x.
4. Square x.	0.27415567	x^2
5. Write result down.		Write x^2.
6. Multiply by −6.	−1.6449340	
7. Add 15.	13.355066	
8. Write this result down.		Write denominator.
9. Enter −0.27415567.	−0.27415567	From step 5.
10. Add 15.	14.725844	
11. Divide by step 9 result (denominator).	1.1026410	
12. Multiply by x = 0.52359877.		From step 3.
13. Press $\boxed{=}$.	0.57734147	tan 30°

To test your ability to calculate *tan x*, try the following examples. Compare your results to the table values and check whether your answer is within the errors shown in Table 3-3.

Calculate	Table Value
tan 10°	0.1763270
tan 22°	0.4040262
tan 40°	0.8390996
tan 65°	2.1445069
tan 130°	−1.1917536

Other values of the tangent for angles greater than 45° can be found using relations similar to those for *sin x*. For example:

For 45° ⩾ x ⩾ 90°

$$\tan x = \frac{1}{\tan (90° - x)} \qquad (3\text{-}15)$$

For 90° ⩾ x ⩾ 135°

$$\tan x = \frac{-1}{\tan (135° - x)} \qquad (3\text{-}16)$$

For 135° ⩽ x ⩽ 180°

$$\tan x = -\tan (180 - x) \qquad (3\text{-}17)$$

You are now in a position to calculate *sin x*, *cos x*, or *tan x* with an equivalent angle accuracy which is guaranteed to 1 sec

Table. 3-4. Trigonometric Functions.

x_o	Sin x_o	Cos x_o	Tan x_o
1	0.0174 524	0.9998 477	0.0174 551
2	0.0348 995	0.9993 908	0.0349 208
3	0.0523 360	0.9986 295	0.0524 078
4	0.0697 565	0.9975 641	0.0699 268
5	0.0871 557	0.9961 947	0.0874 887
6	0.1045 285	0.9945 219	0.1051 042
7	0.1218 693	0.9925 462	0.1227 846
8	0.1391 731	0.9902 681	0.1405 408
9	0.1564 345	0.9876 883	0.1583 844
10	0.1736 482	0.9848 078	0.1763 270
11	0.1908 090	0.9816 272	0.1943 803
12	0.2079 117	0.9781 476	0.2125 566
13	0.2249 511	0.9743 701	0.2308 682
14	0.2419 219	0.9702 957	0.2493 280
15	0.2588 190	0.9659 258	0.2679 492
16	0.2756 374	0.9612 617	0.2867 454
17	0.2923 717	0.9563 048	0.2057 307
18	0.3090 170	0.9510 565	0.3249 197
19	0.3255 682	0.9455 186	0.3443 276
20	0.3420 201	0.9396 926	0.3639 702
21	0.3583 679	0.9335 804	0.3838 640
22	0.3746 066	0.9271 839	0.4040 262
23	0.3907 311	0.9205 049	0.4244 748
24	0.4067 366	0.9135 455	0.4452 287
25	0.4226 183	0.9063 078	0.4663 077
26	0.4383 711	0.8987 940	0.4877 326
27	0.4539 905	0.8910 065	0.5095 254
28	0.4694 716	0.8829 476	0.5317 094
29	0.4848 096	0.8746 197	0.5543 091
30	0.5000 000	0.8660 254	0.5773 503
31	0.5150 381	0.8571 673	0.6008 606
32	0.5299 193	0.8480 481	0.6248 694
33	0.5446 390	0.8386 706	0.6964 076
34	0.5591 929	0.8290 376	0.6745 085
35	0.5735 764	0.1891 520	0.7002 075
36	0.5877 853	0.8090 170	0.7265 425
37	0.6018 150	0.7986 355	0.7535 541
38	0.6156 615	0.7880 108	0.7812 856
39	0.6293 204	0.7771 460	0.8097 840
40	0.6427 876	0.7660 444	0.8390 996
41	0.6560 590	0.7547 096	0.8692 867

x_o	Sin x_o	Cos x_o	Tan x_o
		Table 3-4. Con't.	
42	0.6691 306	0.7431 448	0.9004 040
43	0.6819 984	0.7313 537	0.9325 151
44	0.6946 584	0.7193 398	0.9656 888
45	0.7071 068	0.7071 068	1.0000 000

Direct Functions

Terms: $\alpha = (x - x_o)/K$

$K = 57.29578$

$\sin x = \sin x_o (1 - \alpha^2/2) + \alpha \cos x_o$

$\cos x = \cos x_o (1 - \alpha^2/2) - \alpha \sin x_o$

$\tan x = (\tan x_o + \alpha)/(1 - \alpha \tan x_o)$

Note: $\alpha^2/2$ term may be omitted for 4-place accuracy.

Inverse Functions

$2K = 114.59156$

$x = x_o + 2K (\sin x - \sin x_o)/(\cos x + \cos x_o)$

$x = x_o + 2K (\cos x_o - \cos x)/(\sin x + \sin x_o)$

$x = x_o + K (\tan x - \tan x_o)/[1 + \tan x(\tan x_o)]$

Simpler formulas apply for 4-place accuracy.

of arc or better. All you need is your pocket calculator and the routines illustrated in this chapter. The simpler formulas may be used in each case if equivalent angular accuracies of 1 min of arc are acceptable.

The methods presented thus far are capable of generating *sin x, cos x,* and *tan x* functions for any angle, to several parts per million in function and well within 1 sec of arc in equivalent angle. However, different formulas are required for each of these functions and for the inverse functions to be described shortly. A simpler method, using tables (see Table 3-4), is capable of higher accuracy with less calculation. In essence, the new method depends on the use of tables which contain the baseline functions, plus simple interpolation formulas which supply corrections to the baseline value. This is described in the next section

INVERSE TRIGONOMETRIC FUNCTIONS

The preceding sections showed how to generate trigonometric functions directly from the angle, x, using series expansions and elementary or intermediate calculators. Now we will show how to determine the *angle*, once the function is given. This process of finding the inverse function, or the angle corresponding to the given function, is generally more difficult and requires more care. Let us start by defining terms.

If $y = sin\ x$, then x is the inverse sine of y, or $x = $ arc *sin y*. Similarly if $y = cos\ x$, then $x = $ arc *cos y*. Sometimes $x = $ arc *sin y* is written as $x = sin^{-1}y$. In either case, x is referred to as "the angle whose sine is y." Both notations are used in the literature and in scientific calculators. For convenience, we will use the following terms for the inverse trigonometric function: $x = $ arc *sin y*, $x = $ arc *cos y*, and $x = $ arc *tan y*.

The usual series expansions for the inverse functions generally converge quite slowly. The operator must evaluate many terms in the series to achieve 4- or 5-figure accuracy. Furthermore, the expansions for the inverse functions are much different than the expansions for the direct functions and place a greater demand on the user's memory.

What follows is a simple approach to the calculation of the inverse trigonometric functions which has several advantages over the series expansion method. This approach involves the use of a simple table of tigonometric functions and a set of formulas, both of which can be put on a wallet-sized card. Basically, Table 3-4 can be used to provide an initial estimate (x_o) of the desired angle, and the formulas of Table 3-5 can be used to calculate the correction to the angle. These simple formulas involve ordinary arithmetic operations, which are ideally suited for the elementary calculator. The initial estimates of Table 3-4 can be used with the more accurate formulas listed at the bottom of the table if greater accuracy is desired.

The simple formulas of Table 3-5 can be used to attain 4- or 5-figure accuracy using the elementary calculator. The accurate formulas, Eqs. 3-20 to 3-24, are capable of 6- or 7-figure accuracy, although an intermediate calculator is desirable for the square root operation. Even better angular accuracy is possible in most cases, providing the table of sine, cosine, and tangent functions are extended to the desired eight or nine places.

The advantages of the table and correction method for trigonometric functions are many:

1. It can be used for both *direct* and *inverse* functions with slight modifications to the formulas.
2. All correction formulas can easily be memorized.
3. It involves only a few arithmetic operations on the ordinary calculator.
4. It is capable of extremely high accuracy.
5. The original tables can be used to provide simple checks.
6. The table of trigonometric functions is a single card.

The table and correction method is also very useful for the calculation of direct and inverse logarithms, as will be explained later. In fact, this interpolation technique is generally applicable to the calculation of more complex functions, such as hyperbolic functions, compound interest problems, and logarithmic functions.

Use of the Tables

To explain the correction method, we will discuss first the use of Table 3-4 and the formulas for the correction angle, α. Table 3-4 gives the values of the sine, cosine, and tangent functions to seven places for the angle x_o, up to 45°, in 1° intervals. To use the table, the operator locates the given value of the function between two entries of the table and records the nearest angle, x_o, and the corresponding function values, $sin\ x_o$ and $cos\ x_o$.

For example, suppose we wanted to find the angle $x = $ arc $sin\ 0.5060338$. Then, $sin\ x = 0.5060388$ is found between 30° and 31°. The table shows the following:

x_o	$sin\ x_o$	$cos\ x_o$
30°	0.5000000	0.8660254
31°	0.5150381	0.8571673

Since $sin\ 30°$ is closer to 0.5060338, the nearest value of x_o is 30°; $sin\ x_o = 0.5000000$ and $cos\ x_o = 0.8660254$. The formula for the correction angle, α, is Eq. 3-18, shown in Table 3-5.

Table. 3-5. Simple Formulas for Inverse Sine and Cosine.

Equation	Inverse Function	Desired Angle
3-18	$x = \sin^{-1} y$ or $x = \text{arc sin } y$ where $y \leqslant 0.707$	$x = x_o + \alpha$ * $\alpha = \dfrac{\sin x - \sin x_o}{\cos x_o}$
3-19	$x = \cos^{-1} y$ or $x = \text{arc cos } y$ where $y \leqslant 0.707$	$x = x_o + \alpha$ * $\alpha = \dfrac{\cos x - \cos x_o}{-\sin x_o}$
3-20	$x = \tan^{-1} y$ or $x = \text{arc tan } y$ where $y \leqslant 1.000$	$x = x_o + \alpha$ * $\alpha = \dfrac{\tan x - \tan x_o}{1 + \tan x (\tan x_o)}$

* Multiply α by 57.29578 to obtain the correction in degrees.

The correction angle, α, in radians, is calculated from Eq. 3-18.

$$\alpha = \frac{\sin x - \sin x_o}{\cos x_o} = \frac{0.5060338 - 0.5000000}{0.8660254}$$

$$= 0.0069672 \text{ rad}$$

In degrees $\alpha = 0.0069672 \ (57.29578)$

$$= 0.3991930°$$

Finally, $x = x_o + \alpha = 30.39919°$

The true value of x is 30.4000000°. Therefore the error in x is less than 0.001°, or less than 1 part in 30,000. Of course, the initial value of $x_o = 30°$, selected from the table, provided the first two figures. Example 3-9 shows the calculator steps used to find the value of the angle x using the baseline functions from Table 3-4.

Example 3-9. Find $x = \text{arc } \sin 0.5060338$, using Eq. 3-18 and $x_o = 30°$, $\sin 30° = 0.500$.

Entry or Operation	Display	Comment
Enter 0.5060338.	0.5060338	$\sin x$ (given)
− 0.5000000	0.0060338	$\sin x - \sin x_o$
÷ 0.8660254	0.00696723	α (radians)
· 57.29578	0.39919300	α (degrees)
· 30	30.399193	x (degrees)

Notice that only subtract, divide, multiply, and add operations were required. These directions are intended to be independent of the specific type of calculator used. Therefore the first column shows the desired operation and the second column shows the desired display.

Larger values of α and x_o cause larger errors, as shown in example 3-10.

Example 3-10. Find $x = $ arc $sin\,0.713250$, using Eq. 3-18 and $x_o = 45°$, $sin\,45° = 0.7071068$.

Entry or Operation	Display	Comment
Enter 0.7132504.	0.7132504	$\sin x$
$\boxed{-}$ 0.7071068	0.0061437	$\sin x - \sin 45°$
$\boxed{\div}$ 0.7071068	0.0086885	$\cos 45°$. α in radians
$\boxed{\times}$ 57.29578	0.4978139	α (degrees)
$\boxed{-}$ 45	45.49781	x (degrees)

Since the true angle x is 45.50000°, the error in the angle is about −0.0022° for $\alpha = 0.5°$. This is the largest error in the arc *sin* calculation, because the largst angle (45°) and the largest value of α were used. For example, if α were 0.20°, the error would reduce to −0.000350°.

Estimates of error for $x = $ arc *sin* y, $x = $ arc *tan* y are given at the end of the chapter.

If the answer were required in radians, then the correction (α), expressed in radians, would be added to the angle x_o, converted to radians. This gives x (radians) = $0.0069672 + 30/57.29578 = 0.5305660$. The error in x is only about 1.4×10^{-5} rad, which is less than 1 sec of arc.

Inverse Cosine Function

The calculation of arc *cos* y is very similar.

Example 3-11. Find $x = $ arc *cos* 0.8633956, using Eq. 3-19 and $x_o = 30°$, $cos\,30° = 0.8660254$.

Entry or Operation	Display	Comment
Enter 0.8633956.	0.8633956	$\cos x$
$\boxed{-}$ 0.8660254	−0.0026299	$\cos x - \cos 30°$
$\boxed{\div}$ −0.5000000	0.0052597	$-\sin x_o$. α in radians
$\boxed{\times}$ 57.29578	0.3013590	α (degrees)
$\boxed{+}$ 30	30.301359	x (degrees)

The true value is 30.3000° and, therefore, the error is about +0.0014°. We can save operations by reversing the first two numbers (as shown in example 3-12) and eliminate the need for changing signs.

Example 3-12. Find x = arc *cos 0.9640954*, using Eq. 3-19 and x_o = 15°, *cos* 15° = 0.9640954.

Entry or Operation	Display	Comment
Enter 0.9659258	0.9640954	cos 15°
[−] 0.9640954	0.0018304	cos 15° − cos x
[÷] 0.2588190 (sin 15°)	0.0070722	α (radians)
[×] 57.29578	0.4052976	α (degrees)
[+] 15	15.40521	x (degrees)

The true angle is 15.40000°, and the error is about 0.005°, or about 1 part in 3000. Note that errors for x = arc *cos y* are higher for smaller angles than for larger angles.

However, the equivalent error in the function *cos* 15.4° is only

$$\cos 15.40° - \cos 15.40521° = 0.000024$$

Inverse Tangent Function—Accurate Formula

The use of the interpolation method really pays off in calculating the inverse tangent functions. The usual series expansion converges slowly for x = arc *tan y* and would tax the operator's patience and skill. In contrast, the simple method offered here is capable of 6−8 place accuracy in angles, with far less calculation. This formula is so simple and accurate that there is no need to use any other.

Let $\quad x$ = arc tan y

assume $\quad x = x_o + \alpha$

and $\quad x = \dfrac{\tan x - \tan x_o}{1 + \tan x \tan x_o}$ $\qquad$ (3-20)

Although it has a somewhat different appearance, Eq. 3-20 has the same form as 3-18 and 3-19, namely:

$$\alpha = \frac{\text{difference in function}}{\text{slope of function}}$$

Some examples will illustrate the power of this formula. Only the desired operations will be shown, not the actual calculator sequence.

Example 3-13. Find arc *tan 0.7106630*, using Eq. 3-20 ($x_o = 35°$, *tan* $x_o = 0.7002075$).

Entry or Operation	Display	Comment
Enter 0.7106630.	0.7106630	tan x
$\boxed{-}$ 0.7002075 $\boxed{=}$ $\boxed{M+}$	0.0104555	tan x − 35°
0.7106630 $\boxed{\times}$ 0.7002075	0.4976116	tan x × tan 35°
$\boxed{+}$ 1 $\boxed{-}$ $\boxed{MR}$	0.0069814	α (radians)
$\boxed{\times}$ 57.29578	0.4000065	α (degrees)
$\boxed{+}$ 35	35.400006	$x = x_o + \alpha$ (degrees)

The true value of arc *tan 0.7106630* is 35.4000°, and the error is only 0.0000065°, or less than 1 part in 5 million in angle.

The formula is equally good for small angles, as shown in example 3-14.

Example 3-14. Find arc *tan 0.0927672*, using Eq. 3-20 ($x_o = 5°$, *tan* 5° = 0.0874887).

Entry or Operation	Display	Comment
Enter 0.0927672	0.0927672	
$\boxed{-}$ 0.0874887 $\boxed{=}$ $\boxed{M+}$	0.0052785	tan x − tan 5°
0.0927672 $\boxed{\times}$ 0.0874887	0.0081161	tan x × tan 5°
$\boxed{+}$ $\boxed{1}$ $\boxed{-}$ $\boxed{MR}$	0.0052360	α (radians)
$\boxed{\times}$ 57.29578	0.3000027	α (degrees)
$\boxed{+}$ 5.0	5.3000027	x (degrees)

The error in angle is only 0.0000027, or only about 1 part in 2 million in angle. The error analysis shows that the *theoretical* error for the arc tangent function is only about $\alpha^3/3$ rad (or $\alpha^3 \times 0.0001°$) and is independent of the angle. The reader can verify that this theoretical error applies to examples 3-13 and 13-4.

Accurate Formulas for Arc Sin and Arc Cos

The previous section showed that the angular errors for arc *sin y* decreased with angle x, and the errors for arc *cos y* increased with x. In constrast, the following formulas are independent of x and are capable of much greater accuracy. Of course, there is some extra work required for this accuracy.

The previous examples will now be recalculated to show the increase in accuracy.

Table 3-6. Accurate Formulas for arc sin y and arc cos y.

Equation	Inverse Function	Formula
3-21 3-22	$x = \text{arc sin } y$ $0 < y \leq 0.707$	$x = x_0 + \alpha$ $* \; \alpha = \dfrac{2(\sin x - \sin x_0)}{\cos x + \cos x_0}$ $\cos x = \sqrt{1 - \sin^2 x}$
3-23 3-24	$x = \text{arc cos } y$ $0.707 \leq y$ ≤ 1.000	$x = x_0 + a$ $* \; \alpha = \dfrac{2(\cos x_0 - \cos y)}{\sin x_0 + \sin x}$ $\sin x = \sqrt{1 - \cos^2 x}$

* Multiply α by 57.29578 to convert to degrees.

Examples 3-15. Calculate $x = $ arc $sin\ 0.5060338$, using Eq. 3-21. Use $x_0 = 30°$, $sin\ 30° = 0.500$.

Entry or Operation	Display	Comment
Enter 0.5060338	0.5060338	$\sin x$
$-$ 0.5000000	0.0060338	$\sin x - \sin 30°$
$\times$ 2 $=$ M $+$	0.0120676	Store $2(\sin x - \sin 30°)$.
0.5070338 x^2 CHS	-0.2560702	$-\sin^2 x$
$+$ 1. $\sqrt{x}$	0.8625136	$\cos x = \sqrt{1 - \sin^2 x}$
$+$ 0.8660254	1.7285391	$\cos x + \cos 30°)$
$\div$ $\searrow$ MR	0.00698.14	α (radians)
$\times$ 57.29578	0.04000040	α (degrees)
$+$ 30	30.400004	x (degrees)

The previous error of 0.0008°, using Eq. 3-18, is now reduced by a factor of 200 to 1, down to 0.000004°. However, there are nine more calculator operations (or twice as many) required to achieve this increased accuracy.

The $=$ M $+$ sequence serves to store in memory the quantity $2(sin\ x - sin\ 30)$ for subsequent recall (MR) and division by $cos\ x + cos\ x_0$ to obtain $\alpha = 0.0069814$.

Example 3-16. Calculate $x = $ arc $sin\ 0.7132504$, using Eq. 3-21, $x_0 = 45°$, $sin\ 45° = 0.7071068$.

Entry or Operation	Display	Comment
Enter 0.7132504	0.7132504	$\sin x$
$-$ 0.7071068	0.0061436	$\sin x - \sin 45°$
$\times$ 2 $=$ M $+$	0.0122872	Store $2(\sin x - \sin 45°)$.
0.7132504 x^2 CHS	-0.4912739	$-\sin^2 x$

Entry or Operation	Display	Comment
[+] 1 $\sqrt{x}$	0.7009093	$\cos x = \sqrt{1 - \sin^2 x}$
[+] 0.7070168	1.4080161	$\cos x + \cos 45°$
[÷] [×] [MR]	0.0087266	α (radians)
[×] 57.29578	0.4999976	α (degrees)
[+] 45	45.499998	x (degrees)

The previous error of 0.0022° using the simple formula is reduced to 0.0000024°, or by a factor of almost 1000 to 1, for $\alpha = 0.5°$. The appendix shows that the *theoretical* error for Eq. 3-21 depends only on the value for α and is approximately:

$$\frac{\alpha^3}{12} \text{ radians or about } 2.5 \times 10^{-5}\alpha^3 \text{ degrees}$$

We can now rework previous examples for arc *cos y*, using the more accurate Eq. 3-23 for the arc cosine functions, and compare results. The error reductions are equally startling and are also independent of the angle x_o.

Example 3-17. Find $x =$ arc *cos 0.8633956*, using Eq. 3-23 and $x_o = 30°$, $\cos 30° = 0.8660254$.

Entry or Operation	Display	Comment
Enter 0.8660254	0.8660254	$\cos 30°$
[−] 0.8633956	0.0026298	$\cos 30° - \cos x$
[×] 2 [=] [M] [+]	0.0052596	Store $2(\cos 30° - \cos x)$.
0.8633956 [x^2] [CHS]	−0.7454520	$-\cos^2 x$
[+] 1 $\sqrt{x}$	0.5045275	$\sin x$
[+] 0.5000000	1.00045275	$\sin x + \sin x_o$
[÷] [÷] [×] [MR]	0.0052359	α (radians)
[×] 57.29578	0.2999951	α (degrees)
[+] 30	30.299995	x (degrees)

The error of 0.0014° is now reduced to 0.000005° or by about 300 to 1 for $\alpha = 0.3°$

Example 3-18. Find $x =$ arc *cos 0.9640954*, using Eq. 3-23 and $x_o = 15°$, $\cos 15° = 0.9650258$.

Enter or Operation	Display	Comment
Enter 0.9640954	0.9640954	$\cos x$
[−] 0.9650258	−0.0018304	$\cos x - \cos x_o$
[×] 2 [=] [M] [+]	−0.0036609	Store $2(\cos x - \cos x_o)$
0.9640954 [x^2] [CHS]	−0.9294799	$\cos^2 x$
[+] 1 $\sqrt{x}$	0.2655561	$\sin x$
[+] 0.2588190	0.5243752	$\sin x + \sin x_o$
[÷] [÷] [×] [MR]	0.0069814	α (radians)
[×] 57.29578	0.4000047	α (degrees)
[+] 15	15.400005	x (degrees)

69

The error is reduced from 0.0052° to about 0.000005°, or by 1000 to 1. The theoretical error is about 0.000003°; the difference is due to the use of 7-place values for $\sin x$ and $\cos x$ rather than 8-place or more.

Use of Tables for Direct Trigonometric Functions

The same set of tables can be used to calculate the trigonometric functions directly from the given angle, $x = (x_o + \alpha)$. As before, the value of x_o is chosen from Table 3-4, and the value of α is the difference between the given angle, x, and the table angle, x_o.

The operations are very simple and can be performed on the elementary 4-function calculator. The interpolation formula to calculate these functions directly from the table are as follows:

$$\sin (x_o + \alpha) = B \sin x_o + \alpha \cos x_o \qquad (3\text{-}25)$$

where
$$B = (1 - \alpha^2/2) \qquad (3\text{-}26)$$

$$\cos (x_o + \alpha) = B \cos x_o - \alpha \sin x_o \qquad (3\text{-}27)$$

$$\tan (x_o + \alpha) = \frac{\tan x_o + \alpha}{1 - \alpha \tan x_o} \qquad (3\text{-}28)$$

If only moderate (4−5 place) accuracy is required, the constant B in Eqs. 3-25 and 3-27 can be set to equal unity. The calculation takes only the three steps shown in example 3-19 below. The maximum error is about $\alpha^2/2$ for $\sin x$ or $\cos x$. If B is set equal to $1 - \alpha^2/2$, then the maximum error in Eqs. 3-25 and 3-27 reduces to $\alpha^3/6$ radian, or less than 1×10^{-7}, for $\alpha = 0.50°$.

The error in Eq.3-28 for $\tan (x + \alpha)$ is about $\alpha^3/3$ $\cos^2 x$, or about 4.5×10^{-7} in function for $\alpha = 0.500°$ and $x = 45°$.

You should try calculating the direct trigonometric functions both by the series equations of Tables 3-1, 3-2, and 3-3, and then by the methods indicated here. You may well decide to use the tables and correction formulas for all direct and inverse trigonometric calculations because of the convenience and the accuracy of using the same method for all functions.

Following is a comparison of the use of Eq. 3-25 and with $B = 1$, and $B = 1 - \alpha^2/2$, which is much more accurate.

Example 3-19. Find $sin\ 31.4°$. Use Eq. 3-25, $B = 1$, and $x_0 = 31°$.

Entry or Operation	Display	Comment
Enter 0.40 $\div$ 57.26578	0.00698132	α (radians)
$\times$ 0.8571673	0.0059842	$\alpha \cos x_0$ ($x_0 = 31°$)
$+$ 0.5150391	0.5210222	$sin\ x_0 + \alpha \cos x_0$

The error in function $sin\ 31.4$ is

$$error = 0.5210086 - 0.5210222$$

or about 1.3×10^{-5}. Now suppose $B = 1 - \alpha^2/2$.

Example 3-20. Find $sin\ 31.4°$, using Eq. 3-25 and $B = -\alpha^2/2$.

Entry or Operation	Display	Comment
Enter 0.40. $\div$ 57.29578	0.0069813	α
STORE x^2 CHS	-0.0000487	$-\alpha^2$
$\div$ 2 $+$ 1	0.9999756	$B = 1 - \alpha^2/2$
$\times$ 0.5150381	0.5150255	$B \sin x_0$
RCL 0.0069813	0.0069813	α
$\times$ 0.8571673	0.0059842	$\alpha \cos x_0$
$+$ 0.5150255	0.5210097	$B \sin x_0 + \alpha \cos x_0$

The result is $sin\ x = sin\ (x_0 + \alpha) = 0.5210097$. The error in $sin\ 31.40°$ is now only 1×10^{-7} in function, which is very good for such a simple calculation.

Let us illustrate the use of the tables when x_0 is greater than x.

Example 3-21. Find $tan\ 36.86990$. Use $x_0 = 37°$ (α is negative).

Entry or Operation	Display	Comment
36.86990 $-$ 37	-0.13010	α (degrees)
$\div$ 57.29578 STO	-0.0022707	α (radians)
$+$ 0.7535541	0.7512834	$tan(x_0 + \alpha)$
0.7535541 $\times$ RCL	-0.0017111	$\alpha \tan x_0$
CHS $+$ 1	1.0017111	$1 - \alpha \tan x_0$
$\div$	0.7500001	$tan (x_0 + \alpha)$

Hence $tan\ 36.8690° = 0.7500001$, and there is no visible error in this calculation. Notice that the value of α can be negative if the value of x_0 is larger than the desired x.

Table 3-7. Typical Errors in Inverse Sine and Cosine for Simple Formulas.

Inverse Function	Error in x (Radians)	Typical Errors in x (Degrees)		
		x	$\alpha = 0.25°$	$\alpha = 0.5°$
$x = \arcsin y = x_o + \alpha$ $\alpha = \dfrac{\sin x - \sin x_o}{\cos x_o}$	$\dfrac{\alpha^2}{2} \tan x_o$	15° 30° 45°	1.5×10^{-4} 3.2×10^{-4} 5.5×10^{-4}	5.6×10^{-4} 1.3×10^{-3} 2.2×10^{-3}
* $x = \arccos y = x_o + \alpha$ $\alpha = \dfrac{\cos x_o - \cos x}{\sin x_o}$	$\dfrac{\alpha^2}{2} \dfrac{1}{\tan x_o}$	15° 30° 45°	2.0×10^{-3} 1.0×10^{-3} 5.5×10^{-4}	8.1×10^{-3} 3.8×10^{-3} 2.2×10^{-3}

* When x is less than 10°, use $x = \sqrt{2(1 - \cos x)}$.

Observe that the errors in arc *sin y* increase with increasing x, and that the errors in arc *cos y* decrease with increasing x. The accuracy of these simple formulas for the angles shown is from 50 to 500 times slide rule accuracy.

These errors in inverse sine and cosine functions depend on the value of x_o. The errors in x for the accurate formulas shown in Table 3-8 depend only on α, the angle correction, and are about 1000 times smaller for the same values of α when $x_o = 45°$.

Table 3-8. Accurate Formulas for Typical Errors in Inverse Functions.

Inverse Function ($x = x_o + \alpha$)	Error in x (α in radians)	* Typical Errors in $x = (x_o + \alpha)$	
		$\alpha = 0.25°$	$\alpha = 0.50°$
$x = \arcsin y$ $\alpha = \dfrac{2(\sin x - \sin x_o)}{\cos x + \cos x_o}$ $\cos x = \sqrt{1 - \sin^2 x}$	$\dfrac{\alpha^3}{12}$	7.0×10^{-9} rad or 4.0×10^{-7} deg	5.6×10^{-8} rad or 3.2×10^{-6} deg
$x = \arccos y$ $\alpha = \dfrac{2(\cos x_o - \cos x)}{\sin x_o + \sin x}$ $\sin x = \sqrt{1 - \cos^2 x}$	$\dfrac{\alpha^3}{12}$	7.0×10^{-9} rad or 4.0×10^{-7} deg	5.6×10^{-8} rad or 3.2×10^{-6} deg
$x = \arctan y$ $\alpha = \dfrac{(\tan x - \tan x_o)}{1 + (\tan x \times \tan x_o)}$	$\dfrac{\alpha^3}{3}$	2.8×10^{-8} rad or 1.6×10^{-6} deg	2.2×10^{-7} rad or 1.3×10^{-5} deg

* Errors are independent of angle x_o.

Calculating the Logarithms of Numbers

The logarithm is perhaps the most useful tool for complex calculations that has been invented since the decimal system. The simplest use for logarithms is to multiply or divide many large numbers in sequence to any practical degree of accuracy. All it takes is the ability to add or subtract the logarithms of each number and to find the corresponding antilog in log tables. In fact, the use of logarithms can be regarded as a powerful shortcut method for getting accurate answers to almost any calculation involving multiplication, division, powers, and extraction of roots.

APPLICATIONS OF LOGARITHMS

Logarithms have their greatest application for operations which are difficult or impossible to carry out by ordinary arithmetic methods. For instance, logarithms can be used to raise any positive number to any power. Suppose we know that the odds against getting 60 heads in a row in 60 tosses of a coin are 2^{60} to 1. It is easy to show by logarithms that

$$2^{60} \approx 1.153 \times 10^{18}$$
$$1,153,000,000,000,000,000$$

To get this result, first find log 2 = 0.30103 from log tables. Then multiply 0.30103 by 60 to get the logarithm of the answer.

$$\log 2^{60} = 0.30103 \times 60 = 18.0618$$

The *characteristic*, or whole number, part of the logarithm determines the magnitude of the answer. In this case the characteristic, 18, determines the magnitude, 10^{18}. The *mantissa* or decimal part of the logarithm determines the significant figures in the answer. In this case the mantissa, 0.0618, corresponds to the figures *1.153*. The final result is found by multiplying the significant figures by the magnitude to get the answer, 1.153×10^{18}. The number corresponding to the given logarithm is called the *antilogarithm*, or the *antilog*. In the example, 1.153×10^{18} is the antilog of 18.0618.

By using logarithms, it would have been just as easy to find $1.5^{3.5}$, or $0.72^{3.14}$. In the above example, the exact answer, found by direct multiplication, is

$$2^{60} = 1,152,921,504,606,846,976$$

The saving in computational labor is tremendous, provided only four significant figures are required. Of course, log tables are available for accuracies up to seven places and higher. Remember, in any calculation by logarithms, only the significant figures of the answer may be found by log tables. The power of 10 is determined by the characteristic.

COMMON AND NATURAL LOGARITHMS

There are two kinds of logarithms in general use: logarithms to the base 10, or *common* logarithms; and *natural* logarithms to the base e, ($e = 2.7182818$). We will show how to calculate logarithms to either base 10 or base e.

The logarithm of a number to the base 10 is defined as the exponent to which 10 must be raised to get the number. Stated in algebraic terms, if

$$N = 10^x \tag{4.1}$$

Then

$$x = \text{logarithm of } N \text{ to the base 10, or}$$
$$x = \log N \text{ (exponent to base 10)} \tag{4.2}$$

Conversely, $N = \text{antilog } x$, or the number corresponding to log x. These definitions lead directly to the rule for multiplication.

SIMPLE MULTIPLICATION USING LOGS

To multiply two numbers, N_1 and N_2:

Let

$$x = \log N_1 \text{ and } y = \log N_2 \tag{4.3}$$

Then

$$N_1 = 10^x \text{ and } N_2 = 10^y \tag{4.4}$$

$$N_1 N_2 = 10^x, 10^y = 10^{x+y} \qquad (4\text{-}5)$$

Taking logarithms of both sides of Eq. 4-5,

$$\log N_1 N_2 = x + y$$
$$= \log N_1 + \log N_2 \qquad (4\text{-}6)$$

This result says that the log of the product of two numbers is equal to the sum of the individual logs.

In a similar way, it is easy to show that

$$\log \frac{N_1}{N_2} = \log N_1 - \log N_2 \qquad (4\text{-}7)$$

Just let

$$\frac{N_1}{N_2} = \frac{10^x}{10^y} = 10^{x-y} \qquad (4\text{-}8)$$

Then

$$\log \frac{N_1}{N_2} = x - y = \log N_1 - \log N_2 \qquad (4\text{-}9)$$

In a similar fashion we can show that

$$\log N^y = y \log N \qquad (4\text{-}10)$$

and

$$\log N^{1/y} = \frac{1}{y} \log N \qquad (4\text{-}11)$$

These equations tell us all we need to know about the use of logarithms for calculation. But to get the most accuracy out of a given set of log tables, we must first be able to find the logarithm of numbers that are not listed in the tables.

For example, Tables 4-1 and 4-2 list the common and natural logs of numbers separated by 0.05 or 0.10. In fact, all numbers listed, starting from 3.0, have only two significant figures. Nevertheless, we will show how your calculator, aided by these tables, can determine the log of arbitrary values of N up to 6- or 7-place accuracy when the numbers, N, have up to seven significant figures

LOGARITHMIC INTERPOLATION

The process of finding the value of a function that lies between two known functions reasonably close together is

Table 4-1. Common Logarithms.			
N_o	Log N_o	N_o	Log N_o
1.00	0.0000 000	4.2	0.6232 493
1.05	0.0211 893	4.3	0.6334 685
1.10	0.0413 927	4.4	0.6434 527
1.15	0.0606 978	4.5	0.6532 125
1.20	0.0791 812	4.6	0.6627 578
1.25	0.0969 100	4.7	0.6720 979
1.30	0.1139 434	4.8	0.6812 412
1.35	0.1303 338	4.9	0.6901 961
1.40	0.1461 280	5.0	0.6989 700
1.45	0.1613 680	5.1	0.7075 702
1.50	0.1760 913	5.2	0.7160 033
1.55	0.1903 317	5.3	0.7242 759
1.60	0.2041 200	5.4	0.7323 938
1.65	0.2174 839	5.5	0.7403 627
1.70	0.2304 489	5.6	0.7481 880
1.75	0.2430 380	5.7	0.7558 749
1.80	0.2552 725	5.8	0.7634 280
1.85	0.2671 717	5.9	0.7708 520
1.90	0.2787 536	6.0	0.7781 513
1.95	0.2900 346	6.1	0.7853 298
		6.2	0.7923 917
2.0	0.3010 300	6.3	0.7993 405
2.1	0.3222 193	6.4	0.8061 800
2.2	0.3424 227	6.5	0.8129 134
2.3	0.3617 278	6.6	0.8195 439
2.4	0.3802 112	6.7	0.8260 748
2.5	0.3979 400	6.8	0.8325 089
2.6	0.4149 733	6.9	0.8388 491
2.7	0.4313 638	7.0	0.8450 980
2.8	0.4471 580	7.1	0.8512 583
2.9	0.4623 980	7.2	0.8573 325
3.0	0.4771 213	7.3	0.8633 229
3.1	0.4913 617	7.4	0.8692 317
3.2	0.5051 500	7.5	0.8750 613
3.3	0.5185 139	7.6	0.8808 136
3.4	0.5314 789	7.7	0.8864 907
3.5	0.5440 680	7.8	0.8920 946
3.6	0.5563 025	7.9	0.8976 271
3.7	0.5682 017		
3.8	0.5797 836	8.0	0.9030 900
3.9	0.5910 646	8.1	0.9084 850
		8.2	0.9138 139
4.0	0.6020 600	8.3	0.9190 781
4.1	0.6127 839		

Table 4-1. Con't.

Common Logarithms			
N_o	Log N_o	N_o	Log N_o
8.4	0.9242 793	9.2	0.9637 878
8.5	0.9294 189	9.3	0.9684 829
8.6	0.9344 985	9.4	0.9731 279
8.7	0.9395 193	9.5	0.9777 236
8.8	0.9444 827	9.6	0.9822 712
8.9	0.9493 900	9.7	0.9867 717
9.0	0.9542 425	9.8	0.9912 261
9.1	0.9590 414	9.9	0.9956 352

$\log N$ = common log

$\log N = \log (N_o + oc)$

$\quad \alpha = N - N_o$, $\log N_o$ = table value

$\log N = \log N_o + \dfrac{0.4342945\,\alpha}{N_o + 0.5\alpha}$

Antilogs:

$N = N_o + \alpha$

$\alpha = KN_o / (\log e - 0.5K)$

$K = \log N - \log N_o$

Table 4-2. Natural Logarithms.

N_o	Ln N_o	N_o	Ln N_o
1.00	0.0000 000	2.3	0.8329 091
1.05	0.487 902	2.4	0.0754 687
1.10	0.0953 102	2.5	0.9162 907
1.15	0.1397 619	2.6	0.9555 114
1.20	0.1823 216	2.7	0.9932 518
1.25	0.2231 436	2.8	0.0296 194
1.30	0.2623 643	2.9	1.0647 107
1.35	0.3001 046	3.0	1.0986 123
1.40	0.3364 722	3.1	1.1314 021
1.45	0.3715 636	3.2	1.1631 508
1.50	0.4054 651	3.3	1.1939 225
1.55	0.4382 549	3.4	1.2237 754
1.60	0.4700 036	3.5	1.2527 630
1.65	0.5007 753	3.6	1.2809 338
1.70	0.5306 283	3.7	1.3083 328
1.75	0.5596 158	3.8	1.3350 011
1.80	0.5877 867	3.9	1.3609 766
1.85	0.6151 856	4.0	1.3862 944
1.90	0.6418 539	4.1	1.4109 870
1.95	0.6678 294	4.2	1.4350 845
2.0	0.6931 472	4.3	1.4586 150
2.1	0.7419 373	4.4	1.4816 045
2.2	0.7884 574	4.5	1.5040 774

	Natural Logarithms		
N₀	Ln N₀	N₀	Ln N₀

N_0	Ln N_0	N_0	Ln N_0
4.6	1.5260 563	7.3	1.9878 743
4.7	1.5475 625	7.4	2.0014 800
4.8	1.5686 159	7.5	2.0149 030
4.9	1.5892 352	7.6	2.0281 482
5.0	1.6094 379	7.7	2.0412 203
5.1	1.6292 405	7.8	2.0541 237
5.2	1.6486 586	7.9	2.0668 628
5.3	1.6677 068	8.0	2.0794 415
5.4	1.6863 990	8.1	2.0918 641
5.5	1.7047 481	8.2	2.1041 342
5.6	1.7227 666	8.3	2.1162 555
5.7	1.7404 662	8.4	2.1282 317
5.8	1.7578 579	8.5	2.1400 662
5.9	1.7749 524	8.6	2.1517 622
6.0	1.7917 595	8.7	2.1633 230
6.1	1.8082 888	8.8	2.1747 517
6.2	1.8245 493	8.9	2.1860 513
6.3	1.8405 496	9.0	2.1972 246
6.4	1.8562 980	9.1	2.2082 744
6.5	1.8718 022	9.2	2.2192 035
6.6	1.8870 696	9.3	2.2300 144
6.7	1.9021 075	9.4	2.2407 097
6.8	1.9169 226	9.5	2.2512 918
6.9	1.9315 214	9.6	2.2617 631
7.0	1.9459 101	9.7	2.2721 259
7.1	1.9600 948	9.8	2.2823 824
7.2	1.9740 810	9.9	2.2925 348

ln N = natural log	Antilogs:
ln N = ln $(N_0 + \alpha)$	$N = N_0 + \alpha$
$\alpha = N - N_0$, ln N_0 = table value	$\alpha = CN_0/(1 - 0.5C)$
ln N = ln $N_0 + \alpha/(N_0 + 0.5\alpha)$	$C = \ln N - \ln N_0$

called *interpolation*. In general, you are performing interpolation every time you estimate your weight on a graduated scale or when you read a speedometer. To find the common logarithm of a number which falls between two entries in Table 4-1, we offer a simple interpolation formula, which is very straightforward and takes only four steps on your calculator.

Let

N = given number

$\log N$ = logarithm of N to base 10

$$N_o = \text{nearest number in log table}$$
$$\log N_o = \text{logarithm of } N_o \text{ to base 10}$$
$$\alpha = N - N_o$$

Then

$$\log N = \overbrace{\log N_o}^{\text{nearest log}} + \overbrace{\frac{0.434294\,\alpha}{N_o + \alpha/2}}^{\text{correction}} \tag{4-12}$$

This calculation is quite simple because each term on the right side is known in terms of N_o and α. The logarithm of N_o is found directly from Table 4-1; the correction term, α, is the known difference $N - N_o$; and $N_o + \alpha/2$ is a simple calculation. The calculation of the correction term is easy to do by machine. The applicability of Eq. 4-12 to machine calculation is best understood with reference to some simple examples.

Example 4-1. Find *log 1.22* using Eq. 4-12 and Table 4-1.

Let $\log 1.22 = \log (1.20 + 0.02)$
$N_o = 1.20,\ \alpha = 0.02,\ N_o + \alpha/2 = 1.21$
From Table 4-1 $\log 1.2 = 0.0791812$
Then, from equation (4.12)

$$\log 1.22 = \log 1.20 + \frac{0.434294\,(0.02)}{1.21}$$
$$= 0.0791812 + 0.0071784$$
$$= 0.0863596 \text{ (by calculator)}$$

From 7-place log tables $\log 1.220 = 0.0863598$. The difference is only 2 in the last place, or 2×10^{-7}!

The correction to the logarithm can also be negative, as shown by the next example.

Example 4-2. Find *log 2.28*, using Eq. 4-12.

Let $\log 2.28 = \log (2.30 - 0.02)$
$N_o = 2.30,\ \alpha = -0.02,\ N_o + \alpha/2 = 2.29$
From Table 4-1
$\log 2.30 = 0.3617178$
From equation 4-12

$$\log 2.28 = \log 2.30 + \frac{0.439294\,(-0.02)}{2.29}$$
$$= 0.3617278 + 0.0037930$$
$$= 0.3579348 \text{ (by calculator)}$$

From 7-place log tables, $\log 2.28 = 0.3579348$. In this case there is no visible error in the seventh place.

Let us try one more simple case, just to show the generality of the method, then illustrate how the calculation would be done by any elementary calculator.

Example 4-3. Find $\log 5.25$, using Eq. 4-12.

Let $\log 5.25 = \log (5.20 + 0.05)$
$N = 5.2. \; \alpha = 0.05. \; N_0 + \alpha/2 = 5.225$
From Table 4.1 $\log 5.2 = 0.7160033$

Then $\log 5.25 = \log 5.2 + \dfrac{0.434294 \, (0.05)}{5.225}$

$\qquad\qquad = 0.7160033 + 0.0041559$

$\qquad\qquad = 0.7201592$ (by calculator)

From 7-place log tables, $\log 5.25 = 0.7201593$. The error is only 1 in the seventh place, or 1×10^{-7}.

Suppose now we had a simple 4-function calculator. First we would calculate the correction, and then add on $\log 5.2$ from Table 4-1, as follows:

Example 4-3. Find $\log 5.25$, using a calculator.

Step or Operation	Desired Result	Comment
Enter 0.434294.	0.434294	Constant
Multiply by 0.05.	0.0217147	—
Divide by 5.225.	0.0041559	Correction
Add $\log 5.2 = 0.7160033$.	0.7201592	$\log 5.25$

It is best to perform the calculation of the correction term first and then add the known $\log 5.2$, rather than enter $\log 5.2$ first and then calculate the correction. This is because the machine would not retain $\log 5.2$ while performing the subsequent calculations unless it had memory.

Notice that this is a quite simple procedure for obtaining logs to 6- or 7-place accuracy. In general, the theoretical error for average values of the logarithm will be less than 1×10^{-7}.

Logs of Multidigit Numbers

As we stated earlier, this accuracy is not limited to logarithms of numbers with only two or three significant figures. The logarithms of numbers with many significant figures can be found just as easily with your calculator.

Example 4-4. Find the logarithm of 5.23456.

Let $\log 5.23456 = \log (5.2 + 0.03456)$
$N_0 = 5.2. \; \alpha = 0.03456. \; N_0 + \alpha/2 = 5.21728$

$\log 5.23456 = \log 5.2 + \dfrac{0.434294 \, (0.03456)}{5.21728}$

$\qquad\qquad = 0.7160033 + 0.0028768$

$\qquad\qquad = 0.7188802$

This log is correct to all seven places.

The operations on the calculator are just as simple as in the previous example because the calculator does all the extra work.

Example 4-4. Find *log 5.23456*, using a calculator and Eq. 4-12.

Step or Operation	Desired Result	Comment
Enter 0.434294	0.434294	Constant
Multiply by 0.03456.	0.0150092	8
Divide by 5.21728.	0.0028768	Correction
Add log 5.2 = 0.7160033.	0.7188802	log 5.21728

NATURAL LOGARITHM CALCULATIONS

The equation corresponding to Eq. 4-12 is even simpler to use. All terms have the same meaning as in Eq. 4-12, except that the natural logarithm ($\ln N$) is now used instead of the common log ($\log N$).

$$\ln N = \ln N_o + \frac{\alpha}{N_o + \alpha/2} \qquad (4\text{-}13)$$

Notice that the constant *0.434294*, or log *e*, is not required for calculation of natural logs.

Examples of Natural Logarithm Calculations

Example 4-5. Calculate ln 1.425, using Eq. 4-13 and Table 4-2.

Let $\ln 1.425 = \ln (1.400 + 0.025)$
$N_o = 1.4$, $\alpha = 0.025$, $N_o + \alpha/2 = 1.4125$
From Table 4-2 ln 1.4 = 0.3364722
From Equation 4.13

$$\ln 1.425 = \ln 1.4 + \frac{0.434294\,(0.025)}{1.4125}$$

$$= 0.3364722 + 0.0176991$$

$$= 0.3541713 \text{ of } 0.354171 \text{ (six places)}$$

From 7-place log tables, ln 1.425 = 0.3541718, or 0.354172 (six places).

The error for 7-place results is $0.3541710 - 0.3541718 = 5 \times 10^{-7}$. This is equivalent to 1×10^{-6} for 6-place results, since the calculated result is rounded down and the table result is rounded up. These errors are larger than those previously discussed because the magnitude of a natural log for a given N is 2.3 times the error of the common log for the same number. Errors are discussed at the end of this chapter.

One more example will illustrate the difference between ln N and log N calculations. Note that ln N now has an integer part.

Example 4-6. Calculate ln 6.25, using Eq. 4-13 and Table 4-2.

Let $\ln 6.25 = \ln (6.20 + 0.05)$

Then $N_0 = 6.20$, $\alpha = 0.05$, $N_0 + \alpha/2 = 6.225$

From Table 4-2, $\ln 6.2 = 1.8245493$.

$$\ln 6.25 = \ln N_0 + \frac{\alpha}{N_0 + \alpha/2}$$

Then $\ln 6.25 = \ln 6.2 + \dfrac{0.05}{6.225}$

$\qquad\qquad = 1.8245493 + 0.0080321$

$\qquad\qquad = 1.8325814$

From 7-place tables, the true logarithm is $\ln 6.25 = 1.8325815$. The error is only 1×10^{-7}, or about 1 part in 18 million!

The steps by any machine would be as follows.

Example 4-6. Calculate ln 6.25, using Eq. 4-13 and Table 4-2.

Step or Operation	Desired Result	Comment
Enter 0.05	0.05	$\alpha/2 = 0.025$
Divide by 6.225.	0.0080321	Correction
Add ln 6.2 = 1.8245493.	1.8325814	log 6.25

You are now in a position to calculate the logarithm of any number to the base 10.

Natural Logs of Numbers Greater Than 10

For the natural log of a number greater than 10, the previous procedure is modified as follows. First, express the number in scientific notation. For example:

$$52.5 = 5.25 \times 10^1$$

Then use one of the following two procedures. The first is to determine the natural log of the standard term, then add ln 10.

Example 4-7. Calculate ln 52.5

$$\ln 52.5 = \ln 5.25 + \overbrace{2.3025851}^{\ln 10}$$
$$= 1.6582281 + 2.3025851$$
$$= 3.9608132$$

Similarly, the natural log of a larger number can be calculated the same way. For example

$$\ln 525 = \log (5.25 \times 10^2)$$
$$= \ln 5.25 + \overbrace{2 (2.3025851)}^{2 \ln 10}$$
$$= 1.6582281 + 4.6051702$$
$$= 6.2633982$$

82

An alternate and equally acceptable procedure is to use Eq. 4-14. Here, we calculate (or have available) log N, or the common log of the number. We then multiply log N by the constant in Eq. 4-14.

$$\ln N = 2.3025852 \,(\log N) \qquad (4\text{-}14)$$

The logarithm of N is easily found by expressing N in scientific notation and proceeding as follows:

$$\ln 52.5 = 2.3025851 \,(\log 52.5)$$

From example 4-3, *log 52.5 = 1.7201593*.

Then

$$\ln 52.5 = 2.3025851 \times 1.7201593$$
$$= 3.9608132$$

which gives the same result as before.

For practice, calculate the following logarithms and compare to the table values.

Common Log	Table Value	Natural Log	Table Value
log 3.75	0.5740313	ln 3.75	1.3217558
log 7.67	0.8847954	ln 7.67	2.0373166
log 32.2	1.5078559	ln 32.2	3.4719665
log 175	2.2430381	ln 175	5.1647860

ERRORS IN CALCULATING LOGARITHMS

For the maximum values of the difference α, the theoretical errors for log N and ln N will range from about 1×10^{-6} for the lowest numbers to about 6×10^{-9} for the highest numbers. Typical errors are shown in Table 4-3.

Table 4-3. Typical Errors for Equations 4-12 and 4-13.

Number N	Maximum Difference α	Maximum Error	
		log N	ln N
1.025	0.025	6×10^{-7}	1.3×10^{-6}
3.05	0.05	2×10^{-7}	4×10^{-7}
5.05	0.05	4×10^{-8}	8.3×10^{-8}
9.05	0.05	6×10^{-9}	1.4×10^{-8}

Error Analysis for Logarithmic Calculations

The formulas for the errors, E, for any values of α and N_o are given in Eqs. 4-15 and 4-16.

$$E_{\log} = \frac{1}{28} \left(\frac{\alpha}{N_o}\right)^3 \tag{4-15}$$

$$E_{\ln} = \frac{1}{12} \left(\frac{\alpha}{N_o}\right)^3 \tag{4-16}$$

The derivation of these formulas is given below.

Consider the general series for $\ln(1 + x)$:

$$\ln(1 + x) = x - \frac{x^2}{2} + \frac{x^3}{3} - \frac{x^4}{4} + \dots \tag{4-17}$$

where

$$x < 1$$

Now let

$$\Delta \ln N = \ln(N_o + \alpha) - \ln N_o = \text{ correction} \tag{4-18}$$

$$= \ln\left(\frac{N_o + \alpha}{N}\right) = \ln(1 + \alpha/N_o) \tag{4-19}$$

Let $x = \alpha/N_o$ and substitute in Eqs. 4-17 and 4-19.

$$\Delta \ln N = \frac{\alpha}{N_o} - \frac{1}{2}\left(\frac{\alpha}{N_o}\right)^2 + \frac{1}{3}\left(\frac{\alpha}{N_o}\right)^3 \dots \tag{4-20}$$

Now suppose that the correction, $\Delta \ln N$, is given by

$$\Delta \ln N = \frac{\alpha}{N_o + \alpha/2} = \frac{\alpha}{N_o(1 + \alpha/2\,N_o)} \tag{4-21}$$

Expanding Eq. 4-21 and multiplying,

$$\Delta \ln N = \frac{\alpha}{N_o} - \frac{1}{2}\left(\frac{\alpha}{N_o}\right)^2 + \frac{1}{4}\left(\frac{\alpha}{N_o}\right)^3 \dots \tag{4-22}$$

Equation 4-20 gives the true correction, and Eqs. 4-21 and 4-22 give the approximate correction, which is suitable for the calculator. The error in the natural log, $E_{\ln}$ is the difference between Eqs. 4-20 and 4-22. Subtracting these two equations, the first two terms cancel, leaving

$$\text{Error in } \ln N = \left(\frac{1}{3} - \frac{1}{4}\right)\left(\frac{\alpha}{N_o}\right)^3$$

$$= \frac{1}{12}\left(\frac{\alpha}{N_o}\right)^3 \text{ (for natural logs)} \tag{4-16}$$

Error in log N

$$= \frac{1}{28} \left(\frac{\alpha}{N_o}\right)^3 \text{ (for common logs)} \qquad (4\text{-}15)$$

In Table 4-3, for example, let $\alpha = 0.05$, $N = 3.00$, and

$$\frac{\alpha}{N_o} = \frac{1}{60}$$

Then $\qquad E_{ln} = \frac{1}{12} \left(\frac{1}{60}\right)^3 = 3.8 \times 10^{-7}$

and $\qquad E_{log} = \frac{1}{28} \left(\frac{1}{60}\right)^3 = 1.7 \times 10^{-7}$

This verifies the maximum errors given in Table 4-3.

INVERSE LOGARITHMS

In the beginning of this chapter we indicated that the use of logarithms permitted us to evaluate an expression like 2^{60}.

If $\qquad\qquad\qquad N = 2^{60}$

Then $\qquad\qquad\qquad \log N = 60 \log 2$

$$= 60 \, (0.301030)$$

$$= 18.06180$$

In base 10 notation, the integer part of log N corresponds to the magnitude of N, or 10^{18} in this case. But what about the significant figures which correspond to the decimal part of *log N*, or 0.06180 and which are also needed to determine N from its logarithm?

The number N which corresponds to a given logarithm, *log N*, is called the *antilogarithm of N*, or *antilog N*. It is just as important to be able to determine the inverse logarithm or the antilog of a number as it is to find the log of any number:

$$\text{antilog } 18.0618 = 1.153 \times 10^{18}$$

We will show that the process of finding *antilog N* for either common or natural logarithms is basically the inverse of the process of finding *log N*. Before we turn to the calculator, we will develop the procedure for finding N, or *antilog N*. Essentially, the process consists of locating, in Table 4-1, *log N_o* nearest to the given *log N* and calculating a correction (α). Then α is added to N_o to find N, or

$$N = N_o + \alpha \qquad (4\text{-}23)$$

From Eq. 4-12

$$\log (N_o + \alpha) = \log N_o + \frac{\log e \, (\alpha)}{N_o + \alpha/2} \qquad (4\text{-}24)$$

or
$$\log (N + \alpha) - \log N_o = \frac{\log e}{N_o + \alpha/2}$$

Let the left side of Eq. 4-24 $= K$, and solve for α:

$$K = \frac{(\log e) (\alpha)}{N_o + \alpha/2} \qquad (4\text{-}25)$$

$$(\log e) (\alpha) - (K) (\alpha/2) = KN_o \qquad (4\text{-}25)$$

For *common logs*
$$\alpha = \frac{K N_o}{\log e - K/2} \qquad (4\text{-}26a)$$

where
$$\log e = 0.4342945$$
$$K = \log N - \log N_o \qquad (4\text{-}26b)$$

For *natural logs*
$$\alpha = \frac{CN_o}{1 - C/2} \qquad (4\text{-}27a)$$
$$C = \ln N - \ln N \qquad (4\text{-}27b)$$

Equation 4-26 gives the correction α to the nearest number, N_o, for common logs, and Eq. 4-27 gives the correction to the nearest number for natural logs. If only 4-place accuracy is desired, then the $K/2$ and $C/2$ terms can be omitted.

Antilog Examples

Example 4-8. Find $N = antilog\ 0.4668760$ (base 10).

$\log N = 0.4668760 = \log (N_o + \alpha)$
Nearest log $N_o = 0.4623980$ ($N_o = 2.9$) (Table 4-1)
$K = \log (N_o + \alpha) - \log N_o = 0.00446960$
From equation 4.20a

$$\alpha = \frac{(0.00446960) (2.9)}{0.4342945 - 0.00223480}$$

$$= 0.0300001$$
$$N = N_o + \alpha = 2.9300001$$

The true antilog is 2.9300000 and the error is only 1×10^{-7}, or 1 part in 29 million. Suppose, now, we programed this problem on the ordinary 4-function calculator, as in the example below.

Example 4-9. Calculate *antilog 0.4698220*, using Eq. 4-26.

Step	Key or Operation	Desired Result	Comment
1	Enter 0.4668760.	0.4668760	$\log N$
2	Subtract 0.4623980.	0.0044696	K
3	Write result.		K for step 7.
4	Divide by -2.	-0.0022348	$-K/2$
5	Add 0.4342945.	0.4320597	Denominator.

Step	Key or Operation	Desires Result	Comment
6	Write result.		For step 9.
7	Enter 0.0044696.	0.0044696	K. from step 3.
8	Multiply by 2.9.	0.0129618	Numerator.
9	Divide by 0.4320597.	0.0300000	α
10	Add $N_o = 2.9$.	2.9300000	$N = N_o + \alpha$

The fact that there is no visible error in the seventh place is just a coincidence due to the cancellation of rounding errors in the particular calculator used for this example.

Now suppose we want to find the natural antilog using Eq. 4-27.

Example 4-10. Find *antiln 1.556031*.

$$\text{Nearest } \ln N_o = 1.5575625 \ (N_o = 4.7)$$

$$C = \ln N - \ln N_o = 0.0084746$$

$$\alpha = \frac{(0.0084746)\ 4.7}{1 - 0.0042373}$$

$$\alpha = \frac{0.0398306}{0.9957627} = 0.040001$$

$$N = N_o + \alpha = 4.7400001$$

Again the error is 1×10^{-7}, or 1 part in 47 million. The calculation by machine would be as follows.

Example 4-11. Calculate *antiln 1.5560371*, using Eq. 4-27.

Step	Key or Operation	Desired Result	Comment
1	Enter 1.5560371.	1.5560371	$\ln N$
2	Subtract 1.5475625.	0.0084746	C
3	Write result.		For step 7.
4	Divide by -2.	-0.0042373	$-C/2$
5	Add 1.	$+0.9957627$	Denominator.
6	Write result.		For step 9.
7	Enter 0.0084746.	0.0084746	C. from step 3.
8	Multiply by 4.7.	0.0398306	Numerator.
9	Divide by 0.9957627.	0.0400001	α
10	Add 4.7.	4.7400001	$N = N_o + \alpha$

If your calculator has a reciprocal function $(1/x)$, then step 6 in both examples can be replaced by the reciprocal, and step 7 replaced by "multiply by K" instead of "enter K." Notice the rather extraordinary accuracy of these two very typical sample calculations.

Antilogs of Numbers Greater Than 10

Now suppose that $log\ N$ was given for a number greater than 10. There is no conceptual difference in determining the common antilogarithm of N. Simply convert the characteristic (integer) part of the logarithm directly into a power of 10; then determine the antilog of the decimal part. For example, let us verify that $antilog\ 18.0618 = 1.1529 \times 10^{18}$.

$$N = \text{antilog } 0.06180 \times 10^{18}$$
$$= 1.1529 \times 10^{18}$$

But suppose the natural log was given for this number.

$$\ln N = 41.5888308$$

The simplest procedure is to multiply $\ln N$ by $log\ e$, where $log\ e = 0.4342945$, to get $log\ N$, and then convert as before.

$$\log N = 0.4342945\ (\ln N) \qquad (4\text{-}28)$$
$$= 0.4342945\ (41.588831)$$
$$= 18.061800$$

As before,

$$N = 1.1529 \times 10^{18}.$$

Let us try one final example.

Example 4-12. Find $antiln\ 3.4468079$, using Eqs. 4-26 and 4-28).

$\ln N = 3.4468079$
$\log N = 3.4468079\ (0.4342945)$
$\log N = 1.4969297$ $N = \text{antilog }(0.4969297) \times 10^1$
$\log N_0 = 0.4913617$ $N_0 = 3.1$
Add 1 to the Table 4-2 value. $\log N_0 = 1.4913617$. Then
$K = \log N - \log N_0 = 0.0055680$

$$\alpha = \frac{K\,N_0}{\log e - K/2}$$

$$= \frac{0.0055680\ (31)}{0.4342945 - 0.0027840}$$

$$= 0.4000088$$

$N = N_0 + \alpha = 3.1400009 \times 10^1 = 31.400009$

The true value is 31.4, and the error is about 1 part in 3 million. Notice that the power of 10 was determined by the integer part of the given log, which was 1 in this case. Therefore, the calculated value of N was multiplied by 10^1.

You might try an alternate approach in which you subtract multiples of $\ln 10 = 2.3$ and reduce $\ln N$ to a number less than ln 10. The N which results from this operation is then multiplied by 10^x where x is the number of multiples of ln 10 used in the calculation.

For practice, verify the following antilogarithms, given log N or ln N.

log N	N	ln N	N
0.3483049	2.2300	1.8309802	6.2400
0.4971509	3.1416	1.1447322	3.1416
1.7201593	52.5000	4.3489868	77.4000
1.9380191	86.7000	4.1351666	62.5000

Chapter 5

Extending the Precision of Pocket Calculators

The ordinary electronic calculator has an 8-digit capacity, which is quite suitable for the vast majority of calculations. Sometimes, however, calculations are required to higher precision—up to 10 or even 12 significant figures. For example, what is the exact product of two 6-figure numbers? What interest must a corporation pay on a debt of \$32,750,525 at 7.5% interest per year, or 0.625% interest per month?

Presented here is a straightforward method to extend the precision of a pocket calculator with a capacity of, say, 8 digits to at least 12 significant figures. The method works easily for extended multiplication, where it can be used to obtain 12-digit products with an 8-digit calculator, or 15-digit products with a 10-digit calculator. This method merely requires the operator to combine two machine calculations into one continuous number. This extended capability certainly covers the vast majority of applications for pocket calculators. If still greater precision in calculations is required for some extraordinary applications, then the method can be used, with some extra effort, to extend the accuracy to double precision, or up to twice the calculator capacity. This means up to 16 figures for an 8-digit calculator and up to 20 figures for a 10-digit calculator. For multiplication, this requires the calculation of four partial products by machine, and the careful assignment of decimal places, plus a manual addition by the operator. This extra effort is well worthwhile on the few occasions when such precision is required.

It might appear offhand that there is really no practical way to extend the precision of the calculator to division by similar methods. This is because the remainders which are required to extend the divisions must somehow be recovered by the operator from the machine. This is not possible with present-day pocket calculators. With some ingenuity, however, it is possible to extract the remainder using the methods for extended division described in this section. Then the machine can be used to extend the precision in division to at least 12 figures as in extended multiplication.

EXTENDED MULTIPLICATION FOR GREATER ACCURACY

The process for extended multiplication requires the following four steps:

1. Determine the total number of figures in the product by inspection.
2. Multiply the two given numbers by machine as usual, to obtain the *most significant* figures. This, of course, gives eight figures for an 8-digit calculator. Add dashes for the missing figures.
3. Multiply the last four digits of each number together by machine to obtain the last four *least significant* figures.
4. Connect the two resulting numbers to obtain the final product, using the least significant digits to supply the missing figures. (We'll use the abbreviations *MS* and *LS* for *most significant* and *least significant* figures from this point on.)

For products of 9, 10, or 11 digits, there will be figures in the MS and in the LS which are common and can be used to further check the result. Once this procedure is mastered, the final answer can be written as one continuous number. In essence, the procedure depends on the fact that the multiplication of the last four digits of two large numbers always gives the last four digits of the product *exactly*, no matter how large each multiplier. Although this statement is true in general for the last n digits of two numbers, four digits were chosen to stay within the 8-digit capacity of the simple calculator.

Example 5-1. Multiply $56,789 \times 34,567$ for a 10-digit product.

$$56.789 \times 34.567 = 1.963.025.3\text{--} = MS$$
$$6789 \times 4567 = \quad \text{--}.\text{--}5.363 = LS$$
$$\text{Final product} = 1.963.025.363$$

The two dashes shown after the 3 in the MS indicate that there are two missing figures which must be supplied by the last two figures in the LS.

The two common figures in the MS and the LS are 5 and 3, which are retained as the seventh and eighth figures of the final product. The answer could be written as one continuous number, by simply placing the last two figures, 6 and 3, at the end of the MS and eliminating step 3. However, the third step will be retained in the following examples to clarify the procedure and to separate the final product from the MS.

For multipliers with two or more digits, there is a simple and direct method for determining the number of digits in the product of the numbers. Suppose the two numbers to be multiplied are N_1 and N_2, and the desired product is B. Then

$$N_1 \times N_2 = p$$

The number of digits in N_1 will be called n_1, and the number of digits in N_2 is n_2. Let the *first* digits of the numbers N_1 and N_2 be called m_1 and m_2. The product of m_1 and m_2 determines the number of digits in the answer, P. If $m_1 \times m_2$ is greater than or equal to 10, the number of digits in the answer will be the sum of the number of digits in the two multipliers. That is

$$\text{digits in } P = n_1 + n_2$$

If the product of the two leading numbers ($m_1 \times m_2$) is less than 10, the number of digits in the answer,

$$P = (n_1 + n_2) - 1$$

The simplicity of the method becomes apparent in the series of examples shown in Table 5-1.

The actual value of $m_1 \times m_2$ is not important, and usually it can be determined by inspection whether the value of $m_1 \times m_2$ is greater than or less than 10. That fact is all that is

Table 5-1. Determining the Number of Digits in a Product.

N_1	N_2	n_1	n_2	m_1	m_2	$m_1 \times m_2$	Digits in P	P
49	25	2	2	4.9	2.5	12.25 > 10	4	1225
35	25	2	2	3.5	2.5	8.75 < 10	3	875
500	20	3	2	5.0	2.0	10 = 10	5	10,000
3456	789	4	3	3.4	7.8	26.52 > 10	7	
2468	13, 579	4	5	2.4	1.3	3.12 < 10	8	
12, 345, 678	75, 737, 170	8	8	1.2	7.5	9.0 < 10	15	

needed to determine the number of digits which will be found in the product of N_1 and N_2.

Example 5-2. Multiply $456,789 \times 123,456$ for an 11-digit product. (There are only 11 digits, because 4.5×1.2 is less than 10.)

$$456.789 \times 123.456 = 56.393.342.\text{---} = MS$$
$$6789 \times 3456 = \text{----}2.784 = LS$$
$$\text{Final product} = 56.393.342\,784$$

Three dashes are shown in the MS to indicate that three figures must be supplied by the LS (784 in this case). There is only one common digit in the MS and the LS; namely, 2. Four dashes are shown *before* the LS to emphasize the fact that they are not used for the final product.

Example 5-3. Multiply $987,654 \times 345,679$ for a 12-digit product. (There are 12 digits because 9×3 is more than 10.)

$$987.654 \times 345.679 = 341.411.24\text{-}.\text{---} = MS$$
$$7654 \times 5679 = \qquad \text{--}.\text{--}7.066 = LS$$
$$\text{Final product} = 341.411.247.066$$

This time there is no common digit for check purposes, because every one of the LS digits is required to supply the four missing figures in the final product. For 12-digit products, it is necessary to know whether your 8-digit calculator rounds up the last digit or not, in view of the digits that might follow. For example, suppose that the calculator does not round up the last digit. Then the 4 of the MS in this example is retained intact. If the calculator did round up the last figure, then the last 4 must be reduced to 3, because the next digit to follow is known to be 7; hence the 4 must have been rounded up by the machine. Otherwise the final product would be in error by $+1000$.

Your calculator can easily be checked for the roundup characteristic by calculating $\frac{2}{3}$. The answer, to nine decimals, is 0.666,666,666. If your 8-digit machine product is 0.666,666,66 , then the answer *is not* rounded. If the product is 0.666,666,67, then the answer *is* rounded up and must be corrected for many other 12-digit products. The Hewlett-Packard HP-35, for example, rounds up the 10th figure when required, and must be corrected for extended products when the 11th digit is found to be 5 or greater.

EXTENDED DIVISION

The basic method for extended division is now summarized briefly and then followed by detailed examples.

1. First divide the two numbers, N and D, as usual. Record the seven digits of N/D as the *most significant figures of the quotient*, or MSQ. For example,

$$\frac{5678}{7979} = 0.7116179 = \text{MSQ}$$

2. Multiply the denominator, D, by a reduced quotient, formed by dropping the last three digits from MSQ. This gives a new number, N', which is less than N and will be used to find the remainder, R. In this case, $7979 \times 0.7116 = 5677.8564 = N'$

3. Subtract N' from N to form an exact remainder, R. In this case,

$$
\begin{array}{r}
5678.0000 \\
-5677.8564 \\
\hline
0.1436
\end{array}
$$

The remainder, R, $= 0.1436$. The subtraction can easily be done mentally.

4. Divide R by D, the original denominator, to obtain the *least significant figures of the quotient*, or LSQ.

$$\frac{0.1436}{7979} = 0.00001799742 = \text{LSQ}$$

To obtain the desired number of significant figures, the calculator was given the division, 1436/7979.

5. Combine the figures in steps 1 and 4 to obtain the final quotient. Use common figures to align and check the result. In this case

$$
\begin{array}{l}
0.7116179\text{----} = \text{MSQ from step 1} \\
\underline{0.00001799724} = \text{LSQ from step 4} \\
0.71161799724 = \text{final quotient}
\end{array}
$$

The procedure is very similar to the last step in extended multiplication. The *common* digits, *179*, are retained in the final quotient, and the *additional* least significant figures, *9724*, follow. In summary, then, the calculation appears as follows:

1. $\dfrac{5678}{7979} = 0.7116179\text{----} = \text{MSQ}$

   Remainder by direct product
2. $7979 \times 0.7116 = 5677.8564 = N'$
3. Remainder $= \dfrac{\text{- - - }1436}{5678.0000} = R$

   $5678.0000 = N$

4. $\dfrac{1436}{7979} = \dfrac{R}{D} = 1799724 = \text{LSQ}$

5. $Q = 0.71161799724 = \text{final quotient}$

As in extended multiplication, step 5 can be eliminated by simply placing the additional figures *9724* after the common digits *179* in the MSQ in step 1. The arrows show the flow of the calculations.

One more 4-figure division will further illustrate the basic method. Then 5- or 6-figure denominators will be used in other examples to show the need for extended multiplication to form the number N', which is used to obtain the exact remainder.

Example 5-4. Divide 7979 by 5678.

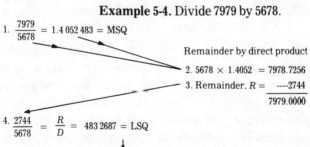

1. $\dfrac{7979}{5678} = 1.4\,052\,483 = \text{MSQ}$

   Remainder by direct product
2. $5678 \times 1.4052 = 7978.7256$
3. Remainder, $R = \dfrac{\text{----}2744}{7979.0000}$

4. $\dfrac{2744}{5678} = \dfrac{R}{D} = 483\,2687 = \text{LSQ}$

5. Final quotient $= 1.4052|483|2687$ (12 figures)

This time the calculator shows all eight significant figures in step 1. The decimal point is dropped for $R = 0.2744$, in steps 3 and 4, in order to get the seven significant figures in step 4. The final quotient is shown in step 5 but could be shown in step 1 as explained in the previous example.

Example 5-5. Divide 45678 by 56789

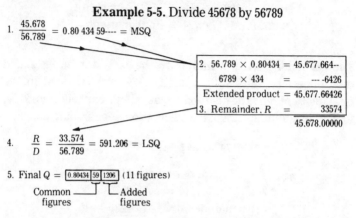

1. $\dfrac{45.678}{56.789} = 0.80\ 434\ 59\text{----} = \text{MSQ}$

2. $56.789 \times 0.80434 = 45.677.664\text{--}$
   $6789 \times 434 = \text{--- -}6426$

   Extended product $= 45.677.66426$

3. Remainder, $R = 33574$

   $45.678.00000$

4. $\dfrac{R}{D} = \dfrac{33.574}{56.789} = 591.206 = \text{LSQ}$

5. Final $Q = \boxed{0.80434\ |59|\ 1206}$ (11 figures)

   Common figures ⌐ ⌐ Added figures

The final answer has 11 significant figures, or 4 more than was contained in the first division. Extended multiplication was used in step 2 to get a more accurate remainder R; this results in more significant figures in the final quotient Q. However, direct multiplication could have been used in step 2 to get a quicker answer with only nine significant figures (0.804345912). Here the machine shows the first zero before the decimal point as a significant figure. If the decimal point in the denominator is moved to, say, 5.6789 in step 4, more significant figures result.

4. $\dfrac{R}{D} = \dfrac{33574}{5.6789} = 5912.0604$ (8 figures)

5. Final $Q = 0.80434|5912|0604$ (13 figures)
   Common   Additional

This example shows that 13 significant figures for extended division are readily attainable, for a 5-figure divisor. Even more precision is possible by making greater use of extended multiplication. This will be shown in the next 6-figure division example. Remember, these procedures for extended division must be modified slightly if your calculator rounds up the last figure in division.

Example 5-6. Divide 456,789 by 234,567 for maximum precision.

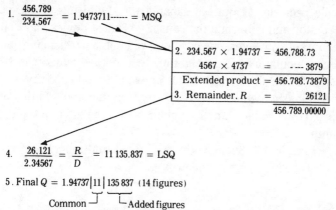

1. $\dfrac{456.789}{234.567} = 1.9473711\text{------} = \text{MSQ}$

2. $234.567 \times 1.94737 = 456.788.73$

   $\qquad 4567 \times 4737 \quad = \qquad\text{- --- }3879$

   Extended product $= 456.788.73879$

3. Remainder, $R \quad = \qquad\qquad 26121$

   $\qquad\qquad\qquad\qquad\qquad \overline{456.789.00000}$

4. $\dfrac{26.121}{2.34567} = \dfrac{R}{D} = 11\,135.837 = \text{LSQ}$

5. Final $Q = 1.94737|11|135\,837$ (14 figures)

   Common ⌐   ⌐Added figures

In this example, 14 significant figures were obtained using an extended product of 11 figures and getting full precision in step 4 by moving the denominator decimal as previously discussed.

You will note that considerable liberty is taken with the decimal point in steps 2, 3, and 4. This is because the only purpose served by those steps is to supply additional figures for steps 1 and 5.

One final word of perspective. There is no point in extending the precision of the multiplication or division if the application does not warrant the extra care and effort. If you want only two or three more significant figures, then the use of the direct product may do the job. If you must guarantee 12 or more figures, then extended products should be used to obtain the more accurate remainders.

DOUBLE PRECISION

By *double precision* we mean the ability of the calculator to determine the results of a multiplication or division to twice the number of figures that it can normally display. For example, double precision for an 8-digit display calculator means that it can determine a 16-digit product for two multipliers of eight digits each. Obviously, the entire product cannot be displayed by the calculator at one time; the result must somehow be shown in two separate displays.

Of course, double precision is required even if the total product contains less than 16 digits; say, 14 or 15. In any case, double precision is quite a capability to build into a pocket calculator and is beyond the capacity of most devices now on the market. However, one can achieve double precision for an 8-digit calculator by a straightforward method which can be applied to calculators with 6-, 10-, or even 12-digit capacity.

The basic method involves the calculation and addition of four partial products and is explained with the aid of a typical example.

Example 5-7. Suppose the two given multipliers and the desired product P are as follows:

$$
\begin{array}{rl}
3.256.782 & \text{(7 digits)} \\
\times\ 45.679.327 & \text{(8 digits)} \\
\hline
P = 148.767.609.945.714 & \text{(15 digits)}
\end{array}
$$

1. Break up each multiplier into two separate parts, each with no more than four nonzero digits. Call these four numbers A, B, C, and D. For the two multipliers in our example, the four numbers are:

$$
3.256.782 \begin{cases} A = 3.256.000 \\ B = 782 \end{cases}
$$

$$
45.679.327 \begin{cases} C = 45.670.000 \\ D = 9327 \end{cases}
$$

2. Convert the numbers to power of 10 as follows:

$$
\begin{aligned}
A &= 3256 \times 10^4 = \alpha \times 10^3 \\
B &= 782 \qquad\quad = b \\
C &= 4567 \times 10^4 = c \times 10^4 \\
D &= 9327 \qquad\quad = d
\end{aligned}
$$

3. Multiply A, B, C, and D together algebraically and form four partial products.

$$
\begin{aligned}
P &= (A + B)\ (C + D) \\
&= AC + BC + AD + BD
\end{aligned}
$$

In our example, using the values from step 2,

$$
P = (ac \times 10^7) + (bc \times 10^4) + (ad \times 10^3) + bd
$$

4. Determine the partial products ac, bc, ad, and bd using the calculator. Record each product, together with the proper power of 10. Remember, AC should have 15 figures all told: 8 from the partial product, ac, and 7 from 10^7.

In our example.

$$AC = ac \times 10^7 = 148,701,520,000,000$$
$$BC = bc \times 10^4 = 35,713,940,000$$
$$AD = ad \times 10^3 = 30,368,712,000$$
$$\underline{BD = bd = 7,293,714}$$
$$P = \text{product} = 148,767,609,945,714$$

5. Add the four partial products by hand, with due regard for the power of 10 for each product. For safety's sake, assign zeros as shown, to account for the total number of figures required for each partial product.

Although this calculation involves a certain amount of care and labor, it is well worth the trouble for the rare occasion when such a precise result is needed. It is also worth noting that all the multiplication is done by the calculator; the operator need only assign the powers of 10 and add the partial products. It is worthwhile to check the final product P against the original multipliers by the method of *9s remainders*, described in the author's forthcoming book (TAB No. 675). The operations on the calculator would then follow the sequence shown in example 5-8.

Example 5-8. Perform the following double-precision multiplication: $3,256,782 \times 45,679,327$.

	Desired Result	Comment
1. Enter $a = 3256$.	3256	
2. Multiply by $c = 4567$.	1487 0152	ac
3. Record $ac \times 10^7$.	---------	AC
4. *Enter $a = 3256$.	3256	
5. Multiply by $d = 9327$.	3036 8712	ad
6. Record $ad \times 10^3$.	---------	AD
7. Enter $b = 782$.	782	
8. Multiply by $c = 4567$.	357 1394	bc
9. Record $bc \times 10^4$.	---------	BC
10. *Enter $b = 782$.	782	
11. Multiply by $d = 9327$.	729 3714	$bd = BD$

12. Manually add partial products as shown in previous example.

  * Not necessary with many calculators; can be retained by machine.

You are now in a position to use the double-precision method for a variety of applications. Obviously, this procedure can be used in the extended-multiplication examples previously described. However, the additional labor is not warranted for those applications. Instead, try using double-precision on these examples:

$35{,}797{,}234 \times 24{,}686{,}348 = ?$ (answer $= 883{,}702{,}975{,}961{,}432$)

$7{,}243{,}469 \times 4{,}578{,}264 = ?$ (answer $= 33{,}162{,}513{,}357{,}816$)

Shortcut Double Precision

Up to now we have discussed how to handle two factors with products of up to 12 digits. Suppose instead that we had two factors with eight digits each. It turns out that the extended-multiplication method can be used for both a 12-digit and a 16-digit product for such factors. Obviously, such a method will work for smaller factors.

Essentially, the method to be described consists of forming two extended products from the two factors and then adding them, with due regard for the power of ten. The procedure is best understood by reference to a specific example. Consider the multiplication 76345678×27482924.

1. Break up the two numbers into a, b, and c parts as shown.

       a

    76345678 part a has eight digits.

     b c

    2748 2924 parts b and c have four digits each.

2. Multiply a $\times$ b using extended multiplication.

```
76345678
×   2748
─────────────────
20979792- - - - MS digits of a × b
        3144   LS digits of a × b
─────────────────
209797923144   extended product, a × b
```

3. Multiply $a \times c$, for *eight significant figures only*.

```
76345678
×   2924
─────────────────
22323476- - - - MS digits of a × c
```

4. Add results of steps 2 and 3 and supply the power of 10.

```
             209797923144   (Step 2) Extended product, a × b
Extended        22323476   (Step 3) MS digits, a × c
            ─────────────────
 product = 209820246620   (Step 4) Sum
```

But the final product must have 16 digits in this case. Therefore, this 12-digit product must be multiplied by 10^4, or four zeros must be added to the extended product. The final product is

$$2.098,202,466,200,000 =$$
$$2.098,202,466\ 2\ \times 10^{15}$$

This procedure works automatically for calculators that do not round up the last digit in multiplication, as previously explained.

To minimize the effort, it is efficient to record the extended product from step 2 on a sheet which is ready to accept the result of step 3. You can then perform the final addition of step 4 without repeating any of the extended products. In other words, all of the work can be compressed into step 4, as shown on the previous page.

Suppose, now that a 16-digit (double precision) product was required in the above example. It is only necessary to add one more step:

5. Multiply the last four digits of a by b. Add the last four digits of this result to the extended 12-digit product of step 4.

```
     5678  Last four digits of a
   × 2924  b
   ----2472  Last four digits of final product
```
Final product = 2,098,202,466,202,472 (double precision)

One more example will be shown to clarify this procedure.
Example 5-9. Multiply 37242918 × 15962174.

Step 1.

$$a$$
$$37242818$$
$$\begin{matrix} b & c \end{matrix}$$
$$\begin{matrix} 1596 & 2174 \end{matrix}$$

15-digit product because
$(3.7 \times 1.5 < 10)$

Steps 2, 3, and 4.

$$a \times b = 59439697128$$
$$a \times c = \underline{80966103}$$
$$594477937383 \text{ Extended product}$$
$$594,477,937,383,000 \text{ Answer, to 15 digits}$$

Finally, if double precision is required, add step 5.

Step 5. Multiply the last four digits of a by c.

$$\begin{array}{r} 2918 \\ \times\ 2174 \\ \hline \end{array}$$
----3732 LS of final product

The double-precision answer is 594,477,937,383,732.

This method of obtaining either 12- or 16-digit accuracy is much less work than using conventional double precision, which involves the calculation and addition of four partial products. However, care must be exercised in either method in aligning the figures correctly.

One final exercise: Determine both 12- and 14- digit products for these multipliers:

$$54{,}321{,}978 \times 856{,}372 = ?$$

The process becomes easier when using calculators which have the wraparound decimal feature. The following shortcut double-precision technique, together with the wraparound decimal, makes it possible to do fewer operations and simplifies aligning the numbers for the final addition. First multiply the complete numbers together as follows:

a	b		c	d		*display*
3256	782	$\times$	4567	9327	$=$	1487676.0 E (OVF)

The E indicates an overflow and that the true decimal point is eight places to the right of the indicated decimal point. Therefore, you can write

Answer = **1487676.0** --------calculator decimal point   8 places

Now perform the partial products bc, ad, and bd, but enter the numbers as if there were only four significant digits maximum, and with the remaining digits set to zero with the proper decimal point position.

$$a = 3256000 \qquad\qquad c = 45670000$$
$$b = 782 \qquad\qquad\qquad d = 9327$$

$$ab \times cd = 1487676 \;.\; 0 \quad 9\;9\;4\;5\;7\;1\;4$$
$$bc = \qquad 357 \;.1 \quad 3\;9\;4\;0$$
$$ad = \qquad 303 \;.\; 6 \quad 8\;7\;1\;2$$
$$bd = \qquad\qquad 7 \quad 7\;2\;9\;3$$

$ab \times cd$ double precision $= 1487676 \;.\; 0 \quad 9\;9\;4\;5\;7\;1\;4.$

Calculator decimal   (15 places)
True decimal

Now sum the digits to fill in the blanks.

$$
\begin{array}{r}
3940 \\
8712 \\
8712 \\
7293 \\
\hline
1\ 9945
\end{array}
$$

The carry beyond the 4-digit sum is ignored, and the sum fills in the blanks.

Chapter 6

Scientific Calculators or Electronic Slide Rules

Up to now, the emphasis has been on the discussion and application of elementary pocket calculators with the typical design features indicated in Table 1-2. Although these calculators are the most popular by far, they are severely limited in their ability to handle scientific and engineering problems.

It is now appropriate to look at the next two levels of calculators suitable for such applications. The first class will be called the *intermediate slide rule* calculator, and is typified by the Melcor 400, Texas Instruments SR-11, and Summit SI81, (Figs. 6-1 through 6-3). The second class will be called the *scientific calculator* (or the *electronic slide rule*). Examples are the Hewlett-Packard HP-35, the Texas Instruments SR-50, and the Rockwell 61R (see Figs. 6-4 through 6-6). The key features of intermediate and scientific calculators were briefly summarized in Tables 1-3 and 1-4. This section presents their general characteristics and special operating features in greater detail.

INTERMEDIATE SLIDE RULE CALCULATORS

This classification is chosen to indicate that this type of calculator is one step along the way to a true electronic slide rule. These calculators not only possess the arithmetic capabilities previously described but also offer the following two types of computing functions not available in simpler calculators:

Algebraic Functions. These are generally available with one or two key strokes and consist of the following (see Figs. 6-1 through 6-3):

Fig. 6-1. Melcor 400 intermediate calculator.

Square roots ($\sqrt{x}$)
Squares (x^2)
Reciprocals ($1/x$)

Scientific Notation. This permits a number to be entered, or a result to be calculated, with a fixed decimal point after the first digit, followed by a 2-digit exponent. For example, the number *36.235* can be written as 3.6235×10^4 and entered in the calculator as 3.6235   04, and the decimal 0.0000475 can be written as 4.75×10^{-5} and entered in the calculator as 4.75$-$05 (see SR-11 in Fig. 6-2). The calculators with this capability generally possess the equivalent of an $\boxed{\text{EEX}}$ (enter exponent) key, or $\boxed{\text{EE}}$ key.

The significance and applications of these calculator features will be discussed in this chapter. It is important to note that scientific (power-of-10) notation, which increases the price and requires extra digits in the display, is not available in many models of intermediate calculators or even in certain advanced electronic slide rules. The reader will be able to judge whether this feature is important to him after reading

Fig. 6-2. Texas Instruments SR-11 calculator.

Fig. 6-3. Summit International SI80 calculator.

the discussion on scientific notation which follows later in this chapter.

Square Roots

The calculation and application of square roots were discussed in Chapter 2. Many operations were required to compute a square root using an elementary calculator with memory. This square root function is now available with a single key stroke using the Texas Instruments SR-10 or the Melcor 400 slide rule calculators. The Sears Slide Rule II requires two key strokes for the square root: the function key, $\boxed{f}$, and the $\boxed{\sqrt{x}}$ key. In all cases, the number in the display is replaced by the square root. All calculators compute the square root using the maximum number of figures available, but they may display the result to only two decimals, if so commanded. In that case, the displayed result should be displayed as $\sqrt{5} = 2.24$, not 2.23. It is wise to check your calculator for this rounding feature, especially for simple division. For example, ⅔ should equal 0.67, not 0.66.

All calculators will accept a floating-decimal number and correctly position the decimal point in the square root. This feature is a decided asset to any calculator.

Squares

This feature is really available in two key strokes, using the elementary calculators previously described. The square of a number—for example—$5^2 = 25$—can be computed in two key strokes using the sequence $\boxed{\times}\boxed{=}$ e.g.,5 $\boxed{\times}\boxed{=}$ yields 25. However, the x^2 feature permits more flexible operations involving squares. For example, to solve $\sqrt{16 + 3^2} = 5$, the operations are 3 $\boxed{x^2}$ $\boxed{+}$ $\boxed{16}$ $\boxed{\sqrt{x}}$ (display = 5).

Reciprocals

The reciprocal of a number, x, is unity divided by x. This feature in a calculator is valuable because it means that you can always use the number in the display as a divisor. For example, you may have a number x in the display. You want to divide it *into* another number, N, not yet entered. Normally, you would have to write x down, enter N, then press $\boxed{\div}$ and enter x. With the reciprocal key, you can press $\boxed{1/x}$, multiply $\boxed{\times}$, and then enter the number N. Notice that a single key stroke, $\boxed{1/x}$, replaces two operations—writing and entering x.

There is one minor pitfall to be guarded against when using the $\boxed{1/x}$ key for large numbers in a calculator without scientific notation. Suppose you wanted to convert 275 feet into miles (275/5280). There might be two ways to do the calculation:

1. $\dfrac{275}{5280} = 275\ \boxed{\div}\ 5280\ \boxed{=}\ 0.0520833$

2. $\dfrac{275}{5280} = 5280\ \boxed{1/x}\ \boxed{\times}\ 275\ \boxed{=}\ 0.0521575$

The first answer is correct, but the second answer is low by about 0.000026. This is because 5280 is a large number, and its reciprocal has only four significant figures in an 8-digit display ($1/5280 = 0.00001893$). Therefore, if accuracy is important, it is a good idea to arrange your calculation (if possible) so that the divisors are either less than or comparable to the numerators in any calculation. This precaution is not necessary with scientific notation, where the full number of significant figures is always available.

Scientific Notation

The ability to express numbers in scientific notation (powers of 10) is one of the distinguishing features of the true scientific calculator. Of the various intermediate slide rules shown in this chapter, only the Texas Instruments SR-10 and SR-11 possess this capability. Other calculators with scientific notation include the higher priced HP-35 and HP-45, as well as newly released calculators such as the Texas Instruments SR-50, Summit SI90, and Sinclair Scientific.

One advantage of this notation is to practically eliminate the limitations imposed by overflow and underflow conditions. Calculators with scientific notation are set up to automatically revert to this notation when a number exceeds the machine capability (larger than 10^8) or is too small to be displayed (smaller than 10^{-8}). The HP-35 reverts to scientific notation when the result is larger than 10^{10} and smaller than 10^{-10}. There is also no need to clear the calculator under these conditions, since overflow does not exist. There are, of course, practical limitations, even with scientific notation. The calculator cannot handle numbers equal to or greater than 10^{100} or numbers equal to or less than 10^{-100}.

Figures 6-2, 6-4, and 6-5 show numbers displayed in scientific notation. The *mantissa*, or significant figure part of the number, is shown on the left, while the *exponent*, or power of 10 is shown on the right. The sequence of entry is shown in the following examples.

To enter, say, 43,560 in scientific notation with the Texas Instruments SR-10, the steps are as follows:

- Express the given number in scientific notation.
  $43,560 = 4.356 \times 10^4$
- Enter 4.356   Display shows 4.356.
- Press $\boxed{\text{EE}}$ key.   Display shows 4.356↔00.
- Enter 04   Display shows 4.356↔04.

To enter a small decimal such as 0.0000785, proceed as follows:

- Express the number in scientific notation.
  $0.0000785 = 7.85 \times 10^{-5}$
- Enter 7.85.   Display shows 7.85
- Press $\boxed{\text{EE}}$ key.   Display shows 7.85   00.
- Enter 05   Display shows 7.85   05.
- Press $\boxed{^+/_-}$ key.   Display shows 7.85   −05
                         (7.85×10^{-5}).

You can now use this number for your next calculation. Observe that the power of 10 appears at the extreme right edge of the display.

These additional examples serve to show how scientific notation overcomes certain calculator limitations.

Multiplication overflow, Rockwell 61R;
      $555,555^2 = 3086.4125$ (overflow indicates 10^8)

Scientific notation, SR-10 or HP 35:
      $555,555^2 = 3.0864135 \ \ 11 = 3.0864135 \times 10^{11}$

Multiplication underflow, elementary calculators:
      $0.000026^2 = 0.0000000$, or zero

Scientific notation. SR-10 or HP-35:

$$0.000026^2 = (2.6 \ -05)^2 = 6.76 \ -10 = 6.76 \times 01^{-10}$$

There are many conversion factors and physical constants which normally appear in scientific notation and would cause considerable confusion if written otherwise. For example:

One circular mil = 7.853982×10^{-7} square inches
Gravitational constant = 6.673×10^{-8} cm³/(g × sec³)
Mass of hydrogen atom = 1.67339×10^{-24} gram
Velocity of light = 2.997925×10^{10} cm/sec
One light year = 5.8785×10^{12} miles

An example from physics demonstrates the necessity for scientific notation when using very large numbers. What is the distance to the nearest star, expressed in miles, if it is 4.5 light years away? Assume that there are 30.48 cm per foot and 5280 ft per mile. The distance is given by

d = velocity × time

$= \text{velocity} \left(\dfrac{\text{mi}}{\text{sec}} \right) \times \dfrac{\text{sec}}{\text{yr}} \times 4.5 \, \text{yr}$

$= \dfrac{2.998 \times 10^{10}\,\text{cm/sec}}{30.48\,\text{cm/ft} \times 5280\,\text{ft/mi}} \times 4.5\,\cancel{\text{yr}} \times 365\,\dfrac{\cancel{d}}{\cancel{\text{yr}}} \times \dfrac{24\,\cancel{\text{hr}}}{\cancel{d}} \times 3600\,\dfrac{\text{sec}}{\cancel{\text{hr}}}$

$= 2.643637 \times 10^{13}\,\text{mi}$

On the SR-10 intermediate slide rule, we would enter the following:

2.998 $\boxed{\text{EE}}$ 10 $\boxed{\div}$ 30.48 $\boxed{\times}$ 4.5 $\boxed{\div}$ 5280
$\boxed{\times}$ 365 $\boxed{\times}$ 24 $\boxed{\times}$ 3600 $\boxed{=}$ 2.643637 13 (display)

Therefore, the distance to the nearest star is about 2.64×10^{13} miles, or about 26 trillion miles.

The next example illustrates the use of scientific notation for very small numbers. What is the area of a wire 1 mil (0.001 in.) in diameter?

$A = \pi r^2$, where r = radius = 0.0005 in.
$= 3.1415 \times 0.0005^2$ sq in.

The sequence on the calculator is shown below.

$$3.1416 \quad \boxed{\times} \quad 5 \quad \boxed{EE} \quad 04 \quad \boxed{^+/_-}$$

Therefore, the area of the wire is 7.954×10^{-7} sq in.

Slide rule calculators which do not use scientific notation may be used so that overflow does not occur. Basically, the technique is the same as the technique used with "slipstick" slide rules: Express the number in scientific notation and do the arithmetic in two segments. One segment performs the computation and the other computes the exponent. For instance, the volume of space, in cubic miles, of a sphere with a radius r out to the nearest star is as follows:

$$r = vt$$

$$= \frac{2.998 \times 10^{10}\text{cm/sec}}{(30.48 \text{ cm/ft}) (5280 \text{ ft/mi})} \times \frac{3600 \text{ sec}}{\text{hr}} \times \frac{24 \text{ hr}}{\text{d}} \times \frac{365 \text{ d}}{\text{yr}} \times 4.5 \text{ yr}$$

$$= \frac{(2998 \times 10^{10}) (3.6 \times 10^3) \quad (2.4 \times 10^1) (3.65 \times 10^2) (4.5)}{(3.048 \times 10^1) \quad (5.280 \times 10^3)}$$

$$= 26.436371 \times 10^{(10 + 3 + 1 + 2 - 1 - 3)} = 2.6436371 \times 10^{13}$$

$$v = \frac{4}{3} \pi r^3 = 77.391658 \times 10^{13 \times 3} = 7.7391658 \times 10^{40} \text{ cu mi}$$

Note that the number of key strokes may be less, since the number of zeros which may be dropped on entry may be more than the exponent manipulator required.

The manufacturer generally explains the detailed operation of each key in a manual which is furnished with each model. However, as a special feature, the manuals supplied with the Texas Instruments SR-10 and SR-11 describe how these models can generate additional functions, such as $sin\ x$, $cos\ x$, $tan\ x$, inverse trigonometric functions, and logarithms. The methods used differ from the ones discussed in Chapters 2, 3, and 4, but you may find it informative to compare both methods and choose the routines suited to your particular needs if you have the operating manual of one of these TI models.

Characteristics of Current Scientific Calculators

There are at least 15 scientific pocket calculators of varying capability and prices on the market. Naturally, the computing power of the calculators varies markedly with the price. Table 6-1 lists the relative prices, design characteristics, and key features of representative scientific calculators.

Below are listed most of the manufacturers or distributors which carry their label on pocket-sized or portable scientific calculators.

Bowmar Consumer Products Div.

Casio Consumer Products Div.

Commodore Business Machines

Hewlett-Packard

John Colling Enterprises (JCE)

Kingspoint

Lloyd's Electronics

Monroe, The Calculator Co.

Rockwell International

Sears, Roebuck and Co.

Sanyo Electric Trading

Litronix

Sharp Electronics

Sinclair Radionics

Summit International

Texas Instruments

Calculators which can execute programs automatically, such as the Monroe 324 or the Hewlett-Packard HP-65, are excluded from this comparison because they are beyond the price class under consideration. (These calculators are discussed later.)

It is impossible to adequately cover each make and model of scientific calculator. Instead, this chapter will cover the key features and capabilities of several representative models in the "typical" price range. Models considered representative are the following:

Hewlett-Packard HP-35. (See Fig. 6-4.)

Texas Instruments SR-50. (See Fig. 6-5.)

Rockwell 61R. (See Fig. 6-5.) Other calculators in this class include the Sears Electronic Slide Rule, the Lloyd's Accumatic 999 and the Bowmar MX 140-1.

Summit International SI90. (See Fig. 6-7.)

Commodore 1400. (See Fig. 6-8.)

Bowmar MX 140-1. (See Fig. 6-9.)

Casio FX-10. (See Fig. 6-10.)

Sinclair Scientific. (See Fig. 6-11.)

The HP-35 was the first true scientific pocket calculator to appear on the market. It was followed by the Unicom 202 and

Table 6-1. Comparison of Typical Scientific Pocket Calculators.

FEATURES	Texas Instruments SR-50	Summit Int'l SI-90	Spectrum SP-70	Sinclair Scientific	Rockwell 61SR / Unicom 202 SR	Lloyds Accumatic 999	Kingspoint SC-40/KP-40	Hewlett Packard HP-45	Hewlett Packard HP-35	Commodore SR-1400	Casio FX-10	Bowmar MX-140
Price (Dec 1974) (1)	$130	$130	$120	$70	$100	$120	$140	$325	$225	$100	$80	$140
Type of Display (2)	LED	LED	LED	LED	GD	GD	LED	LED	LED	LED	GD	LED
Digits, Mantissa/Exponent	10/2	10/2	10/2	5/2	8/0	8/0	10/2	10/2	10/2	10/2	8/0	10/2
Rechargeable Batteries	Yes	Yes	Yes	No	Yes	Yes	Yes	Yes	Yes	Yes	Yes	Yes
Number of Keys	40	36	39	18	20	20	38	35	35	36	29	25
Storage Registers (Memories)	1	1	1	0	1	1	1	9	1	1	0	1
Scientific Notation	Yes	Yes	Yes	Yes	No	No	Yes	Yes	Yes	Yes	No	Yes
Degree/Radian Modes	Yes	Yes	Yes	No	Yes	Yes	Yes	Yes	Yes	No	Yes	Yes
Parentheses or Stack	No	Yes	Yes	Yes	No	No	Yes	Yes	Yes	No	No	Yes
FUNCTIONS												
Primary — Direct Tig. (Sin, Cos, Tan)	Yes	Yes	Yes	Yes	Yes	Yes	Yes	Yes	Yes	Yes	Yes	Yes
Inverse Trig (Arc Sin, etc)	Yes	Yes	Yes	Yes	Yes	Yes	Yes	Yes	Yes	Yes	Yes	Yes
Logarithms (e, 10)	Yes	Yes	Yes	Yes	Yes	Yes	Yes	Yes	Yes	e	Yes	Yes
Antilogs (e, 10)	e	e	e	10	e	Yes	e	e	Yes	Yes	e	e
Power Function (X^Y)	Yes	Yes	Yes	No	Yes	Yes	Yes	Yes	Yes	Yes	Yes	(4)
Square Root ($\sqrt{X}$)	Yes	Yes	Yes	No	(3)	(3)	Yes	Yes	Yes	No	Yes	Yes
Squares (X^2)	Yes	Yes	Yes	No	Yes	Yes	Yes	Yes	Yes	Yes	Yes	Yes
Reciprocal (1/X)	Yes	Yes	Yes	No	Yes	Yes	Yes	Yes	Yes	Yes	Yes	Yes
Pi (π)	Yes	Yes	Yes	No	Yes	Yes	Yes	Yes	Yes	Yes	Yes	Yes
Radian/Degree Conversion	Yes	No	No	No	No	No	No	Yes	No	No	No	No
Secondary — Deg/Min/Sec to Decimal	No	No	No	No	No	No	No	Yes	No	No	No	No
Polar-Rectangular Conversion	No	No	No	No	No	No	No	Yes	No	No	No	No
Hyperbolic Functions	No	No	No	No	No	No	No	No	No	No	No	No
Factorials (X!)	No	Yes	No	No	No	Yes	Yes	Yes	Yes	No	Yes	Yes
Sum and Store (E)	Yes	Yes	Yes	Yes	No	No	Yes	Yes	Yes	No	Yes	Yes
Statistical Mean/Deviation	No	No	No	No	No	No	No	Yes	Yes	No	No	No

(1) Prices and models as of Dec. 1974
(2) GD = Gas Diode, LED = Light Emitting Diode
(3) Provides (X^2 + Memory) instead
(4) Integer Powers, 1-9 only

the Lloyd's and Sears electronic slide rules. Then Hewlett-Packard released its advanced scientific calculator, the HP-45, about a year after the HP-35. Finally, the Texas Instruments SR-50 calculator was announced early in 1974, followed by the Bowmar 140-1, Rockwell 61R, and Kingspoint SC-40. Quite recently, scientific calculators in the $100 class have made their appearance—notably the Casio FX-10, the Commodore 1400, and Sinclair *Scientific*.

ROCKWELL 61R

The Rockwell 61R is manufactured by the Rockwell International Microelectronics Group. Its main characteristics are listed in Fig. 6-6. It features an 8-digit display with large, attractive numerals. It has a special tube which provides overflow and negative indicators at the extreme left of the display. The keyboard has 20 dual-function keys. The second function is engraved on the keyboard above the keys. The function is commanded by first pressing the function key, $\boxed{F}$, and then pressing the key below the desired function, as shown below.

Desired Function	Press		Number of Operations
$\log x$	$\boxed{F}$	LOG x $\boxed{8}$	2 keys
x^y	$\boxed{F}$	x^y $\boxed{6}$	2 keys
$\tan$	$\boxed{F}$	TAN $\boxed{3}$	2 keys
arc sin	$\boxed{F}$	ARC SIN $\boxed{0}$ $\boxed{1}$	3 keys

The calculator provides direct and inverse trigonometric functions, which are available in either the degrees or radian mode of calculation. It also provides common and natural logarithms ($\log x$ and $\ln x$) as well as common and natural antilog functions (10^x and e^x).

Once executed, each function replaces x in the display and is available for the next calculation.

The algebraic or power functions available include square root ($\sqrt{x}$), reciprocal ($1/x$), and the power function (x^y). This model does not provide instant squaring (because the dual operation $\boxed{\times}$ $\boxed{=}$ can be used for squaring), nor does it offer scientific notation.

The Rockwell 61R provides more memory flexibility than either the HP-35 or the SR-50. Memory operations include $\boxed{x \longleftrightarrow M}$, interchange display and memory; $\boxed{M+}$, add display to memory; $\boxed{M-}$, subtract display from memory, and $\boxed{M + x^2}$, add the square of the display to memory. The last capability is quite useful for statistical summing calculations involving the sum of squares. In addition, it provides $\boxed{x \longrightarrow M}$, transfer display to memory (or *store display*), and $\boxed{x \longleftarrow M}$, transfer memory to display (or *recall memory.*) In common with all Rockwell models, it has the ability to multiply, divide, add, and subtract in the automatic constant mode (explained in Chapter 1.) A change sign key, $\boxed{+/-}$, and function key, $\boxed{\pi}$, complete the function capability of this model.

Aside from the newly released Casio FX-10 and Sinclair *Scientific*, this calculator was priced lower than the other calculators under comparison. This calculator is quite suitable for users who do not require scientific notation and prefer algebraic logic and a large bright display at an attractive price.

To partially offset the need for scientific notation, the Rockwell 61R offers the *wraparound decimal* feature. This permits the operator to multiply two numbers whose product exceeds 10^8. The answer is determined by multiplying the display by 10^8 to get the desired result. For example:

Display Supplied by operator

$$1,111,111 \times 1,111,111 = \underbrace{12345.676}_{} \times 10^8$$

The Sears Electronic Slide Rule has identical functional capability with a different keyboard design. The Bowmar MX 140-1 has replaced the earlier model, the MX 100-1. It differs in that it displys 10 digits and has scientific notation and triple-function keys.

Each of these calculators operates in algebraic notation and has two working registers plus a memory register. As we shall see, the Hewlett-Packard line of calculators has major differences.

Fig. 6-4. A scientific calculator, the Hewlett-Packard HP-35.

HEWLETT-PACKARD'S HP-35 SCIENTIFIC CALCULATOR

The Hewlett-Packard HP-35, shown in Fig. 6-4, revolutionized the pocket calculator field when it first came out in 1972 with a full complement of trigonometric, logarithmic, and exponential functions, capped off with scientific notation. In addition, it offers 10 decimal digits with rounding, a light-emitting diode (LED) display, and 35 single-function keys. It features the kind of arithmetic logic known as *reverse Polish* notation, which reverses the order of the arithmetic operations. In multiplication, for example, one multiplier is placed in the y-register, the other multiplier in the x-register, and *then* the $\boxed{\times}$, or multiply, key is pressed. Referring to the HP-35 keyboard, the arithmetic operations are

For $a \times b$: a [ENTER ↑] b [×]

For $a \div b$:   ; a [ENTER ↑] b [÷]

For $a + b$: a [ENTER ↑] b [+]

The a [ENTER ↑] places a in the X and Y registers. The answer to every arithmetic operation appears directly in the display without the need for an [=] key.

Further calculations typical of the Hewlett-Packard calculators will be discussed since they form the basis for understanding the operation of the HP-45 and HP-65 presented in later chapters.

The following examples extracted from the Hewlett-Packard operating manuals illustrate how the HP-35 (or HP-45) solves problems in reverse Polish notation (RPN).

Example 6-1. Sums of Products (HP-35). Suppose you sold 12 items at $1.58 each and 8 items at $2.67 each. The total sale price is

$$(12 \times \$1.58) + (8 \times \$2.67) = \$40.32$$

The answer is found without writing down or storing intermediate results.

Press	Display	Comments
12	12.	
[ENTER ↑]	12.	
1.58	1.58	
[×]	18.96	$12 \times \$1.58$
8	8.	
[ENTER ↑]	8.	
2.67	2.67	
[×]	21.36	$8 \times \$2.67$
[+]	$40.32	Answer

Example 6-2. Product of Sums HP-35. Problems like $(7 + 3) \times (5 + 11) = 160$ are done just like sums of products, with all the [×] and [+] key strokes interchanged.

Press	Display	Comments
7	7.	
ENTER ↑	7.	
3	3.	
+	10.	7 + 3
5	5.	
ENTER ↑	5.	
11	11.	
+	16.	5 + 11
×	160.	(7 + 3) (5 + 11)

Trigonometric Examples

As in all calculators, the sine, cosine, or tangent of the angle x replaces x in the display.

Right Triangle Solution. Given the two legs of a triangle, a and b, find the hypotenuse, c, and the angle, A. An efficient procedure is shown below.

$A = \arctan (a/b)$
$c = a/\sin A$

Example 6-3. Right Triangle Solution (HP-35).

Key—Operations	Display	Comment
3 ENTER ↑ ENTER ↑ 4 ÷ ARC TAN	36.86989764	Angle. A
SIN ÷	5.000000003	Side. C

This requires a total of only nine steps to solve for both the hypotenuse c and the angle A. Notice that input variables a and b need be entered only once, and the calculation is completed without using the memory.

Example 6-4. What is the great-circle distance between San Francisco and Miami?

The equation for the great-circle distance, a, in a nautical miles, is

$$a = 60 \arccos [\cos b \cos c + \sin b \sin c \cos A]$$

From the diagram,

$b = 90° - 37.6° = 52.4°$
$c = 90° - 25.7° = 64.3°$
$A = 122.4° - 80.1° = 42.3°$

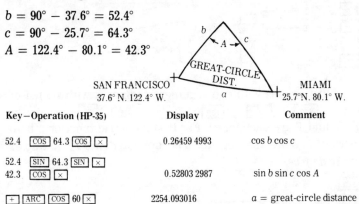

SAN FRANCISCO
37.6° N. 122.4° W.

MIAMI
25.7°N. 80.1° W.

Key–Operation (HP-35)	Display	Comment
52.4 [COS] 64.3 [COS] [×]	0.26459 4993	cos b cos c
52.4 [SIN] 64.3 [SIN] [×] 42.3 [COS] [×]	0.52803 2987	sin b sin c cos A
[+] [ARC] [COS] 60 [×]	2254.093016	a = great-circle distance

The operation of the logarithmic keys—$\boxed{log\ x}$, $\boxed{ln\ x}$, and $\boxed{e^x}$—is quite straightforward. The desired function simply replaces the contents of the x registers, just as in square root, reciprocal, or trigonometric calculations.

Operational Stack

The most significant feature of the HP-35 is the operational stack, which stores intermediate answers as they occur and automatically drops them into place for the next calculation.

The stack consists of four registers, which are identified by the letters X, Y, Z, and T. The contents of the stack are identified by the *lowercase* letters x, y, z, and t. The three keys shown below are used for entries into the stack, exchanging the contents of the X and Y registers, and "rolling down" the registers for viewing the display.

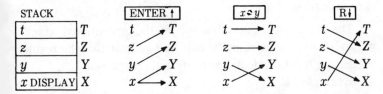

Arithmetic operations occur from the interaction between the contents of the X and Y registers. Answers appear in the X register and are automatically displayed, as shown on the left. The stack also drops, as shown on the right.

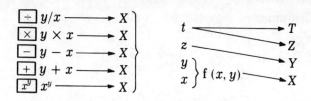

All functions with one argument replace x with $\mathbf{f}(x)$. For keys $\boxed{1/x}$, $\boxed{\sqrt{x}}$, $\boxed{\log}$, $\boxed{\ln}$, and $\boxed{e^x}$, registers Y, Z, and T are unchanged. For trigonometric functions, both forward and inverse, register Z is duplicated into T. *All angles are in degrees.*

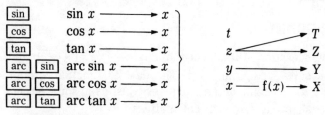

The operational stack allows typical problems to be solved with a minimum number of key strokes, when solving equations with several terms or nested parentheses.

The following examples have been chosen to show how the stack functions in actual use. The stack operation charts that following show:

- **Bottom row**—the successive key strokes used to evaluate the expression.

- **Top four rows**—the contents of the stack following each operation.

- **Next-to-bottom row**—the contents of the display after each operation.

The following chart shows how the operational stack works for a simple arithmetic calculation. Note that the result of each arithmetic calculation is instantly displayed.

Example 6-5.

$$(3 \times 4) + (5 \times 6) = 42$$

	T						12	12		
	Z						12	12		
	Y		3	3		12	5	5	12	
Display	X	3.	3.	4.	12.	5.	5.	6.	30.	42.
	Key	$\boxed{3}$	$\boxed{\uparrow}$	$\boxed{4}$	$\boxed{\times}$	$\boxed{5}$	$\boxed{\uparrow}$	$\boxed{6}$	$\boxed{\times}$	$\boxed{+}$

The following chart illustrates how the operational stack functions using mixed calculations.

Example 6-6.

$$\frac{(2 + 3) \times 4/5}{\sin 30°} \times 4^{15} = 1.0$$

T								
Z								
Y		2	2		5		20		4
Display X	2	2	3	5	4	20	5	4	30
Key	2	↑	3	+	4	×	5	÷	30
T									
Z						8	8		
Y	4		8	8	−1.5	−1.5	8		
Display X	0.5	8	1.5	−1.5	−1.5	4	0.125	1	
Key	sin	÷	1.5	CHS	↑	4	x^y	×	

This chart shows how intermediate results are conveniently made available in a more complex calculation using each register in the operational stack. There is no need to use a memory in this calculation.

Example 6-7. Find the monthly payment on a 30-year (360-payment) loan of $30,000 which has an annual interest of 6% (0.5% per month), where P is principal, i is monthly interest, and n is the number of monthly payments.

$$M = \frac{Pi}{1 - |1/(1 + i)^n|} = \frac{30.000 \times 0.005}{1 - |1/1.005^{360}|}$$

T						
Z					150		150
Y		30000	30000		150	1		1
Display X	30000	30000	.005	150	1	1	360
Key	30000	ENTER ↑	.005	×	1	ENTER ↑	360
	(P)		(i)				(n)

T	150	150	150	150	150	150
Z	1	1	150	150	150	150
Y	360	360	1	1	150	150
Display X	360	1.005	6.0225	0.16604	0.83395	179.86
Key	ENTER ↑	1.005	x^y	$1/x$	−	÷

The payment is $179.86.

Accuracy

The accuracy of the HP-35 depends on the operation being performed. Elementary add, subtract, multiply, divide, reciprocal, and square root functions have a maximum error of plus or minus one count in the 10th (least significant) digit. Errors in these operations are caused by rounding answers to the 10th digit.

The square root of 5, for example, will appear as 2.236067977, correct to one part in the last digit.

The accuracy of trigonometric, logarithmic, and exponential operations depends on the argument (x). The answer that is displayed will be the correct value for an input argument within ± 1 counts in the 10th least significant digit of the original input argument. Typical errors for these functions are shown below.

Operation	Equivalent Error in Argument ($\pm n$ Counts in Last Place)
$\log x$, $\ln x$, e^x	2
Trigonometric functions	3
x^y	4 in x 7 in y

There is an additional error of $\pm 1 \times 10^{-9}$ in the displayed answer for trigonometric functions. As an example of errors, using the above table, consider $\ln 5 = 1.609437912$ shown on the display. The argument, to 10-figure accuracy, is 5.000000000. The accuracy statement says that 1.609437012 is the natural logarithm of a number between 4.999999998 and 5.000000002, or $5 \, (\pm 2 \leqslant 10^{-9})$.

Any computation or data entry resulting in a magnitude equal to or greater than 10^{100} causes 9.999999999 99 to be displayed. Computations or data entries having a magnitude less than 10^{-99} are displayed as zero. Answers greater than 10^{10} and smaller than 10^{-2} are displayed in scientific notation.

Finally, if you attempt an improper calculation, such as division by zero, a blinking zero appears. To reset, press $\boxed{\text{CL}x}$. The following operations are improper:

- Division by zero
- Square root of a negative number
- $\ln x$, $\log x$, or x^y, where $x \leqslant 0$
- $arc \sin x$ or $arc \cos x$, where $x > 1$

TEXAS INSTRUMENTS SR-50

Early in 1974, Texas Instruments announced a new slide rule pocket calculator, the SR-50, in direct competition with the HP-35. In packaging and appearance it is quite similar to the HP-35, yet it offers several additional functions at a significantly lower price. These extra features include: $\boxed{x!}$, x factorial; $\boxed{x^2}$, x squared; $\boxed{\sqrt[x]{y}}$, xth root of y; $\boxed{\Sigma}$, sum and store; $\boxed{\text{HYP}}$, hyperbolic functions; and a switch for the *degree* or *radian* mode of calculation. Finally, the SR-50, in contrast to the HP-35, uses the familiar algebraic notation with the $\boxed{=}$ sign to complete calculations.

In common with the HP-35, the SR-50 displays 10 significant figures with sign, a 2-digit exponent with sign, and the full complement of trigonometric, logarithmic, and exponential functions. All in all, this recent entry in the scientific calculator race represents formidable competition in

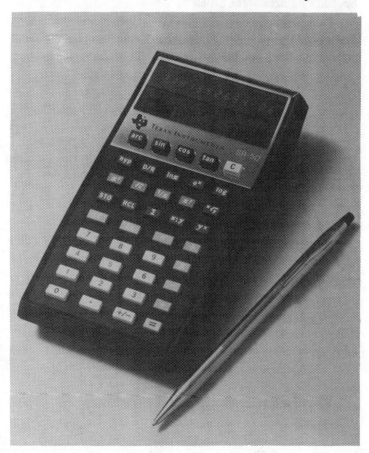

Fig. 6-5. Texas Instruments SR-50 scientific calculator.

the marketplace. Other operating features are similar to those of the HP-35. The calculator indicates overflow and underflow conditions by a flashing display rather than by a fixed set of nines or zeros. It also provides a flashing display to indicate illegal operations, such as trying to find the square root of a negative number, the factorial of a noninteger, or the logarithm of a negative number. The flashing display can be terminated by the use of the $\boxed{C}$ key.

Rather than explain functions that are common to those of the HP-35, we will summarize briefly the functions that are unique to the SR-50 in its price range.

Special Features of the SR-50

Following are some examples to ilustrate the special features of this calculator. Advanced applications of the SR-50, HP-35, and Rockwell 61R calculators will be discussed later.

Factorial x, $\boxed{x!}$

Factorial x is a single-function key, $\boxed{x!}$, which calculates the following function: $x! = (x)(x-1)(x-2)(x-3)...$ For example, $4! = (4)(3)(2) = 24$. To calculate $4!$, just enter 4, press $\boxed{x!}$, and read 24 in the display. The factorial function may be used as part of another calculation, as shown next.

Example 6-8. Calculate $60/5! = 0.5$.

Key–Operation	Display	Comment
60 $\boxed{\div}$	60	
5 $\boxed{x!}$	120	5 factorial.
$\boxed{=}$	0.5	Answer.

Calculating the xth Root of y

This key evaluates the function $\boxed{\sqrt[x]{y}}$ or $y^{1/x}$.
Example 6-9. Evaluate $\sqrt[1.3]{4.8}$, or $4.8^{1/1.3}$.

Key–Operation	Display	Comment
4.8 $\boxed{\sqrt[x]{y}}$	4.8	Base Number.
1.3 $\boxed{=}$	3.42194507	Answer.

Example 6-10. Evaluate $\sqrt[3]{20} = 2.714417617$.

Key–Operation	Display	Comment
20 $\boxed{\sqrt[x]{y}}$	20	Base number.
3 $\boxed{=}$	2.714417617	Answer.

Of course, this calculation can be performed on the HP-35 or any calculator with the $\boxed{y^x}$ or $\boxed{a^x}$ function. Simply press the reciprocal $\boxed{1/x}$ key after entering x and before completing the operation.

Radian Calculation Mode

This feature is possessed by the Rockwell 61R, Bowmar *Scientific*, Texas Instruments SR-50, and others. It permits the calculator to handle arithmetic operations involving the angle, expressed in radians, and functions of the angle, including inverse functions.

Example 6-11. Evaluate the expression $5-3\ sin/6$.

Key—Operation	Display	Comment
Set DEG RAD switch to RAD.		
$\boxed{\pi}$ $\boxed{\div}$ 6 $\boxed{=}$	0.5235987756	Value of angle in radians.
$\boxed{\sin}$ $\boxed{\times}$ 3 $\boxed{=}$	1.5	$3 \sin \pi/6$
$\boxed{+/-}$	−1.5	Change of sign.
$\boxed{+}$ 5 $\boxed{=}$	3.5	Answer.

If the angle were given in degrees, the degree-to-radian conversion switch, $\boxed{D/R}$, could be used to convert automatically.

Hyperbolic Functions

There are six hyperbolic functions that can be found on the SR-50, which are analogous to the trigonometric functions. These are hyperbolic sine $\boxed{\sinh}$, hyperbolic cosine $\boxed{\cosh}$, hyperbolic tangent $\boxed{\tanh}$, and the inverse functions $\boxed{\text{arc}}$ $\boxed{\cosh}$, and $\boxed{\text{arc}}$ $\boxed{\tanh}$. These functions have such diverse applications as conic sections, transmission line and waveguide theory, and cable geometry. The calculation of these functions on the SR-50 is precisely the same as for the trigonometric functions.

Example 6-13. Evaluate $cosh\ 0.78 = 1.319939138$.

Key—Operation	Display
0.78 $\boxed{\text{hyp}}$ $\boxed{\cos}$	1.319939138

Example 6-13. Evaluate $arc\ sinh\ 0.886 = 0.7984245338$.

Key—Operation	Display
0.886 $\boxed{\text{arc}}$ $\boxed{\text{hyp}}$ $\boxed{\sin}$	0.7984245338

Fig. 6-6. Rockwell 61R scientific calculator.

Sum and Store $\boxed{\Sigma}$

This key is used to sum desired display entries into a special summing register or memory. The sum can then be recalled for subsequent calculations and retained in the memory. The clear key, $\boxed{C}$, does not erase memory; therefore, a zero should be entered into memory to clear it unless the calculator has just been turned on. Either negative or positive quantities may be summed by the $\boxed{\Sigma}$ key. This key may be used independently without affecting the display or data processed in the working registers.

SUMMIT INTERNATIONAL SI90

The SI90 calculator, shown in Fig. 6-7, features almost all of the scientific functions previously described, including trigonometric, logarithmic, and exponential capability. It has a somewhat larger LED readout than the HP-35, with a full 10-digit display and 2-digit exponent with sign, and an addressable memory. It also features an $\boxed{x^y}$ key; a degree—radian mode key; and logical parenthesis keys, $\boxed{(}$ $\boxed{)}$, which allow complex expressions to be evaluated without requiring additional memory registers.

For example, the parentheses permit the operator to evaluate the expression below in a straightforward manner.

$$\left[\sin \frac{1}{\sqrt{\dfrac{5+2}{900} - \dfrac{9-3}{900}}}\right]^3 = 0.125$$

The sequence for evaluating this expression is as follows:

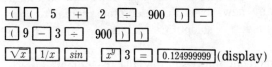

$\boxed{(}$ $\boxed{(}$ 5 $\boxed{+}$ 2 $\boxed{\div}$ 900 $\boxed{)}$ $\boxed{-}$

$\boxed{(}$ 9 $\boxed{-}$ 3 $\boxed{\div}$ 900 $\boxed{)}$ $\boxed{)}$

$\boxed{\sqrt{x}}$ $\boxed{1/x}$ $\boxed{\sin}$ $\boxed{x^y}$ 3 $\boxed{=}$ $\boxed{0.124999999}$ (display)

This answer is within the functional accuracy of the SI90. Notice that the double parentheses enclose both terms of the denominator, and that the number of left parentheses, $\boxed{(}$, equals the number of right parentheses, $\boxed{)}$. Another convenient feature is the single memory key, $\boxed{M\ \updownarrow}$, which can be used to enter data into memory or retrieve data from memory. However, this places certain restrictions on the memory operations which depend on the sequence that precedes depression of the $\boxed{M\ \updownarrow}$ key.

The calculator comes equipped with an ac charger—adapter, and the price is well below that of the HP-35.

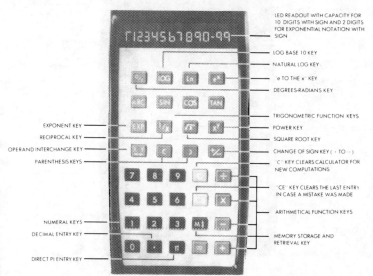

Fig. 6-7. Summit International SI90 scientific calculator.

COMMODORE 1400 SLIDE RULE

Another recent scientific calculator is the Commodore 1400, shown in Fig. 6-8, which represents further competition to the Texas Instruments SR-50, Hewlett-Packard HP-35, and Rockwell 61R. In Table 6-1 it can be seen that the Commodore 1400 has at least three important features that are desirable in any new scientific calculator: radian—degree calculating modes, scientific notation, and logical parentheses.

The functional capabilities of the 1400 are indicated in Fig. 6-8. Note that the calculator has a *radian* lamp to indicate when radian calculations are in progress. It also has a single memory key, [M], which can be used to store new data from memory. The machine can accept numbers in scientific notation, using the [exp] and [+/-] keys, but it will display the result in ordinary notation where there is no loss of accuracy.

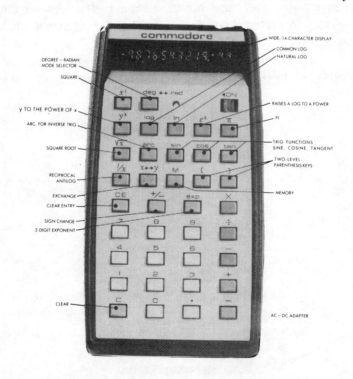

Fig. 6-8. Commodore 1400 scientific calculator.

For example, to evaluate $(9 \times 10^{12})/(3 \times 10^{11})$, press these keys: 9 $\boxed{exp}$ 12 $\boxed{\div}$ 3 $\boxed{exp}$ 11. The display will read *30*.

The use of the 2-level parentheses, $\boxed{[(}$ and $\boxed{)]}$, deserves special mention. It permits the operator to evaluate complex formulas and mixed chain computations without using the memory to record intermediate results or having to master the calculator's internal logic. For example, evaluate:

$$2 + [(4 + 5)^{(1.1 + 2.2)}] = 1411.2897$$

Press keys: 2 $\boxed{+}$ $\boxed{[(}$ $\boxed{(}$ 4 $\boxed{+}$ 5 $\boxed{)}$
$\boxed{y^x}$ $\boxed{(}$ 1.1 $\boxed{+}$ 2.2 $\boxed{)}$ $\boxed{)]}$ $\boxed{=}$.

The display will read 1411.2897.

The calculator measures only $3\frac{1}{4} \times 6 \times 1\frac{3}{4}$ in., and it comes completely equipped with an ac adapter—charger and rechargeable batteries.

CASIO FX-10

This calculator is shown in Fig. 6-10. It features a bright 8-digit Digitron display, without scientific notation. It does

Fig. 6-9. Bowmar MX 140-1 scientific calculator.

Fig. 6-10. Casio FX-10 scientific calculator.

provide common and natural logarithms, the natural antilog (e^x), the power function (a^n), reciprocals ($1/x$), and $\sqrt{x}$. It also features deg−min−sec conversion to decimal degrees and the usual trigonometric functions. Unfortunately, it does not provide the inverse trig functions (*arc cos*, *arc sin*, and *arc tan*), which is a serious omission. Of course, the owner of such a calculator could well use the interpolation routines offered in Chapter 3 for the inverse trig functions. This calculator can be operated on either ac or disposable batteries, good for 17 hours' operation. However, a charger is not offered with this model. The Casio FX-10 measures $5\frac{7}{8} \times 3\frac{3}{4} \times 1\frac{1}{4}$ in. and features a convenient keyboard with large, single-function keys.

It is interesting to note that both the Sinclair *Scientific* and Casio FX-10, priced below the other calculators, lack some capability which you as prospective owner must consider in relation to higher priced calculators. It could be that you do not require the missing functions, in which case either calculator may serve the purpose. Review the functions provided by each model as shown in Table 6-1 to determine which calculator best suits your purpose and pocketbook. The only way to determine the best price for the calculator you want is to get prices from several outlets—just as in the new-car market—and choose the best price that goes with a warranty for one-year service.

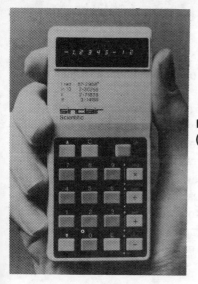

Fig. 6-11. The Sinclair Scientific.
(Courtesy Summit International.)

SINCLAIR SCIENTIFIC

This calculator, shown in Fig. 6-11, is a nice combination of miniature packaging and elegant styling. It offers select scientific functions as well as scientific notation, plus a simplified keyboard for economical design. Of course, there are some shortcuts to meet the popular price. For example, there are only five significant figures in the display, which is fixed in the scientific notation mode. Although this accuracy is much better than that of the the conventional slide rule, it is below the accuracy of any of the other scientific calculators described in this chapter. Nevertheless, it might be quite acceptable to the student, technician, or practicing engineer. Sometimes, the full complement of 10 (or even 8) digits is an annoyance to the user, since only 4 or 5 digits are needed most often in practice.

The calculator does not offer reciprocals, square roots, or natural logs. These functions can be obtained, with a little extra effort, by the use of the $\boxed{x^y}$ key or by simple conversion factors.

For example:

- $\sqrt{x} = x^{0.5}$, so use the $\boxed{x^y}$ key and let $y = 0.5$.
- $e^y = 2.71828^y$, so use the $\boxed{x^y}$ key and let $x = 2.71828$.

131

- ln x = 2.30259 *log x*, so use the $\boxed{\log}$ key and multiply by 2.30259.

To aid in these calculations, the Sinclair *Scientific* has four conversion constants printed on its keyboard under the display.

There are only 18 keys required to process all the functions. The four arithmetic keys each have a triple function. The normal function is enscribed directly on the key; the upper function is selected by the $\blacktriangle$ key, and the lower function is selected by the $\blacktriangledown$ key. The calculator features an *enter exponent*, $\boxed{\text{E}}$ key and uses reverse Polish notation (as does the HP-35). The calculator weighs only 3¾ oz and measures 4⅜ × 2 × $^{11}/_{16}$ in. It comes equipped with batteries good for 25 hours' use. Since this calculator does not provide an ac adapter−charger, it is desirable to have spare batteries handy for emergency operation.

Chapter 7

Some Applications for Scientific Calculators

This chapter shows how different calculators can solve typical problems which require scientific or advanced functions. These exercises will permit you to evaluate different calculators and gain an appreciation of how mathematical operations can be translated into calculator routines for solving scientific or technical problems. Emphasis will be placed on the method of problem solving as well as on the individual characteristics of each calculator.

For simplicity and to minimize repetition, only three calculators will be used to illustrate the applications:

1. Rockwell 61R (same as Lloyd's *Accumatic 999* and Sears *Electronic Slide Rule*)
2. HP-35 (same logic as HP-45)
3. Texas Instruments SR-50

Examples chosen will include typical mathematical problems and specific profession-oriented applications. Mathematical examples include rectangular-to-polar conversion, cosine law solution, quadratic equation solution, monthly payment on a loan, statistical mean, variance and standard deviation, and other special applications from engineering and finance.

To get a feeling for programing the more complex problems, you should review each example to determine the following:

- What was the formula used for each problem?
- What was the actual sequence of operations?
- What specific numerical data was entered in the example?

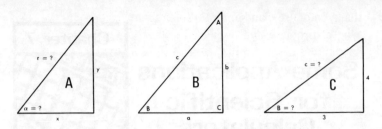

Fig. 7-1. (A) A problem in rectangular-polar conversion; (B) a generalized right triangle; (C) a numerical example to be solved.

- How does the numerical display correlate with the sequence of operations up to that point?
- Can you solve the same problem with a different set of input data?
- Can the number of steps be shortened or can the number of data entries be reduced by the judicious use of memory?
- Can you predict the contents of the display as well as the working and memory registers during the calculation?

If you can answer these questions, you will be ready for the advanced applications discussed in Chapter 8. The procedure followed will be:

1. Define the problem and the given data.
2. State the equations to be solved.
3. Develop a general program on one calculator, then develop a numerical example.
4. Solve the same problem with another scientific calculator to illustrate differences in problem solving.

If you master steps 2 and 3, you will be able to solve a similar problem whenever it arises. The process of specifying the sequence of calculator or computer steps necessary to solve a given problem is called programing.

RECTANGULAR-TO-POLAR CONVERSION

One of the most common problems in physics, surveying, engineering, and science is shown in Fig. 7-1.

The problem may be to convert from rectangular coordinates, x and y, to polar coordinates, r and α, or to find the hypotenuse c and angle B, given the two sides a and b. This type of problem can be solved quite handily by most of the calculators described in Chapter 6.

The object is to enter values for the given sides (a and b) only once and to specify a program which solves for both the hypotenuse c and the angle B, with a minimum number of steps. A general program using symbols for the input data will be shown first; then numerical data will be used to illustrate numerical results. The HP-35 will be used first, then the Rockwell 61R, to illustrate two types of logic and the use of memory. The equations to be solved are

$$B = \text{arc tan } b/a \qquad (7\text{-}1)$$
$$c = b/\sin B \qquad (7\text{-}2)$$

The solution (general program) for rectangular-to-polar conversion with the HP-35 is shown below.

Key—Operations	Display	Comment
b ENTER ↑ ENTER ↑	b	Enter b in X, Y, and Z
a ÷	tan B	Tan B in X, b in Y-register.
ARC TAN	B	Read angle B in X-register.
sin	sin B	Sin B in X, b in Y-register.
÷	c	Read side $c = b/\sin B$.

The desired angle B is found first and is read after the arc tan sequence. Side c is found second, for a total of only nine operations, including the entry of sides a and b. Now let's substitute values for a and b. The data are entered just once.

Example 7-1. If $a = 4$ and $b = 3$, find c and angle B using the HP-35.

Key—Operation	Display	Comment
3 ENTER ↑	3.00	Side b
4 ÷	0.75	tan B
ARC TAN	36.87*	B
SIN	0.60*	sin B
÷	5.00*	side c

* Rounded to two decimal places.

The calculator actually displays a 10-digit readout for angle B—namely, 36.86989764—but only two decimal places are shown for convenience.

Suppose now we use the Rockwell 61R. This calculator offers several memory operations which can be used to solve

Eq. 7-1. Remember, however, that every function operation with this calculator must be preceded by pressing the $\boxed{F}$ (function) key. The numerical example will be shown for comparison with the previous example. The expression in parentheses indicates the alternate function selected by the $\boxed{F}$ key.

Example 7-2. If $b = 3$ and $a = 4$, find c and angle B using the Rockwell 61R.

Key–Operation	Display	Comments
3 $\boxed{F}$ (M + x^2)	3.00	$3^2 = 9$ in memory
$\boxed{\div}$ 4 $\boxed{F}$ (M + x^2)	4.00	$4^2 + 3^2 = 25$ in memory
$\boxed{=}$	0.75	tan B
$\boxed{F}$ $\boxed{ARC}$ $\boxed{TAN}$	36.8699	angle B
$\boxed{F}$ ($x \longleftrightarrow$ M)	25	25 in display. angle b in memory
$\boxed{F}$ $\boxed{\sqrt{x}}$	5	side c

There are 15 steps required, 5 of which were used to activate the $\boxed{F}$ key. The angle B is still available in memory at the end of the calculation and the side c is in the display. You will note that, this time, the familiar Pythagorean equation is used to solve for side c.

$$c = \sqrt{a^2 + b^2}$$

Now for the Texas Instruments SR-50. The next example illustrates its use in rectangular-to-polar conversion.

Example 7-3. If $b = 3$ and $a = 4$, find c and angle B.

Key–Operation	Display	Comments
3 $\boxed{-}$ 4 $\boxed{=}$	0.75	tan B
$\boxed{ARC}$ $\boxed{TAN}$	36.8699	angle B
$\boxed{SIN}$ $\boxed{1/x}$	1.6666	1/sin B
$\boxed{\times}$ $\boxed{=}$	5.000000	$c = b (1/\sin B)$

In this case, the first number entered ($b = 3$) is retained in the register and multiplied by $1/\sin B$ to give side $c = 5$. There are 10 steps required for this calculation. Although the range of total steps for the three calculators was 9−15, the total time for the calculation is much closer since the data entries and data readouts and minimum steps take most of the time.

COSINE LAW SOLUTION

The general problem and a numerical example are shown in Fig. 7-2.

The cosine law can be used to find the third side of a triangle when two sides and the included angle are given, or to find any angle when all three sides are given. The first application for the cosine law is illustrated by Fig. 7-2A, where sides a and b and included angle C are given, and side c must be found.

$$c = \sqrt{a^2 + b^2 - 2ab \cos C} \qquad (7\text{-}4)$$

The general program using the HP-35 is shown in the following example.

Example 7-4. Given a, b, and angle C, find side c, using the HP-35.

Key—Operation	Display	Comment
a [ENTER ↑] [×] [ENTER ↑]	a^2	
b [STO] [ENTER ↑] [×] [+]	$a^2 + b^2$	b in memory
[x⇄y] [RCL] [×] 2 [×]	$2ab$	
C [COS] [×]	$+ 2ab \cos C$	
[−] [√x̄]	side c	

The program involves a total of 19 steps, including 3 data entries; a, b, and angle C. It requires the use of memory to prevent repetition of data entries. The following numerical example illustrates the contents of the operational stack at each step in the calculation.

Example 7-5. With the HP-35, find c if $a = 8$, $b = 12$, and $C = 150$.

Key—Operation	Display	Operational Stack
8	8	8
[ENTER ↑] [ENTER ↑]	8	8, 8, 8
[×]	64	64, 8
12	12	12, 64, 8
[STO]	12	12, 64, 8
[ENTER ↑] [×]	144	144, 64, 8, 8
[+]	208	208, 8, 8, 8
[x⇄y]	8	8, 208, 8, 8
[RCL] [×]	96	96, 208, 8, 8
2 [×]	192	192, 208, 8, 8
150	150	150, 192, 208, 8
[COS]	−0.866 *	−0.8660 *, 192, 208, 8
[×]	−166.27*	−166.27*, 208, 8, 8
[−]	374.27*	374.27*, 8, 8, 8
[√x̄]	19.35*	19.35, 8, 8, 8

* Some decimals are dropped for convenience of explanation.

This program requires 19 steps to find $c = 19.35$. Observe that the input data is entered only once. New values could be

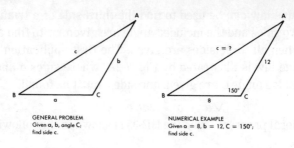

Fig. 7-2. Cosine law problems.

substituted for a, b, and angle C, and the same program used for any similar problem. Let's see how the same problem is solved with the Rockwell 61R.

Example 7-6. With the Rockwell 61R, find c if $a = 8$, $b = 12$, and angle $C = 150$. [In the first column of the table, an expression in parentheses—$(M + x^2)$, for example—denotes a function enscribed above a dual-function key.]

Key—Operation	Display	Comment
150 F COS	−0.866026	minus indicator lights (cos 150 is negative).
× 8 F (M + x^2)	8	$8^2 = 64$ added to memory.
× 12 F (M + x^2)	12	$12^2 = 144$ added to memory.
× 2 =	−166.27699	Minus indicator lights.
F (M−)	−166.27699	Memory now contains $C^2 = 208 + 166.27699$.
F (M → x)	374.27699	c^2 in display.
F F $\sqrt{x}$	19.346239	c = third side.

The above program requires 20 steps, including the 3 data entries (150 and sides 8 and 12). It turns out that the steps saved by the $(M + x^2)$ function are offset by the six steps required to press the F key. For all intents and purposes, both programs take about the same time.

Example 7-7. With the SR-50, find c if $a = 8$, $b = 12$, $C = 150$.

Key—Operations	Display	Comment
8 STO × 12 × 2	192	$2ab$
× 150 COS +/− =	166.2768775	$−2ab\cos C$
+ RCL x^2	64	a^2
+ 12 x^2 =	374.2768775	$a^2 + b^2 − 2ab\cos C$
$\sqrt{x}$	19.34623678	side c

138

This solution requires 19 steps, including 4 data entries ($b = 12$ is entered twice).

MONTHLY PAYMENT ON A LOAN

It may not be obvious to the user, but the scientific calculator can also solve problems in finance, real estate, and business. A typical problem is to determine the monthly payment required to clear a loan or principal P. The basic formula is:

$$M = \frac{P \times i}{[1 - (1 + i)^{-n}]}$$

(7-5)

Where
M = monthly payment
i = monthly interest
n = total number of payments

The solution for the monthly payment is easily programed on any scientific calculator. Let's start with the HP-35.

Example 7-8. Find the monthly payment on a loan (general program).

Key–Operations	Display	Comments
P ENTER ↑ i ×	Pi	Numerator.
1 ENTER ↑ $1 + i$ ENTER ↑	$1 + i$	Operator enters $1 + i$.
n CHS x^y	$(1 + i)^{-n}$	$x = (1 + i)$, $y = -n$
− ÷	M	Answer.

The are only 13 steps required, including 4 data entries: P, i, $1 + i$, and n. The monthly interest may be stored in memory and recalled, but this is generally not necessary. I recommend, however, that you let the calculator determine $i = I/12$, if the yearly rate, I, is not easily divisible by 12 (6.25%, 8.5%, etc.). Now for a numerical example.

Example 7-9. Find the monthly payment on a loan, using the HP.35 ($P = 30,000$, $I = 6\%$, $i = 0.005$, $n = 306$).

Key–Operations	Display	Comment
30,000 ENTER ↑ 0.005 ×	150	$P i$
1 ENTER ↑ 1.005 ENTER ↑	1.005	$1 + i$
360 CHS x^y	0 166042	$(1 + i)^{-360}$
− ÷	179.87	monthly payment

To solve the same problem on the Rockwell 61R, process 1.005^{-360} first, then change sign, add 1, take the reciprocal, and multiply by P and i.

Example 7-10. Find the monthly payment on a loan, using the Rockwell 61R ($P = 30{,}000$, $i = 0.005$, $n = 360$).

Key—Operation	Display	Comment
1.005 $\boxed{\text{F}}$ $\boxed{x^y}$	-0.166074	$-(1 + i)^{-n}$
360 $\boxed{+/-}$ $\boxed{=}$ $\boxed{+/-}$		
$\boxed{+}$ 1 $\boxed{=}$	0.833926	$1 - (1 + i)^{-n}$
$\boxed{\text{F}}$ $\boxed{1/x}$	1.1991471	reciprocal
$\boxed{\times}$ 30,000	30.000	
$\boxed{\times}$ 0.005 $\boxed{=}$	179.87206	monthly payment

This solution requires a total of 17 steps, including 4 data entries.

The solution on the SR-50 would take two steps less, since all operations are single functions and require no $\boxed{\text{F}}$ key.

QUADRATIC EQUATION—MANUAL PROGRAM

The quadratic equation, shown below, is characterized by three variables—a, b, and c—and two answers, or *roots*. It occurs widely in mathematics, scince, and engineering. It is an ideal tool to illustrate the difference in scientific calculators and the need for programing a solution.

The theory of quadratic, or *second-degree*, equations is well known and can be summarized as follows. Given:

$$ax^2 + bx + c = 0 \qquad (7\text{-}6)$$

where a, b, and c are constants for any given problem. This equation has two roots, R_1 and R_2, which are given by the following formulas, provided the quantity under the radical sign is positive:

$$R_1 = \frac{-b}{2a} - \sqrt{\left(\frac{b}{2a}\right)^2 - \frac{c}{a}} \qquad (7\text{-}7)$$

$$R_2 = \frac{-b}{2a} + \sqrt{\left(\frac{b}{2a}\right)^2 - \frac{c}{a}} \qquad (7\text{-}8)$$

If $d = (-b/2a)$ and $(d^2 - c/a)$ is positive,

$$R_1 = d + \sqrt{d^2 - c/a} = d - f \qquad (7\text{-}9)$$
$$R_2 = d - \sqrt{d^2 - c/a} = d + f \qquad (7\text{-}10)$$

where R_1 and R_2 are *real numbers* and $f = c/a$.

If $(d^2 - c/a)$ is negative and $j = \sqrt{-1}$,

$$R_1 = d + j\sqrt{d^2 - c/a} = d + jf \qquad (7\text{-}11)$$
$$R_2 = d - j\sqrt{d_2 - c/a} = d - jf \qquad (7\text{-}12)$$

As a check,

$$R_1 \times R_2 = c/a \qquad (7-13)$$

The mathematical operations to be performed on the calculator are indicated by Eqs. 7-6 through 7-13 and follow this sequence:

1. Calculate $d = -b/2a$; store d in memory.
2. Calculate d^2 and c/a.
3. Calculate $f^2 = d^2 - c/a$)
   If f $f^2 > 0$ use Eqs. 7-9, 7-10.
   If $f^2 < 0$, use Eqs. 7-11, 7-12.
4. Calculate $f = \sqrt{d^2 - c/a}$.
5. Calculate first real root ($R_1 = d - f$).
6. Calculate second real root ($R_2 = d + f$).
7. Calculate imaginary roots ($R_1, R_2 = d \pm jf$).

What we now must do is transform these mathematical directions into a fixed program or calculator sequence of operations which can be used to solve the two real roots of any quadratic equation with real coefficients a, b, and c. The next example shows how the above instructions are translated into a general program for the HP-35.

Example 7-11. Using the HP-35, find the real roots of $ax^2 + bx + c = 0$.

Step	Quadratic Program	Operation Performed
1	b [CHS] [ENTER ↑] a [ENTER ↑] 2 [×] [÷]	$d = -b/2a$
2	[ENTER ↑] [↑] [↑] [×]	With d stored, calculate d^2.
3	c [ENTER ↑] a [÷] [−]	Calculate $f^2 = d^2 - c/a$ *.
4	[√] [ENTER ↑]	Calculate $f = \sqrt{d^2 = c/a}$.
5	[↓] [−]	$R_1 = d - f$, the first root.
6	[↓] [+]	$R_2 = d + f$, the second root.
7	[x⇄y] [↓] [×]	Check $R_1 \times R_2 = c/a$.

* If f^2 is negative, reverse the sign and use Eqs. 7-11 and 7-12 for R_1 and R_2.

There are 23 steps required for the calculation and 3 more for the check, if desired. Notice in step 2 that the [ENTER ↑], [ENTER ↑], [ENTER ↑], and [×] operations serve both to store d in the Z registers and to calculate d^2. Now let us solve a simple quadratic equation with numerical values in place of a, b, and c.

Example 7-12. Find the real roots of a quadratic equation where $a = 2$, $b = 3$, and $c = -2$.

Key—Operation	Display	Comments
3. [CHS] [ENTER↑] 2 [ENTER↑]		
2 [×] [÷]	−0.7500 0000	$d = -b/2a$
[ENTER↑] [ENTER↑] [ENTER↑] [×]	0.56250000	d^2
−2 [ENTER↑] 2 [÷]	−1.00 000 000	e/a
[−] [√] [ENTER↑]	1.250 000 000	f
[↓] [−]	−2.000 000	$R_1 = d - f$
[↓] [+]	0.500 000	$R_2 = d - f$
[x⇄y] [↓] [×]	−1.000000	c/a (check)

Let us now solve a quadratric equation with the Rockwell 61R calculator. The following example, taken from its instruction manual, shows that it takes 27 steps to solve a similar quadratic equation. It also illustrates the use of the *minus* light to indicate negative quantities. Note the use of [F] for memory operations in parts 1 and 2 and the automatic *subtract constant* operation to solve for the two roots in part 3. Key functions in parentheses—for example, ($M + x^2$)—are functions enscribed above dual-function keys.

Example 7-13. Using the Rockwell 61R solve the quadratic equation for $a = 3$, $b = 9$, and $c = 6$.

$$x = \frac{-b \pm \sqrt{b^2 - 4ac}}{2a}$$

$$3x + 9x + 6 = 0$$

$$(3x + 3)(x + 2) = 0$$

$$x = -1 \text{ or } -2$$

Where $a = 3$, $b = 9$, and $c = 6$,

Key—Operation   **Display**   **Comments**

Part 1. $\dfrac{b}{2(-a)}$

Key—Operation	Display	Comments
9	9.	Enter b term.
[÷]	9.	
2	2.	
[÷]	4.5	
3	3.	Enter a term.
[+/−]	−3.	Minus indicator lights.
[=]	−1.5	$b/2(-a) = -1.5$
[F] ($x \to M$)	−1.5	$b/2(-a)$ term entered into memory.

Part 2. $\sqrt{\left[\dfrac{b}{2(-a)}\right]^2 + \dfrac{c}{(-a)}}$

Key—Operation	Display	Comments
6	6.	Enter c term. The $-a$ term is in Y-register as a constant divisor. Minus indicator goes out.
$=$	$-2.$	$c/-a = -2$; Minus indiator lights.
F $(x{\leftrightarrow}M)$	-1.5	$b/2(-a)$ term displayed; $c/-a$ term in memory.
F $(M + x^2)$	-1.5	$[b/2(-a)]^2 + [c/-a] = 0.25$ in memory.
F $(x{\leftrightarrow}M)$	0.25	$b/2(-a)$ term goes into memory. Minus indicator goes out.

Part 3: Roots 1 and 2.

F $(\sqrt{x})$	0.5	$\sqrt{\left[\dfrac{b}{2(-a)}\right]^2 + \dfrac{c}{-a}}$ term
F $(x{\rightarrow}M)$	-1.5	$b/2(-a)$ term. Minus indicator lights.
$+$	-1.5	
F $(x{\leftarrow}M)$	0.5	Minus indicator goes out.
$-$	$-\boxed{1.0} \rightarrow$	Root 1 $= -1$. Minus indicator lights.
$-$	1.5	Restore $b/2(-a)$ term.
$=$	$-\boxed{2.0} \rightarrow$	Root 2. $= -2.0$. Minus light is on.

Let us now solve an equation involving an irrational square root and more complex coefficients. Of course, the program works just as well and solves this problem just as easily.

Example 7-14. Solve equation $ax^2 + bx + c = 0$ where $a = 1.5$, $b = -3.27$, and $c = 0.435$. Use the HP-35.

Key—Operation	Display	Comments
3.27 ENTER↑ 1.5 ENTER↑	1.50000000	
2 $\times$ $\div$	1.09000000	$d = -b/2a$
ENTER↑ ENTER↑ ENTER↑ $\times$	1.18810000	d^2
0.435 ENTER↑ 1.5 $\div$ $-$	0.89810000	f^2 (positive)
$\sqrt{}$ ENTER↑	0.94768138	$f = \sqrt{}$
$\downarrow$ $-$	0.14231862	$R_1 =$ root 1
$\downarrow$ $+$	2.03768138	$R_2 =$ root 2
$x{\rightleftarrows}y$ $\downarrow$ $\times$	0.29000000	$c/a =$ check

This problem illustrates the virtue of the pocket calculator. It is just as easy to solve the quadratic with 8-figure coefficients and roots as it is to solve the equation with 2-figure coefficients and roots.

STATISTICAL MEAN AND STANDARD DEVIATION

The final problem used to compare scientific calculators is the determination of the mean and standard deviation of a set of numbers. A numerical set of data points x_i are given for illustration.

Example 7-15. Find the mean x variance σ^2 and standard deviation σ for a set of values x_i using the Texas Instruments SR-50.

$$x_i = 3, 5, 3, 7, \text{ and } 4$$

$$n = 5 \text{ data points}$$

$$x = \frac{1}{n} \sum_{i=1}^{n} x_i$$

$$x = \frac{1}{5}(3 + 5 + 3 + 7 + 4) = 4.4$$

Enter	Press	Display
3	+	3.
5	+	8.
3	+	11.
7	+	18.
4	= ÷	22.
5	=	4.4

This requires 13 steps for the 5 x_i data entries.

Variance is determined as follows,

$$\sigma^2 = \sum_{i=1}^{n} \left[\frac{x_i^2}{n} - \bar{x}^2 \right]$$

$$= \frac{1}{5}(3^2 + 5^2 + 3^2 + 7^2 + 4^2) - 4.4^2$$

$$= 2.24$$

Enter	Press	Display
3	x^2 +	9.
5	x^2 +	34.
3	x^2	43.
7	x^2	92.
4	x^2 = ÷	108.
5	−	21.6
4.4	x^2 =	2.24

This requires 21 steps for the five data entries.

The standard deviation σ can now be determined.

$$\sigma^2 = 2.24$$

$$\sigma = 1.4996662955$$

Enter	Press	Display
2.24	$\sqrt{x}$	1.496662955

This requires just one step assuming that the variance was in the calculator from the previous example.

The total calculation takes about 35 steps for 5 data entries, or about 7 steps per data entry. However, the 5 data entries are made twice in this routine.

The next example shows how the same type of calculations are performed on the Rockwell 61R.

$$\overline{x} = \frac{\displaystyle\sum_{i=1}^{n} x_i}{n} \qquad \sigma = \sqrt{\frac{\sum (x_i - \overline{x})^2}{n-1}} = \sqrt{\frac{\sum x_i^2 - \frac{(\sum x_i)^2}{n}}{n-1}}$$

Using the second equation for calculating standard deviation σ requires the values of x to be entered only once.

Example 7-16. The results of throwing a die are:

Number of spots 1 2 3 4 5 6
Frequency 31 28 30 30 39 42

Find the mean, variance, and standard deviation.

Key—in	Display	Comments
C CE	0.	
F ($x \rightarrow$M)	0.	Clears memory.
31	31	
F (M + x^2)	31	
+	31	
28	28	
F (M + x^2)	59	
+	59	
30	30	
F (M + x^2)	30	These steps form Σx_i in the X-register
+	89	and $\Sigma (x_i)^2$ in the memory.
30	30	
F (M + x^2)	30	
+	119	
39	39	
F (M + x^2)	39	
+	158	
42	42	
F (M + x^2)	42	
÷	200	Display shows $\Sigma x_i = 200$
6	6.	
×	33.333333	Display shows $x = 33.333333 = $ mean.
=	199.99999	x_i^2
×	199.99999	
÷	39999.996	x^2

Key−in	Display	Comments
6	6.	
=	6666.666	
F (M−)	6666.666	Subtracts $\dfrac{(\Sigma x_i)^2}{n}$ from Σz_i^2 in memory.
F (x↤M)	163.334	
÷	163.334	
5	5.	$5 = (n-1)$, where n is 6.
=	32.6668	Variance,
F ($\sqrt{x}$)	5.7154877	Display shows. = 5.7154877.

The program requires a total of 43 steps, or about 7 steps per data entry. However, each item of data is only entered once. It is interesting to note that the HP-45 can perform this calculation in only 16 steps, because it has a built-in routine for the mean and standard deviation calculations.

HINTS ON CALCULATORS

The following observations and suggestions concern the choice and use of a calculator.

1. There is much controversy regarding the relative merits of reverse Polish notation used by Hewlett-Packard and the more customary algebraic notation used by most manufacturers. In the long run, I feel there is no net advantage of one type of logic over the other. Once the ordinary operator is familiar with his calculator, he can solve a typical set of problems and get the results in about the same time with either type of logic, *provided* the calculator he uses has the same *computing power*. This means the same number of operational, or working, registers and memories and availability of computing aids such as logical parentheses and preprogramed functions. It is these factors plus the type of display and the cost of the calculator that should influence the decision to buy, rather than the type of logic or notation.

2. It is important to know what is in the memory and the operational stack or working registers at each step in the program. Consult the operational manuals for this type of detail.

3. For each application, it is important to record the general sequence of operations as well as a typical

example using numerical data inputs. This enables you to solve similar problems later.

4. Each calculator has its individual characteristics which must be mastered for maximum efficiency. Study your instruction manual carefully and determine *why* each sequence was chosen.

5. Be sure to check your basic program routine by a known example before repeating the calculation for different sets of data points.

6. Be sure to record the answers to your problem as each one is displayed in the machine, particularly if you require more than one result (hypotenuse and angle, mean and standard deviation, etc.).

7. For repetitive problems, spend a little time to be sure you have both the best mathematical and machine solution to your problem. A little research may save a lot of work.

8. Always work out the program formally on paper *first*, then go to the calculator to check your program. Do not use the calculator as a trial and error device.

Chapter 8

Hewlett–Packard HP–45

The Hewlett-Packard HP-45 represents the top of the line in scientific pocket calculators. It posesses all the capabilities of the HP-35 plus a considerable number of preprogramed features, as shown in Fig. 8-1. It has a total of 48 arithmetic and scientific functions and data manipulation capabilities, all packaged in the same size as the HP-35 or the Texas Instruments SR-50. Of course, it carries a higher price tag than its competitors.

The additional functions available in the HP-45 are made possible by the use of dual-function keys, which are enabled by the *gold* key, shown at the upper right in Fig. 8-1. For descriptive purposes, we have designated this key as $\boxed{G}$. The $\boxed{G}$ key is pressed first, followed by the key corresponding to the function engraved (in gold) above it. Referring to Fig. 8-1, the keys $\boxed{G}$ and $\boxed{e^x}$ enable 10^x, $\boxed{G}$ and $\boxed{COS}$ enable cos^{-1}, and $\boxed{G}$ and $\boxed{x^2}$ enable $\sqrt{x}$. Similarly, $\boxed{G}$ commands the degree or radian mode of calculation and the metric conversions cm/in., kg/lb, and ltr/gal (identified by gold letters). Gold key functions will be shown without a box.

The keys and features identified in Fig. 8-1 indicate many capabilities unique to the HP-45. Highlights include the nine addressable memories, the variable decimal point, choice of *fixed* or *scientific notation* mode of calculation, degree—radian—grad modes, percent change ($\Delta\%$), and statistical mean (x) and standard deviation (s) keys. Other important features include rectangular-to-polar conversion

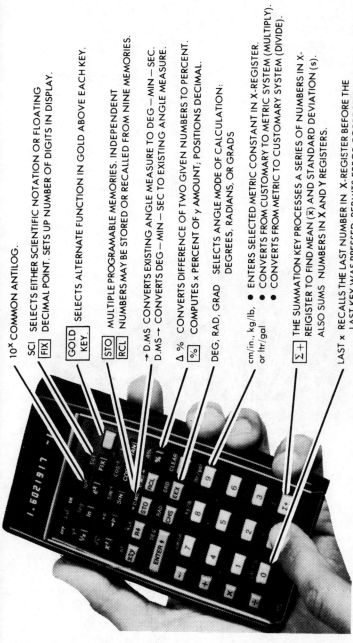

10^x COMMON ANTILOG.

SCI   SELECTS EITHER SCIENTIFIC NOTATION OR FLOATING
FIX   DECIMAL POINT. SETS UP NUMBER OF DIGITS IN DISPLAY.

GOLD   SELECTS ALTERNATE FUNCTION IN GOLD ABOVE EACH KEY.
KEY

STO   MULTIPLE PROGRAMABLE MEMORIES. INDEPENDENT
RCL   NUMBERS MAY BE STORED OR RECALLED FROM NINE MEMORIES.

→ D.MS CONVERTS EXISTING ANGLE MEASURE TO DEG—MIN—SEC.
D.MS → CONVERTS DEG—MIN—SEC TO EXISTING ANGLE MEASURE.

Δ %   CONVERTS DIFFERENCE OF TWO GIVEN NUMBERS TO PERCENT.
%   COMPUTES x PERCENT OF y AMOUNT; POSITIONS DECIMAL.

DEG, RAD, GRAD   SELECTS ANGLE MODE OF CALCULATION:
                  DEGREES, RADIANS, OR GRADS

cm/in., kg/lb,   ● ENTERS SELECTED METRIC CONSTANT IN X-REGISTER.
or ltr/gal   ● CONVERTS FROM CUSTOMARY TO METRIC SYSTEM (MULTIPLY).
                  ● CONVERTS FROM METRIC TO CUSTOMARY SYSTEM (DIVIDE).

Σ+   THE SUMMATION KEY PROCESSES A SERIES OF NUMBERS IN X-
       REGISTER TO FIND MEAN ($\bar{x}$) AND STANDARD DEVIATION (s).
       ALSO SUMS NUMBERS IN X AND Y REGISTERS.

LAST x RECALLS THE LAST NUMBER IN X-REGISTER BEFORE THE
       LAST KEY WAS PRESSED. PERMITS ERROR CORRECTION.

Fig. 8-1. Hewlett-Packard's HP-45 scientific calculator and those features beyond the HP-350.

149

R → CONVERTS POLAR COORDINATES TO RECTANGULAR (x AND y) COORDINATES.

→ P CONVERTS RECTANGULAR (x AND y) COORDINATES TO POLAR.

n! CALCULATES THE FACTORIAL OF THE NUMBER IN THE DISPLAY.

x̄, s CALCULATES THE ARITHMETIC MEAN (x̄) AND THE STANDARD DEVIATION (s) OF A SERIES OF NUMBERS ENTERED IN X, IN CONJUNCTION WITH THE Σ+ KEY.

KEYS 0-9 IDENTIFY NINE ADDRESSABLE MEMORIES AND SELECT 0—9 DECIMALS IN FIXED OR SCIENTIFIC NOTATION.

x² SQUARES NUMBER IN THE DISPLAY.

Fig. 8-1. Con't.

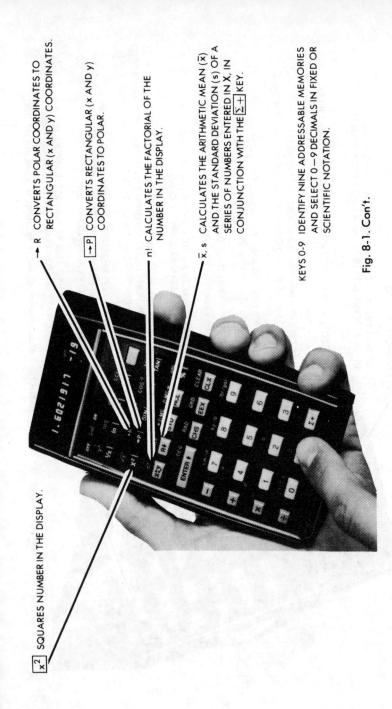

(→ P), polar-to-rectangular conversion (→ R), and the $\boxed{\Sigma+}$ key. When a series of numbers (x_i, y_i) are entered using the $\boxed{\Sigma+}$ key, the calculator provides the number of entries n, the sum (Σx_i), the sum of the squares of the numbers (Σx_i^2), as well as Σy_i, the mean and the standard deviation. All dual outputs are provided by the X and Y registers. For example, in rectangular–polar coordinate conversion, the display shows the first output, magnitude r, and the $\boxed{x \supset y}$ key recovers the angle θ from the Y register.

The truly unique feature of this scientific pocket calculator is the availability of nine separately addressable memory registers which permit general solutions to advanced problems requiring multiple memories, as well as a variety of scientific and engineering problems. Operations available with these memories include storing numbers into the display, arithmetic operations on the display, and retrieving numbers from the display. Once a number is recalled from memory to the display, it can be operated on by any function available in the HP-45 without disturbing the contents of memory. Conversely, register arithmetic can be used to alter the contents of memory using any number or function of the number available in the display.

The following sections will describe the unique features of the HP-45 and give examples that emphasize the use of multiple memory in the solution of advanced mathematical and scientific problems. At the same time, the concept of creating manual programs will be further explored as a prelude to the discussions of programmable calculators presented in the last chapter.

DISPLAY AND ROUNDING OPTIONS (SCI–FIX)

The HP-45 offers two display modes (fixed decimal and scientific notation) and a variety of rounding options. Rounding options affect the display only; the HP-45 always maintains full accuracy internally.

Fixed-decimal notation is specified by pressing $\boxed{\text{FIX}}$ followed by the appropriate number key 0–9 to specify the number of decimal places to which the display is to be rounded. When the calculator is turned on, it "reverts" to *fix 2* (two decimal places). Some examples of the use of the FIX key are shown below.

Press	Display
123.456	123.456
FIX 4	123.4560
FIX 1	123.5
FIX 0	123.

Scientific notation is specified by pressing G SCI, where G is the *gold* key, followed by the appropriate number key to specify the number of decimal places (0−9) to be displayed. For example,

Press	Display
G SCI 6	1.23456002
G SCI 3	1.235302

POLAR—RECTANGULAR CONVERSION

Two functions are provided for polar—rectangular conversion. To convert values in X and Y registers, (representing rectangular *x* and *y* coordinates, respectively) to polar *r* and θ coordinates (magnitude and angle, respectively), press →P.

Conversely, to convert values in X and Y registers representing polar coordinates to rectangular coordinates, we use →R. Polar—rectangular conversions involve storage register 9. Thus, any values previously stored in this register will be overwritten when coordinate conversions are performed.

Example 8-1. Convert rectangular coordinates 4 and 3 to polar form, *r* θ, with the angle expressed in degrees.

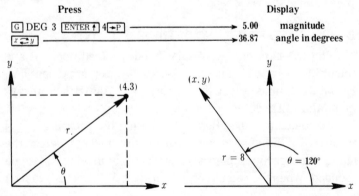

Press		Display	
G DEG 3 ENTER ↑ 4 →P	⟶	5.00	magnitude
x ⇄ y	⟶	36.87	angle in degrees

Example 8-2. Convert $8\underline{/120°}$ to rectangular coordinates x and y.

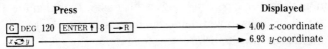

Press		Displayed
G DEG 120 ENTER ↑ 8 →R	———→	4.00 x-coordinate
$x\rightleftarrows y$	———→	6.93 y-coordinate

By combining the polar—rectangular function with the accumulation function, $\boxed{\Sigma+}$, you can add and subtract vector components. The sums of these are contained in storage registers R_7 and R_8:

$$r_7 = x_1 \pm x_2 \pm \ldots \pm x_n = \Sigma x$$
$$r_8 = y_1 \pm y_2 \pm \ldots \pm y_n = \Sigma y$$

To display the contents of registers R_7 and R_8, press $\boxed{RCL}$ $\boxed{\Sigma+}$ to obtain the sum of x coordinates (register 7); then press $\boxed{x\rightleftarrows y}$ to obtain the sum of y coordinates (register 8).

Example 8-3. Sum two vectors, V_1 and V_2, having the polar coordinates (8, 30°) and (12, 60°), respectively. Represent the sum V in the terms of polar coordinates (r/θ).

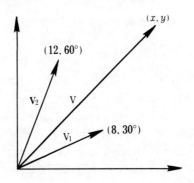

Press		Display
G CLEAR		0.00
30 ENTER ↑ 8 G →R	———→	6.00
Σ+		1.00
60 ENTER ↑ 12 G →R	———→	6.93
Σ+		2.00
RCL Σ+	———→	12.93
→P	———→	19.35 (magnitude r)
$x\rightleftarrows y$	———→	48.07 (angle θ)

FACTORIALS, $\boxed{\text{G}}$ $n!$

The factorial function $n!$ permits you to handle combinations and permutations with ease. To calculate the factorial of a displayed number, merely press $\boxed{\text{G}}$ $n!$. For example, find the factorial of 5 as follows:

Press	Display
5 $\boxed{\text{G}}$ $n!$	120.00 (5!)

Factorials can be calculated for positive integers from 0 through 69. Attempting to calculate the factorial of a fractional or negative value is an improper operation and will result in a blinking display.

Example 8-4. How many different ways may a coach assign players, from a squad of 12, to the 9 positions in a baseball lineup? The equation for permutations of 12 things taken 9 at a time is

$$P(12,9) = \frac{12!}{(12 - 9)!}$$

Press	Display	Comment
12 $\boxed{\text{G}}$ $n!$	4.790016000 08	12!
$\boxed{\text{G}}$ Last x	12.00	Value is retrieved from previous operation.
9 $\boxed{-}$	3.00	
$\boxed{\text{G}}$ $n!$	6.00	3!
$\boxed{\div}$	79833600.00	Number of possible lineups.

DEGREES–MINUTES–SECONDS CONVERSION

Displayed angles can be converted from any decimal angular mode to degrees, minutes, and seconds, in the properly sequenced format by pressing $\boxed{\text{G}}$ → DMS. Conversely, to convert an angle displayed in degrees, minutes, and seconds to the decimal equivalent in the specified angular mode, press $\boxed{\text{G}}$ DMS →.

Note that the result of a $\boxed{\text{G}}$ DMS conversion is rounded to the nearest second, both internally and on the display. Any conversions involving an angle greater than 100,000° is an improper operation.

Example 8-5. Assume a surveyor wants to add two angles 10° 8′56″ and 2° 17′42″. These must first be converted to decimal degrees before adding and then converting back to degrees, minutes, and seconds.

Press	Display
10.0856 $\boxed{G}$ DMS →	10.15 decimal degrees
2.1742 $\boxed{G}$ DMS →	2.30 decimal degrees
$\boxed{+}$	12.44 decimal degrees
$\boxed{G}$ → DMS	12.2638 (12° 26′ 38″)

Example 8-6. Find arc *sin 0.55* in the degrees mode and convert to degrees, minutes, and seconds.

Press	Display
0.55 $\boxed{G}$ SIN^{-1}	33.37 (decimal degrees)
$\boxed{G}$ → DMS	33.2201 (33° 22′ 01″)

FINDING PERCENTAGE

To find the percentage of a number, key in the base number and press $\boxed{\text{ENTER} \uparrow}$. Then key in the percent and press $\boxed{\%}$. For example, find 14% of 300.

Press	Display
300 $\boxed{\text{ENTER} \uparrow}$ 14 $\boxed{\%}$	42.00

Finding Net Amount

An additional feature is that, after finding the percentage, the HP-45 still contains the original base number, from which you may calculate the net amount by simply pressing $\boxed{+}$ or $\boxed{-}$

Press	Display
300 $\boxed{\text{ENTER} \uparrow}$ 14 $\boxed{\%}$	42.00 percentage
$\boxed{+}$	342.00 net amount, base plus percentage

Here is another solution.

Press	Display
300 $\boxed{\text{ENTER} \uparrow}$ 14 $\boxed{\%}$	42.00 percent
$\boxed{-}$	258.00 net amount, base less percentage

Finding Percent Difference $\Delta\%$

To find the percent difference between a number and the base, enter the base number and press $\boxed{\text{ENTER} \uparrow}$. Enter the second number and press $\boxed{G}$ $\Delta\%$. For example, assume that you want to find the rate of increase of your current mortgage payment—say, $240 per month, over what you were paying in rent 15 years ago ($70/mo).

Press	Display
70 [ENTER ↑] 240 [G] Δ%	242.86 percent increase

$$\frac{(240-70)}{70} \times 100$$

METRIC CONVERSION CONSTANTS

The HP-45 provides built-in conversion constants (accurate to 10 digits). The constants shown below normally convert from customary to metric units.

Centimeters to inches, or inches to centimeters: 1 in. = 2.540000000 cm

Kilograms to pounds, or pounds to kilograms: 1 lb = 0.453592370 kg

Liters to gallons, or gallons to liters: 1 gal. = 3.785411784 ltr.

To use these constants, key in the measure to be converted, press [G], then press the desired constant key followed by the applicable operator: Press [×] to obtain *metric* equivalents, [÷] to obtain *customary* (U.S.) equivalents. Note that it isn't necessary to press [ENTER ↑] after keying in the initial value.

Press	Display
12 [G] cm/in.	2.54
[×]	30.48

Example 8-7. If an 8 × 10 in. drawing is to be reduced to 85% of its original size, what is the finished size in centimeters?

Press	Display
8 [ENTER ↑] 85 [%]	6.80 inches
[G] cm/in.	2.54 conversion constant
[×]	17.27 centimeters
10 [ENTER ↑] 85 [%]	8.50 inches length
[G] cm/in.	2.54 conversion constant
[×]	21.59 centimeters
	(The finished size is 17.27 × 21.59 cm.)

Similarly, to convert from a kg to b lb, perform the following operations:

a [ENTER ↑] [G] kg/lb [×]

Convert from a gal. to b liters as follows:

a [ENTER ↑] [G] ltr/gal [×]

STATISTICAL FUNCTIONS

The statistical function ($\bar{x}, s$) is used to find the mean (arithmetic average) and standard deviation (measure of dispersion around the mean) of data entered and summed. Options are provided to enable you to interact with and modify results by adding new data or correcting errors. Also, the number of entries, sum of the squares, and sum of entries in two dimensions can be obtained.

Summation—averaging calculations also use the [Σ+] key to sum the numbers used in calculating means and standard deviations. Because the [Σ+] function uses storage registers R_5-R_8, these registers must be cleared with [G] [CLEAR] before pressing [Σ+], or errors could result. Information is entered as follows:

1. Press [G] [CLEAR] to insure that registers R_5-R_8 are clear of previous data.
2. Key in each value and sum with [Σ+] key. The last [Σ+] pressed provides the number of entries.
3. Press [G] $\bar{x}, s$ to obtain mean x.
4. Press [x ⇄ y] to obtain standard deviation s.
5. If there are more values to be included (e.g., if you want to add to the data sample and modify results), key in and press [Σ+] after each entry. Additional information is available by performing steps 6–10 (in any order).
6. Press [RCL] 5 to obtain number of entries.
7. Press [RCL] 6 to obtain sum of squares for X-register entries.
8. Press [RCL] 7 to obtain sum of X register entries.
9. Press [RCL] 8 to obtain sum of Y register entries.
10. Alternatively, press [RCL] [Σ+] to obtain sum of X register entries, and [x ⇄ y] to obtain sum of Y register entries.

Example 8-8. In a recent survey to determine the average age of the 10 wealthiest people in the U.S., the following data was obtained:

62 84 47 58 68 60 62 59 71 73

Of the ages given, what is the mean? The standard deviation?

Press	Display
CLEAR	0.00
62 $\boxed{\Sigma+}$ 84 $\boxed{\Sigma+}$ 47 $\boxed{\Sigma+}$ 58 $\boxed{\Sigma+}$ 68 $\boxed{\Sigma+}$	
60 $\boxed{\Sigma+}$ 62 $\boxed{\Sigma+}$ 59 $\boxed{\Sigma+}$ 71 $\boxed{\Sigma+}$ 73 $\boxed{\Sigma+}$	10.00 number of entries
$\boxed{G}$ $\bar{x}, s$	64.40 mean
$\boxed{x \rightleftarrows y}$	10.10 standard deviation

Example 8-9. Find the sum of the ages entered, sum of the squares, and number of entries, as well as the mean and standard deviation. (Continue from last example.)

$\boxed{G}$ $\bar{x}, s$	64.40	mean
$\boxed{x \rightleftarrows y}$	10.10	standard deviation
$\boxed{RCL}$ 7	644.00	sum of numbers entered, x-entries
$\boxed{RCL}$ 6	42392.00	sum of squares, x-entries
$\boxed{RCL}$ 5	10.00	number of entries

LAST x **REGISTER**

The last input argument of a calculation is automatically stored in the LAST x register when a function is executed. This feature provides a handy error correction device as well as a facility for reusing the same argument in multiple calculations, since it allows recall of the argument by pressing $\boxed{G}$ $\boxed{\text{LAST } x}$. The register is cleared only when the calculator is turned off or when a new argument replaces (or overwrites) the previous one.

The HP-45 automatically stores the last function performed. For example, suppose you divided 12 by 3 as follows:

12 $\boxed{\text{ENTER} \uparrow}$ 3 $\boxed{\div}$ 4.00

Now to verify the last input argument from the example above.

Press	Display
$\boxed{G}$ $\boxed{\text{LAST } x}$	3.00 (last input argument)

158

As each new function is keyed (executed), the contents of LAST x are overwritten with the new value.

If you want to correct a number in a long calculation, LAST x can save you from starting over. For example, divide 12 by 2.157, after you have divided by 3.157 in error.

Press		Display	
12 ENTER 3.157 $\div$	3.80		Wrong answer—you wanted to divide by 2.157, not 3.157.
G LAST x	3.157		Retrieves last number displayed preceding operation.
$\times$	12.00		You're back at the beginning.
2.157 $\div$	5.56		12/2.157

DATA STORAGE REGISTERS

In addition to the operational stack and LAST x register, the HP-45 provides nine registers for user storage, retrieval, and mathematical operations.

Unrestricted Storage Registers $R_1 - R_4$

Registers $R_1 - R_4$ can be used for temporary storage without restriction. Values stored in these registers are not affected by calculations or by clearing operations. New values are entered by writing over the old contents, that is, by storing a new number. The contents are lost, however, when the HP-45 is turned off.

Restricted Storage Registers $R_5 - R_8$

Registers $R_5 - R_8$ are used internally when performing summations using $\boxed{\Sigma+}$ and $\boxed{G}$ $\bar{x}$, s. When summations are not being performed, these registers may be used for general-purpose storage. However, since registers $R_5 - R_8$ are not overwritten by new values during summing $(\Sigma+)$ functions, they must be cleared of existing values by pressing $\boxed{G}$ $\boxed{CLEAR}$ before they are used in summations.

Register R_9

Register R_9 is required internally when performing trigonometric functions and polar—rectangular conversions;

any values stored there will be lost. Otherwise, register R_9 may be used for general-purpose storage in the same manner as registers R_1-R_5.

STORING AND RECALLING DATA

To store a value appearing on the display (whether the result of a calculation, or a keyboard entry), press $\boxed{\text{STO}}$; then press the number key (1–9) specifying the storage register. To retrieve the value, press $\boxed{\text{RCL}}$; then press the applicable number key. A copy of the recalled value appears on the display (X register); the original value remains in the specified constant storage register. The number previously on the display is loaded into the Y register unless the key stroke immediately preceding $\boxed{\text{RCL}}$ was $\boxed{\text{ENTER} \uparrow}$, $\boxed{\text{CL}x}$, or $\boxed{\Sigma +}$. (These keys do not cause the stack to be pushed up by the next data entry.) For example, add 8, 20, 17, and 43; store the result in R_1; and divide the individual numbers by the stored sum to find what part each is of the total.

Press	Display
8 $\boxed{\text{ENTER}}$ 20 $\boxed{+}$ 17 $\boxed{+}$	43 $\boxed{+}$ = 88.00 (total)
$\boxed{\text{STO}}$ 1	88.00
8 $\boxed{\text{RCL}}$ 1 $\boxed{\div}$	0.09 or 9% of total
20 $\boxed{\text{RCL}}$ 1 $\boxed{\div}$	0.23 or 23% of total
17 $\boxed{\text{RCL}}$ 1 $\boxed{\div}$	0.19 or 19% of total
43 $\boxed{\text{RCL}}$ 1 $\boxed{\div}$ 1 $\boxed{\div}$	0.49 or 49% of total

PERFORMING REGISTER ARITHMETIC

Arithmetic operations ($+$, $-$, $\times$, $\div$) can be performed between the X register (first argument) and a storage register (second argument). To modify the contents of a storage register, press $\boxed{\text{STO}}$, followed by the applicable operator key ($\boxed{-}$, $\boxed{+}$, $\boxed{\times}$, $\boxed{\div}$) and the number key specifying the storage register. | For example, store 6 in register R_1; then increment it by 2.

Press	Display
6 $\boxed{\text{STO}}$ 1	6.00 (6 ⟶ R_1)
2 $\boxed{\text{STO}}$ $\boxed{+}$ 1	2.00 (2 + r_1 ⟶ R_1)

Now see what is now stored in register R_1.

Press	Display
[RCL] 1	8.00 ($r_1 \longrightarrow$ display)

Now subtract a displayed value from the contents of R_1 and store the result back in register R_1. *

Press	Display
13 [STO] $-$ 1	13.00 ($r_1 - 13 \longrightarrow R_1$)
[RCL] 1	-5.00 ($r_1 \longrightarrow$ display)

Conversely, to alter a displayed value without affecting the stored value, (or the Y, Z, and T registers), press [RCL], the applicable operator, and the number key specifying the storage register. For example, add the current value stored in register R_1 (5.00) to a new entry (2).

Press	Display
2 [RCL] [+] 1	-3.00 (2 + $r_1 \longrightarrow$ display)
[RCL] 1	-5.00 ($r_1 \longrightarrow$ display)

Now subtract the contents of register R_1 (-5.00) from a new entry (11).

Press	Display
11 [RCL] [$-$] 1	16.00 (11 $-$ $r_1 \longrightarrow$ display)
[RCL] 1	5.00 ($r_1 \longrightarrow$ display)

Next, combine several operations.

Press	Display
3 [STO] 1	3.00 (3 $\longrightarrow R_1$)
2 [STO] [+] 1	2.00 (2 + $r_1 \longrightarrow R_1$)
35 [STO] [÷] 1	35.00 (35/$r_1 \longrightarrow R_1$)
[RCL] 1	0.14 ($r_1 \longrightarrow$ display)
5 [RCL] [×] 1	0.71 (5 × $r_1 \longrightarrow$ display)

COMPARISON OF HP-45 EFFICIENCY

The worth of any calculator to a user is proportional to the time and labor saved in the performance of a calculation. Therefore, the calculator he buys must be justified on the basis of his computational needs and the savings in time and labor afforded by the calculator. These, in turn, must be traded off

---

* This register arithmetic applies to HP-45 models produced after January 1974.

against the initial cost or investment for the purchase of the calculator.

The time it takes to perform a series of calculations on an electronic slide rule is essentially the time it takes to formulate a program, or sequence of machine instructions, and the time required to press each key in the sequence. In comparing calculators we can assume that the time required to formulate the program is about the same for each calculator. It only remains to compare the time required to press the keys in each program. The following discussions will give some data on the number of steps required to solve typical problems and hence how much time might be needed to solve them.

The time needed to multiply two simple numbers like 2 and 4 is the time needed to press four keys: 2 $\boxed{\times}$ 4 $\boxed{=}$. The answer, 8, appears immediately after the $\boxed{=}$ key is pressed. However, the time required to multiply 98,765,432 by 87,654,321 is proportional to 18 key strokes, which is a significant difference. Assuming 1 sec per key stroke, for convenience, this means that the first multiplication takes only 4 sec, but the second multiplication takes 18 sec—a range of 4½ to 1. The scientific equations and iterative solutions to be discussed in Chapters 8, 9, and 10 require many operations on numbers with six to eight digits. To avoid repeated entry and recording of lengthy numbers, it is wise to make the maximum use of calculator memory to store, recall, and perform operations on these numbers. At the same time, the use of memory also reduces the chance for recording and entry errors in handling these numbers.

It is instructive to compare different calculators in their ability to efficiently solve problems of increasing complexity. To standardize the comparison, we will assume that the entry of a given number is one program step, regardless of the number of digits it may have. Whenever a sample problem is solved, using a given calculator, we will add the number of key operations to the number of data entries, for the total number of program steps. The difference in solution time will be proportional to the difference in program steps, plus the difference in data entries. We may say, for example, that the solution of a quadratic equation for real roots took 21 program steps, including 4 data entries, for a certain calculator and 27 program steps, including 6 data entries, for another calculator. You can judge for yourself, after several such examples, whether the increased capability and cost of one calculator is worth the time and labor saved by that calculator. You may find, after some reflection, that the most powerful calculator is not necessarily the one you need.

To simplify matters, let's compare two calculators with the same logic, made by the same manufacturer, but with different capability; namely, the Hewlett-Packard HP-35 and HP-45, with a price differential of about $100. You will see that these calculators are competitive for many simple scientific problems, but the HP-45 has decided advantages for more complex problems.

Addition of Vectors

The procedure for adding vectors is to find the x and y components of each vector, sum x and y terms separately, and then find the resultant of Σx and Σy. The components of a vector, V, are: $V_x = V \cos \alpha$, and $V_y = V \sin \alpha$.

Example 8-10. Given: $V_1 = 16\underline{/36°}$ more $V_2 = 22\underline{/54°}$

$$\text{Find: } V_R = V_1 + V_2$$
$$= 37.54\underline{/46.43°}$$

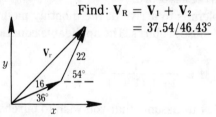

Key—Operation	Display—Comment
16 [ENTER ↑] 36 [sin] [×] 22 [ENTER ↑] 54 [sin] [×] [+]	$27.20 = \Sigma V_y$
16 [ENTER ↑] 36 [cos] [×] 22 [ENTER ↑] 54 [cos] [×] [+] STO	$25.88 = \Sigma V_y$
[÷] [arc] [tan]	$46.43° = $ angle
[cos] [RCL] [$x \rightleftarrows y$] [÷]	$37.54 = V_r$

The vector sum is $37.54\underline{/46.43°}$. There are 31 program steps, including 8 number entires, required for the HP-35.

The same problem can be solved much more efficiently on the HP-45, using the [→R] and [→P] keys.

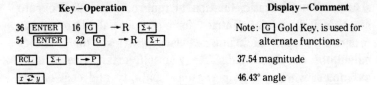

Key—Operation	Display—Comment
36 [ENTER] 16 [G] →R [Σ+]	Note: [G] Gold Key, is used for
54 [ENTER] 22 [G] →R [Σ+]	alternate functions.
[RCL] [Σ+] [→P]	37.54 magnitude
[x ⇄ y]	46.43° angle

This requires only 16 program steps, including 4 number entries, or about half the effort needed for the HP-35. Bear in mind that the overall saving in time, and the possible errors in entry, are quite dependent on the number of data points entered manually and on the number of digits in each entry. Therefore, savings in the number of data entries is quite significant. When a problem is easily handled by the simpler calculator, the additional capability of the HP-45 may not result in a more efficient operation or fewer steps. Consider the following examples.

Compound Interest and Monthly Payments

In the evaluation of investment alternatives it is often desirable to evaluate the cost and gains of real estate or other transactions. An electronic calculator provides rapid and accurate functions which reduce complex calculations to a few simple operations on the keyboard.

A common problem is to arrive at the monthly payment, M, that a loan or purchase requires. The applicable equation is

$$M = \frac{P\,i}{1 - 1/(1 + i)^n} \tag{8-1}$$

Example 8-11. Let us assume that you wish to purchase a $60,000 home with 20% down ($12,000), and the balance is payable in monthly installments for 30 years at a 9% yearly interest rate. Find the monthly payment using the HP-35. The principal (sum of money borrowed) $P = \$48,000$. The interest rate per payment period is 0.75%/mo (9%/yr). The number of payment periods is $n = 30 \times 12 = 360$.

Key—Operation	Display
0075. [STO] 1 [+]	1.0075
360 [x^y] [$1/x$] 1 [x ⇄ y] [−]	0.9321
[$1/x$] [RCL] [×] 48000 [×]	386.2189

164

The solution takes only 15 steps, including 3 data entries, using the HP-35.

Example 8-12. Find the monthly payments using HP-45. The same problem on the HP-45 actually takes three more program steps.

Key – Operation	Display – Comment
.0075, $\boxed{\text{STO}}$ 1, 1 $\boxed{+}$	
360 $\boxed{\text{G}}$ $\boxed{y^x}$ $\boxed{1/x}$ 1 $\boxed{x \leftrightarrows y}$ $\boxed{-}$	
$\boxed{1/x}$ $\boxed{\text{RCL}}$ 1 $\boxed{\times}$ 48000 $\boxed{\times}$	386.22 monthly payment

This solution takes a full 18 program steps because it must identify the memory register by its number code, and it must identify the alternate function, $\boxed{y^x}$, by using the $\boxed{\text{G}}$ key.

Let's try a case involving natural logarithms and compound interest. Suppose we know (1) how much we still owe on a loan, (2) the interest rate, and (3) the monthly payment, and we want to know how many payments n are left. We can calculate n by means of the equation

$$n = \frac{ln\,[1/(1 - Pi/M)]}{ln\,(1 + i)} \qquad (8\text{-}2)$$

Example 8-13. Find the number of payments remaining (using HP-35)

Where
$$P = 32500$$
$$i = 9\%/\text{yr} = 0.75\%/\text{mo} = 0.0075/\text{mo}$$
$$M = \$386.22$$

Key – Operation	Display – Comment
32,500 $\boxed{\text{ENTER} \uparrow}$ 386.22 $\boxed{\div}$	
.0075 $\boxed{\text{STO}}$ $\boxed{\times}$ 1 $\boxed{x \leftrightarrows y}$ $\boxed{-}$	
$\boxed{1/x}$, $\boxed{\text{ln}}$, 1, $\boxed{\text{RCL}}$, $\boxed{+}$ $\boxed{\text{ln}}$ $\boxed{\div}$	133.47 = number of payments

A total of 17 program steps, including 3 data entries, are required.

Now consider use of the HP-45 for solving the same problem.

Example 8-14. Find the number of payments, using the HP-45.

Key – Operation	Display
32500 $\boxed{\text{ENTER} \uparrow}$ 386.22 $\boxed{-}$	
0.0075 $\boxed{\text{STO}}$ 1 $\boxed{\times}$ 1 $\boxed{x \leftrightarrows y}$ $\boxed{-}$	
$\boxed{1/x}$ $\boxed{\text{ln}}$ 1 $\boxed{\text{RCL}}$ 1 $\boxed{+}$ $\boxed{\text{ln}}$ $\boxed{\div}$	133.47

165

This time, 19 program steps were required, including 3 data entries. This is because additional register identifications were required to store and recall memory. Therefore, the less capable machine was slightly more efficient for the two *simple* problems cited. This will be true when we need only one memory and each machine has the required functional capability.

However, if the problem is more *complex* and iteration of routines is required, the more powerful machine comes into its own. In fact, the problems discussed in Chapters 9 and 12 can practically be solved only with a calculator that has six or more addressable memories and the ability to perform register arithmetic. When these problems must be repeated many times, and solved for different values of input data, or if different output data is required, then a programmable calculator represents the best choice.

Advanced Applications of Multiple Memory Calculators

Chapter 9

The availability of a pocket calculator with nine memories and a full complement of scientific functions makes it possible to solve a wide variety of complex equations. These include quadratic, cubic, and simultaneous linear equations. Certain equations, such as trigonometric and logarithmic equations, lend themselves to an *iterative* (systematic trial and error) approach, particularly when exact solutions are not available.

Solving Equations by Iteration

This process was illustrated in Chapter 2, where square roots were found on an elementary calculator using a systematic estimate and correction routine which quickly converged on the final answer. First you make an initial estimate for the desired answer. Then you calculate a correction to the estimate by a series of steps (program) which depends on the equation to be solved. When the correction falls below a desired amount—e.g., 10^{-6} radians, the process is terminated. The formula for the correction may be arbitrary, but it is most often based on the derivative of the given equation or function. The method is illustrated below, using a simple trigonometric equation.

Consider Kepler's equation for orbiting bodies.

$$M = E - e \sin E \qquad (9\text{-}1)$$

where M and E are orbital angles and e is the eccentricity of the orbit.

It is quite simple to solve for angle M if E and e are known. But it is a different matter to solve for E if M and e are known.

You might pick up your scientific calculator and try your hand at solving this equation with $M = 1.01921919$ and $e = 0.300$. One approach is to assume a trial value for E (say, 0.5 radian), calculate an estimate for M (say, M_o) and then find the difference by the equation $\Delta M = M - M_O$. Then assume a new value for E—say, 1 radian—and calculate a new value for ΔM. When the sign of ΔM reverses for two close values of M, the true value for E must lie somewhere in between. The next trial value for E is found by interpolation, and the process is repeated until ΔM is less than some desired value. But there could be many tedious repetitions of this process to achieve an accuracy of 10^{-6} or even 10^{-4} radian.

Let us propose instead a more general and efficient method, which uses derivatives rather than interpolation to correct the initial estimate. This method can be used for a wide range of equations that do not have exact or closed form solutions. Furthermore, the corrections calculated generally converge to the desired answer and automatically carry the correct sign. However, no matter what form of correction routine is used, any iterative solution generally requires additional memories to store the constants of the original equation and to store one or more intermediate results, which may be needed in the various routines. For Eq. 9-1 it is desirable to store two quantities, the given value of M (1.01921919), and the trial value of E that is used in the iterative cycle. These points are best illustrated by the following example.

Example 9-1. Solve Kepler's equation for E, given M and e. Solve the problem by iteration as follows:

1. Assume the first estimate is $E_0 = M$, or $M + e \sin M$.
2. Calculate $\Delta M = M - (E_o - e \sin E_o)$.
3. Differentiate equation 9-1 to find ΔM:
$$\Delta M = (1 - e \cos E_o) \, \Delta E_0$$
4. Calculate $\Delta E_o = \Delta M / (1 - e \cos E_o)$.
5. Calculate the next trial value of $E = E_1 = E_0 + \Delta E_0$.
6. Repeat steps 2 through 4 until ΔM falls below the desired error, say, 10^{-6} radian or 0.2 arc sec.

The HP-45 will be used to solve this problem because it has more than one memory and could store the constant e also, if so desired.

The operations required to solve the equation for E are shown in example 9-2 in terms of HP-45 keys and the constants M, e, and the trial value of E.

Example 9-2. Program the HP-45 to solve

$$M = E - e \sin E \text{ for } E$$

(M and e given).

		Comments	
STEP	Key—Operation	First Guess	Second Guess
1	M ENTER↑ STO 1	Store M.	Step 1 not
	sin e ×	Store E_0.	needed.
	+ STO 2		
2	sin e × RCL 1 +	Calculate M.	Repeat step 2,
	RCL 2 −		using E_1.
3	1 ENTER↑ RCL 2 cos	Calculate E.	Repeat step 3.
	e × − ÷		
4	RCL 2 + STO 2	New guess, E_1.	New guess, E_2.

Note: Box encloses iteration routine.

If your calculator does not have the equivalent of two memories, then you must write each trial value for E as it is calculated, and enter that value into the calculator where the program says "RCL 2". Furthermore, the calculator should have a radian mode of calculation in order to use the program as shown. The Rockwell 61R/63R and the Texas Instruments SR-50 have this feature; the HP-35 does not.

Example 9-3 (on the following page) shows how the same program is used to solve a specific numerical example. It takes only 2 iteration cycles and a total of 54 steps to get a final solution for E that is correct to within 10^{-8} radian.

SATURN CAPTURE MANEUVER AND USE OF MEMORY

Another problem in space travel may serve to illustrate the use of memory to store intermediate results and to vary the conditions of a problem. Suppose a space vehicle has been launched toward the planet Saturn with a certain velocity V_x which allows it to reach Saturn in a prescribed number of

Example 9-3. Find E, given $M_o = 1.01921919$ and $e = 0.300$. (Use two iteration cycles.)

Step	Key-Operation (Radian Mode)	First Iteration Display	First Iteration Symbol	Second Iteration Display	Second Iteration Symbol
1	1.01921919 [ENTER↑] [STO] 1 [sin] 0.3000 [×] [+] [STO] 2	1.27472892	E_o	1.30918221	E_1
2	[sin] 0.300 [×] [RCL] 1 [+] [RCL] 2 [−]	0.03143764	ΔM_o	−0.00017089	ΔM_1
3	1 [ENTER↑] [RCL] 2 [cos] 0.300 [×] [−] [÷]	0.03445328	ΔE_o	−0.00018526	ΔE_1
4	[RCL] 2 [+] [STO] 2	1.30918221	E_1	1.30899694	E_2

First Iteration
Estimate $E_o = M_o + e \sin M_o$.
Calculate $\Delta M_o = M_o - E_o - e \sin E_o$.
Calculate $\Delta E_o = \Delta M / (1 - e \cos E_o)$.
Find $E_1 = E_o + \Delta E$.

Second Iteration
Repeat steps 2, 3 and 4, replacing E_o with E_1.
E_2 is final value of E. error is 10^{-8} radian.
The true value of E is 1.30899693.
The small value of ΔE signals the end of the iteration cycle.

There is a total of 48 program steps and 6 data entries, including 21 steps and 2 entries of $e = 0.300$ for each iteration.

days. It is necessary to find the braking velocity required to bring the spacecraft into a desired elliptical orbit around Saturn. Also required are the total weight of the vehicle W_o and the propellant weight W_p. Finally, it is desired to express these quantities as a function of V_∞ the excess launch velocity. This calls for a manual program which can be repeated for each new value of V_∞.

You will observe, after studying the equation, that not all quantities that might be repeated were stored in memory. For example, $K_t = 0.2$ was entered manually each time it was used. In fact, it may not be worthwhile to store such a simple number if memory locations are scarce. For certain problems, the eccentricity e and the payload W_{pl} are considered variables and hence could well be stored in memory. The following numerical example uses six memories to store the constants.

Example 9-4. The data for the Saturn capture maneuver problem is as follows.

Given data: $\mu_s = 37.897 \times 10^6$ km³/sec² = gravitational parameter
$r_p = 3$ Saturn $R = 3 R_s$ = periapsis of orbit
$r_a = 60$ Saturn $R = 60 R_s$ = apoapsis of orbit

$$e = \frac{(r_a - r_p)}{r_a + r_p} = \frac{57 r_s}{63 r_s} = 0.9047619 = \text{eccentricity}$$

$I_{sp} = 385$ sec = specific impulse
$W_{pl} = 570$ kg = weight of payload
$g_o = 9.80665$ m/sec² = earth gravity factor
$K_t = 0.200$ = tankage factor

Variables: $V_\infty = 8.60, 7.11, 6.13,$ and 5.55 km/sec (corresponding to flight times of 1400 to 2000 days)

Data required: $\Delta V, W_p, W_o$ for each V_∞

Equations: $V_c = \sqrt{\mu/r_p}$ = circular velocity $\qquad$ (9-2)
$V_e^2 = 2V_c^2$ = escape velocity $\qquad$ (9-3)
$V_p = V_c\sqrt{1 + e}$ = velocity at periapsis $\qquad$ (9-4)
$V_h = \sqrt{V_\infty^2 + V_e^2}$ = hyperbolic velocity $\qquad$ (9-5)
$\Delta V = V_h - V_p$ = delta velocity $\qquad$ (9-6)
$K_o = e^{\Delta V/g_o I_{sp}}$ = delta V factor $\qquad$ (9-7)

$$W_o = \frac{W_{pl}}{(1 + K_t)/K_o - K_t} = \text{total weight} \qquad (9-8)$$

$W_p = W_o (1 - 1/K_p)$ = propellant weight $\qquad$ (9-9)
$W_t = K_t W_p$ = tankage weight $\qquad$ (9-10)

The first thing to do is to store quantities that may be repeated in the calculations. To start, store the variables, V_∞ and r_p, since the latter may be changed in subsequent calculations. Additional quantities may be stored as they are calculated if they reappear in subsequent calculations. We store V_c and V_e^2 on this basis. Similarly, V_p and K_o will be stored for future use. Below is the program to solve for the first set of data, for $V_\infty = 8.60$ km/sec.

Step	Program Steps or Operations	Numerical Result
1	$V_\infty = {}_{8.60}$. [STO] 1, r_p [STO] 2	Store V_∞, and r_p.
2	μ_s [ENTER ↑] [RCL] [÷] 2 [√x] [STO] 3 [x²] 2 [×] [STO] 4	$V_c = 14.46538$ km/sec $V_e^2 = 418.49427$ km²/sec²
3	1 [ENTER ↑] e [+] $\sqrt{x}$ RCL [×] 3 [STO] 5	$V_p = 19.96412$ km/sec
4	[RCL] 1 [x²] [RCL] [+] 4 [√x]	$V_h = 22.19131$ km/sec
5	[RCL] [−] 5. 1000 [×] I_{sp} [÷] g_o [÷] [eˣ] [STO] 6	Record $\Delta V = 2227.194$ m/sec. $K_o = 1.80380$
6	W_{pl} [ENTER ↑] 1 [ENTER ↑] 0.2 [+] RCL [÷] 6 0.2 [−] [÷]	Record $W_o = 1225.11947$ kg
7	1 [ENTER ↑] [RCL] 6 [1/x] [−] [×]	Record $W_p = 545.93289$ kg.
8	0.2 [×]	Record $W_t = 109.18658$ kg.

For the next value ($V_\pi = 7.11$) store V_∞ and repeat steps 5 through 8. Repeat this cycle for each new value of V_∞. Use the given data for numerical values of r_p, u_s, e, I_{sp}, g_o, and W_{pl}. The data may be changed if desired. There is a total of 69 program steps for the first set of data, and 43 program steps for each succeeding set of data calculated. Remember to record the outputs of steps 5 through 8 as they are displayed.

ITERATIVE SOLUTION FOR INTEREST RATE

Another use for iteration occurs in certain problems involving monthly payments on a loan. When the interest rate, i, was known in advance (examples 7-8 to 7-10) the monthly payment calculations were quite straightforward. But suppose the problem is somewhat different and requires an iterative, or implicit, solution. For example: What is the monthly interest required to pay off a $30,000 loan in 25 years if the monthly payment is $239.5498? Here $P = \$30,000$, $n = 25 \times 12 = 300$, and $m = \$239.5498$. To solve for i now requires a different method, since i is not defined explicitly in terms of P, M, and n. This problem is worked out in example 9-5 and further illustrates the use of memory and iteration on the calculator. It takes 93 program steps on the HP-45 and only 2 cycles of calculation, or iteration, to solve for i. The solution employs the iterative method using a derivative correction and requires four memories.

Example 9-5. Find the interest rate for a loan as follows. The initial estimate of interest is i_0 and the correction is Δi_0. An iterative routine for Δi_0 is developed from Eq. 9-11 as follows:

Let $P_0 i = M [1 - (1 + i)^{-n}]$	Equation to be solved.	**(9-11)**
Then $K_0 = (1 + i_0)^{-n}$	Assume i_0, calculate K_0.	
$P_1 = \dfrac{M}{i_0} 1 - Ko$	Using K_0, M, and i_0, calculate P_1.	
$\Delta P = P_0 - P_1$	Calculate ΔP, using P_1 and P_0.	
$\Delta i_0 = \dfrac{\Delta P \times i_0}{n\, MK_0 - P_0}$	Calculate Δi_0, using ΔP, nMK_0, i_0, and Δi_0.	
$i_1 = i_0 + \Delta i_0$	Calculate next value, i_1, using i_0 and Δ_0.	
$\Delta i = \dfrac{i\Delta P}{nMK - P}$	Where i becomes i_0, i_1, i_2, etc.	**(9-12)**

Let's apply the above equations to a problem. Suppose the principal amount P, the monthly rate M, and the number of months n are given.

Example 9-6. Find the monthly interest rate i using an HP-45 with an iteration routine based on the above equations.

Store the three constants M, P_0, and i_0 (monthly interest). Assume $i_0 = 0.006$.

Key -Operation	Display	Comment
STO 1 M = 239.5498 = monthly payment		
STO 2 P_0 = 30,000 , STO 4 i_0 = 0.006		
1 ENTER ↑ RCL 4 ÷ ENTER ↑		$n = 300$ mo
300 CHS y^x STO 3	0.16619034	$K_0 = (1 + i_0)^{-n}$

Store the three constants M, P_0, and i_0 (monthly interest). Assume $i_0 = 0.006$.

Key-Operation	Display	Comment
☐ RCL 1 ☒ RCL 4 ☒ RCL 2 xCy ☐	33, 289.823 −3, 289.823	$P_0 = M\,1 - K_0\,/i_0$ $\Delta P_0 = P - P_0$
RCL 4 ☒ 300 ENTER ↑		$n = 300$
RCL 1 ☒ RCL 3 ☒ RCL 2 ☐ ☒	0.00109316	$\Delta i_0 = \dfrac{i_0 \Delta P}{(nM\,K_0 - P_0)}$
RCL 4 ☐ STO 4	0.00709316	$i_1 = {}_0 + \Delta i$

Second Iteration Cycle Interest $\boxed{i1 = 0.00709316}$ (0.709.%).

Key-Operation	Display	Comment
1 ENTER ↑ RCL 4, 1 ☐ ENTER ↑ 300 CHS y^x STO 3	0.11997920	$n = 300$ mo $K_0 = (1 + i_0)^{-n}$
☐ RCL 1 ☒ RCL 4 ☒ RCL 2 $x \rightleftarrows y$ ☐	29, 720.0129 +279.9871	$P_0 = M[(1 - K_0)/i_0$ $\Delta P_0 = P - P_0$
RCL 4 ☒ 300 ENTER ↑ ☒		
RCL 1 ☒ RCL 3 ☒ RCL 2 ☐ ☒	−0.00009290	$i_1 = \dfrac{i_1 \Delta P}{nMK_1 - P_0}$
RCL 4 ☐	−0.00700026	$i_2 = i_0 + \Delta i_1$ $= 0.7000\%$

The monthly interest rate is 0.7000%, and the yearly interest rate is 8.4000% (12 × 0.7000%). The error is negligible.

CUBIC EQUATIONS

In Chapter 7 we developed a general program for the roots of a quadratic equation and gave several examples of the program. Now suppose you were required to solve a general cubic equation. You could use the general formulas given in any standard handbook of mathematical tables. But these formulas might be too complicated for a person unskilled in higher algebra. Here is a straightforward way of finding the first root of a cubic equation by an iterative procedure, applicable to any scientific calculator. However, one with six memories is desirable.

The general cubic equation is

$$ax^3 + bx^2 + cx + d = 0 \qquad (9\text{-}13)$$

The procedure for solving the equation consists of first finding one real root, which must exist for every cubic equation. (The mathematical procedure to be used is described below.) The cubic is then reduced to a quadratic equation, which is solved by the program of example 7-11. The trick is to find the first real root to sufficient accuracy (up to six or eight significant figures) using a systematic process which converges to the answer. Briefly, this process is as follows:

1. Find two trial values of x for the equation below, which cause y to change sign (from plus to minus or from minus to plus).

$$y = ax^3 + bx^2 + cx + d \qquad (9\text{-}14)$$

2. Estimate or interpolate a new value of x_o between the two trial values of x which drives y closer to zero.

3. Find $y_o = ax_o{}^3 + bx_o{}^2 + cx_o + d$. $\qquad (9\text{-}15)$

4. Find s (slope) $= 3ax_o{}^2 + 2bx_o + c$. $\qquad (9\text{-}16)$

5. Calculate $\Delta x = -y_0/s$. $\qquad (9\text{-}17)$

6. Use a new trial value $x_1 = x_o + \Delta x$. $\qquad (9\text{-}18)$

7. Repeat steps 3-6 inclusive $x_1 + \Delta x = x_2$ and for $x_2 + \Delta x = x_3$.

8. Stop when $x_o + \Delta x$ is within desired error.

9. Solve remaining quadratic equation for the last two roots.

This sequence of operations will now be illustrated by a specific numerical example, using a program suitable for the **HP-45 and the Monroe 324,** which have nine addressable memories. This memory capacity eliminates the labor of recording and entering the values of up to eight lengthy constants several times for each iteration cycle. In addition, there is much less chance that the operator will make an error when he uses the calculator's memory.

We will now develop a manual program for the first real root of a cubic equation, based on the previous discussion. It will apply to all equations of the form of Eq. 9-13, where a, b, c, and d are all real numbers. We will store the coefficients a, b, c, and d, and the derivative factors $3a$, $2b$, and c to start the solution. The operator assumes an initial value, x_o, for the first real root, and proceeds to narrow down the solution as indicated in example 9-6. This program makes use of eight memories and illustrates the type of register arithmetic that is used to manipulate the data contained in memory.

The solution for the remaining two roots of the reduced quadratic equation was described in Chapter 7; it would follow the solution of the first real root. The operations required to solve the cubic equation as shown require about 198 steps for the first real root and about 23 steps for the two roots of the reduced quadratic, for a total of about 221 steps. This number of manual steps begins to tax the patience and concentration of an operator, particularly if a series of answers is required for different values of input parameters. The need to perform repeated calculations of this complexity leads to the requirement for a programmable calculator, as discussed in Chapter 12.

Returning to our cubic equation, the iterative routine to be developed follows the mathematical procedure just described for the first real root of the equation.

Numerical Solution of Cubic Equation

Suppose the cubic equation that's given is $y = 0.88x^3 + 1.672x^2 - 2.288x - 4.224$ and we want to find one real root where $y = 0$. To start, assume $x_o = 0$; then $y_o = -4.224$. Using Horner's method, evaluate y for $x = 1$ and $x = 2$,

1. We find for $x_o = 1$, $y_o = -3.960$.

	a	b	c	d	
$\boxed{x_o = 1}$	0.88	1.672	-2.288	-4.224	cubic coefficients
		$+ 0.880$	$+ 2.552$	$+ 0.264$	
		2.552	0.264	$\boxed{-3.960}$	(y_o ordinate, $x_o = 1$)

2. Since the y ordinate is decreasing for $x = 0$ and $x_o = 1$, try $x_o = 2$.

		b	c	d	
$\boxed{x_o = 2}$ 0.88		1.672	-2.288	-4.224	cubic coefficients
		$+ 1.760$	$+ 6.864$	$+ 9.152$	
		3.432	4.576	$\boxed{+4.928}$	(y_o ordinate, $x_o = 2$)

3. We find that y has changed from $y_o = -3.960$ for x_o is about halfway between 1 and 2. Now find y for $x_o = 1.5$.

$$\boxed{x_o = 1.5}\ 0.88 \quad 1.672 \quad -2.288 \quad -4.224 \quad \textbf{cubic coefficients}$$

$$\underline{+\ 1.320 \quad +\ 4.488 \quad +\ 3.330 \qquad\qquad}$$

$$2.992 \quad +\ 2.200 \quad \boxed{-0.924}(y_o \text{ ordinate, } x_o = 1.5)$$

Therefore, $y_o = -0.924$ when $x_o = 1.5$.

4. Now calculate a correction Δ to be added to x_o, as follows:

(a) Let $\Delta = \dfrac{-y_o}{\text{slope of cubic}} = \dfrac{-y_o}{s}$ \hfill (9-17)

(b) The slope of a cubic equation

$$ax^3 + bx^2 + cx + d = 0 \qquad\qquad (9\text{-}13)$$

is given by

$$s = 3ax^2 + 2bx + c \qquad\qquad (9\text{-}18)$$

for any values of $a, b,$ and c.

(c) The slope at $x_o = 1.5$ is given by the same procedure, using coefficients $3a, 2b,$ and c as follows:

$$3a = 3 \times 0.88\ = 2.64$$
$$2b = 2 \times 1.672 = 3.344$$
$$c = -2.288\quad |$$

(d) At $x_o = 1.5$ the slope s is 8.668, as shown below.

$$2.64 \quad +\ 3.344 \quad -2.288 \quad \textbf{coefficients of slope, } s$$

$$\underline{+\ 3.960 \quad +\ 10.956 \qquad\qquad}$$

$$7.304 \quad +\ 8.668 \quad \text{value of } s \text{ at } x_o = 1.5$$

5. The correction Δ is

$$\Delta = \frac{-y_o}{S} = \frac{+\ 0.924}{8.668} = 0.1065990$$

The new value of x is $x_1 = x_o + \Delta$.

$$x_1 = 1.6065990, \text{ or } 1.6066$$

(For the first iteration, it is not necessary to keep all the decimal places.)

Now repeat steps 3, 4, and 5 for $x_1 = 1.6066$. This is left as an exercise for the reader and yields $x_2 = 1.6000260$. The third cycle yields $x_3 = 1.6000000$, which is the exact root desired.

These operations are followed step by step in the next example, which uses the memory available in the HP-45 to store the necessary constants, the estimates for x_o and slope s. The general coefficients, $a, b, c,$ and d are indicated as loaded into the memories, but their numerical values are used in the steps following.

177

Example 9-7. Solve the following cubic equation for the first real root, using the HP-45.

$$0.88x^3 + 1.672x^2 - 2.288x - 4.224 = 0$$

$$\underset{(a)}{0.88}x^3 + \underset{(b)}{1.672}x^2 - \underset{(c)}{2.288}x - \underset{(d)}{4.224} = 0 \quad \longleftarrow \text{ cubic coefficients}$$

Step	Key-Operations	Comments
Load Memory	a STO 2, $\times$ 3 STO 7, b STO 3 $\times$ 2 STO 8, c STO 4, d STO 5, FIX 4 x_0 STO 1	Store cubic coefficients. Store derivative coefficients. Let $x_0 = 1.0$
1	RCL $\times$ 2, RCL $+$ 3, RCL $\times$ 1, RCL $+$ 4, RCL $\times$ 1, RCL $+$ 5	$y_0 = -3.960$
2	2.0 STO 1, repeat of step 1 operations	$x_0 = 2.0, y_0 = 44.928$
3	1.5 STO 1, repeat of step 1. STO 6	$x_0 = 1.5, y_0 = 0.924$
4	RCL 1, RCL $\times$ 7, RCL $+$ 8 RCL $\times$ 1, RCL $+$ 4 RCL $x \rightleftarrows y$ RCL $+$ 1 STO 1,	$s = 8.6680$, slope of curve
5	RCL 6 CHS RCL $+$ 1 STO 1	$\Delta = 0.1066, x_0 + \Delta = 1.6066$
6	Repeat of step 1, FIX 6, STO 6	$y_0 = 0.065064$
7	Repeat of steps 4 and 5	$\Delta = -0.006573, x_0 + \Delta = 1.600026$
8	Repeat of step 1, STO 6	$y_0 = 0.000255$
9	Repeat of steps 4 and 5, if necessary	$\Delta = -0.000026, x_0 + \Delta = 1.600000$

Now assume the true real root is 1.6000000. The quadratic equation that remains is given by the last row of coefficients below: 0.88, 3.080, and 2.640. Use $x = 1.600$.

$$x = 1.6, \quad 0.88 \qquad 1.672 \qquad -2.288 \qquad -4.224$$

$$\begin{array}{cccc}
 & & +\ 1.408 & +\ 4.928 & -4.224 \\
\hline
 & 0.88 & 3.080 & 2.640 \\
\end{array}$$

These become the coefficients of the quadratic

$$0.88x^2 + 3.080x + 2.640 = 0$$

Example 9-7. To solve for the last two roots of the cubic equation, use the quadratic program developed in example 7-11. Use coefficients $a = 0.88$, $b = 3.08$, and $c = 2.64$.

Key–Operations	Display	Comment
3.08 [CHS] [ENTER ↑] 0.88 [ENTER ↑]		
2 [×] [÷] [ENTER ↑] [STO] 2	−1.750 000	$d = -b/2a$
[×] 2.64 [ENTER ↑]		
0.88 [÷] [−]	0.062500	$f^2 = d^2 - c/a$
[√x]	0.250000	f (write)
[RCL] 2 [+]	−1.500 000	R_2 of cubic
[RCL] 2, 0.2500 [−]	−2.000 000	R_3 of cubic

You might wish to store the constants 3.08 and 2.64 into memories 7 and 8 and rewrite the above program accordingly. This would result in one continuous program rather than two segmented programs.

The three roots are

$R_1 = 1.6000\ 000$ from the iteration program, example 9-6.

$R_2 = -1.500\ 000$ from the quadratic program, example 9-7.

$R_3 = -2.000\ 000$ from the quadratic program, example 9-7.

Observe that these roots verify the original equation
$(0.88)\ (x - 1.6)\ (x + 1.5)\ (x + 2.00)$
$$= 0.88\ x^3 + 1.672\ x^2 - 2.288x - 4.224$$

It can be shown that the sum of the roots of the cubic should equal $-b/a$, where a and b are the original constants in the cubic equation. We have $R_1 = 1.6$, $R_2 = -1.5$, and

$R_3 = -2.0$. The sum of the roots is -1.9; the term $-b/a = -1.672/0.88 = -1.9$, which checks.

You can verify that the product of the roots equals $d/a = 4.8$, which is an alternate check.

To solve the cubic equation efficiently for the first real root, it is desirable to store the various constants of the cubic into memory. For the calculation of the slop s the constants to be stored are $3a$, $2b$, and c. The last constant to be stored is each successive value of x_o, x_1, x_2, and so on. This makes a minimum of eight constants required at any one time. A manual program using eight storage registers for these constants was developed for the HP-45. Thus, if a lesser machine without multiple memory is used, the operator must enter these constants many times by hand, which takes more care and time.

It should be noted that there are no scientific functions required for the first real root, and that only the square root function is needed for the reduced quadratic. Therefore, any operator with a simple arithmetic calculator can solve any cubic or quadratic equation following the procedures of this example and the routine shown in Chapter 2 for square roots. There are also intermediate calculators such as the Texas Instruments SR-10 that possess a square root capability, which can be used to solve the quadratic equations with ease.

Steps to Solve Cubic Equation

As a matter of interest, a tabulation of the number of steps required to solve for all three roots by this method is given here. The entry of any given number is assumed to be only one step.

- Store coefficients of original cubic and its derivative   24
- Find y_o for $x_o = 1.0, 2.0$, and 1.5.   62
- Calculate slope s, correction Δ, and new x_o.   23
- Find new y_o, new slope, new Δ, and new x_o second cycle.   45
- Find new y_o, new slope, new Δ, and final x_o (third cycle).   44
- Solve reduced quadratic equation.   23

Total = 221

The third cycle is optional. If omitted, 44 steps are saved. There is a total of 221 steps, if 6-decimal accuracy is required. If an error of 0.00003 in the root R_1 was permitted, then the third cycle could be omitted, and only 177 steps would be required. However, a final check for y_o using some 20 steps is always worthwhile to guarantee your answer.

LINEAR SIMULTANEOUS EQUATIONS

Any number of problems can be expressed as two simultaneous linear equations in two unknowns, x and y. For example, you may be given two different but consistent statements about the ages of two people or about the prices of two quantities of apples and oranges. Such problems can easily be solved with the aid of the simple computer program which is developed below. It will be assumed that eight memories are available in your pocket calculator or in a desk computer at the office.

Suppose you can express two facts about x and y in equation form, as follows:

$$r_4 = r_5 x + r_6 y \qquad (9\text{-}19)$$
$$r_1 = r_2 x + r_3 y \qquad (9\text{-}20)$$

where r_1 through r_6 are known constants or numbers. Then x is given by

$$X = \frac{N_x}{D} = \frac{\begin{vmatrix} r_4 & r_6 \\ r_1 & r_3 \end{vmatrix}}{\begin{vmatrix} r_5 & r_6 \\ r_2 & r_3 \end{vmatrix}} = \frac{r_4 r_3 - r_1 r_6}{r_5 r_3 - 5_2 r_6} \qquad (9\text{-}21)$$

$$\text{where } D = r_5 r_2 - r_2 r_6. \qquad (9\text{-}22)$$

Similarly, y is given by

$$y = \frac{N_y}{D} = \frac{\begin{vmatrix} r_5 & r_4 \\ r_2 & r_1 \end{vmatrix}}{D} = \frac{r_5 r_1 - r_2 r_4}{D} \qquad (9\text{-}23)$$

The constant symbols are chosen to coincide with the number codes for the memory registers in which they will be stored. To solve these two equations by a calculator with eight memories, perform the following operations in order.

1. Store r_4, r_5, and r_6 in memories 4, 5, and 6.
2. Store r_1, r_2, and r_3 in memories 1, 2, and 3.
3. Calculate $D = r_5 r_3 - r_2 r_6$; store in memory 7.
4. Calculate N_x and divide by D. This is x.
5. Calculate N_y and divide by D. This is y.
6. Multiply y by r_6, multiply x by r_5, and add. (This result should equal r_4, as a check.)

Example 9-8. The following table shows the general program for two linear simultaneous equations.

Steps Required	Key—Operation	Comment
18	r_4 STO 4, r_5 STO 5, r_6 STO 6 r_1 STO 1, r_2 STO 2, r_3 STO 3	Store constants.
11	RCL 4, RCL × 3, RCL 1 RCL × 6 −	N_x
13	RCL 5, RCL × 3 RCL 2 RCL × 6 − STO 7	D
3	÷ STO 8	x (Record.)
11	RCL 5 RCL × 1 RCL 2 RCL × 4 −	N_y
3	RCL ÷ 7	(Record.)
9	RCL × 6, RCL 5 RCL × 8 +	Check: 5.00 = R_4.

There are 62 program steps and 6 data entries, for a total of 68 steps. This includes nine steps for the check.

Now let us try a simple problem to exercise our program. Suppose two bottles of wine plus four cans of beer cost \$5, and that the cost of one bottle of wine is \$1 more than one bottle of beer. Find the price of a bottle of wine and a can of beer. To start, let x = price of wine and y = price of beer.

$$\text{Then } 5 = 2x + 4y \tag{9-24}$$
$$1 = x - y \tag{9-25}$$

Example 9-9. Solve Eqs. 9-24 and 9-25 above.

Steps Required	Key—Operation	Comments
19	5 STO 4, 2 STO 5, 4 STO 6 1 STO 1, 1 STO 2, 1 CHS STO 3	Store constants

Steps Required	Key—Operation	Comments
11	RCL 4 RCL × 3. RCL 1 RCL × 6 −	$N_x = -9$
13	RCL 5 RCL × 3. RCL 2 RCL × 6	
	− STO 7	$D = -6.00$
3	÷ STO 8	$\lfloor x = 1.50$
11	RCL 5 RCL × 1. RCL 2. RCL × 4 −	$N_y = -3.00$
3	RCL ÷ 7	$y = 0.50$
9	RCL × 6. RCL 5 RCL × 8 +	Check = 5

We have found that the wine costs $1.50 per bottle, and the beer costs $0.50 per can. There are 54 program steps, 6 data entries, and 9 steps for the check, for a total of 69 program steps for the final solution.

Three Linear Simultaneous Equations

Having solved two simultaneous linear equations, let's move on to the next step, higher order linear equations involving 3 or more unknowns. To solve three linear simultaneous equations in three unknowns would appear offhand to be too difficult a problem to solve even with a 9-memory pocket calculator. In the first place it would seem necessary to store at least 12 constants, 4 for each equation. In addition one would like to store the determinant D, which is required once for each unknown, for a total of 13 constants. However, it is possible to manually program a straightforward, easy-to-remember solution on a pocket calculator with nine memories. This section will give some elementary mathematical analysis on how to solve the equations and then present a method for programing the equations by an elegant use of the nine available memories of the HP-45 or Monroe 324G.

We will proceed using determinants to find the value of the variables x, y, and z. You will find that the formidable set of equations given below can be easily programed on a 9-memory arithmetic calculator. Interestingly, no scientific functions are required. The expansions shown apply only to a

3 × 3 determinant and cannot be generalized to higher orders. However a 4 × 4 determinant can be expanded to a set of four products, each of which makes use of the 3 × 3 determinants expanded below.

Suppose the three simultaneous linear equations have the form

$$k_3 = r_7 x + r_8 y + r_9 z \qquad (9\text{-}26)$$
$$k_2 = r_4 x + r_5 y + r_6 z \qquad (9\text{-}27)$$
$$k_1 = r_1 x + r_2 y + r_3 z \qquad (9\text{-}28)$$

The symbols r_1 through r_9 are chosen to symbolize the constants that will be stored in memory registers 1 through 9. The symbols k_3, k_2, and k_1 are also constants; they will be stored in the calculator at appropriate points in the solution. Your problem can be stated simply as follows:

Given constants $\begin{vmatrix} k_3 \\ k_2 \\ k_1 \end{vmatrix}$, $\begin{vmatrix} r_7\, r_8\, r_9 \\ r_4\, r_5\, r_6 \\ r_1\, r_2\, r_3 \end{vmatrix}$

find x, y, and z.

The solution for one variable—say, x—is easily found using determinants. One could then use this value for x to reduce the set of three equations to only two simultaneous linear equations and then solve for y and z using the program of example 9-8. However, we will use a straightforward method that makes repeated use of 3 × 3 determinants.

The two vertical lines which mark the 3 × 3 array symbolize the determinant D, which is required for the solution to x, y, and z. The diagonal expansion method will be used to evaluate each 3 × 3 determinant as shown in Eqs. 9-29 through 9-31. To solve for x let $x = N_x/D$.

$$= \frac{N_x}{D} = \frac{\begin{vmatrix} k_3\, r_8\, r_9 \\ k_2\, r_5\, r_6 \\ k_1\, r_2\, r_3 \end{vmatrix}}{\begin{vmatrix} r_7\, r_8\, r_9 \\ r_4\, r_5\, r_6 \\ r_1\, r_2\, r_3 \end{vmatrix}} \frac{\begin{array}{l}(k_3 r_5 r_3 + r_8 r_6 k_1 + r_9 k_2 r_2) \\ -(k_1 r_5 r_9 + r_2 r_6 k_3 + r_3 k_2 r_8)\end{array}}{\begin{array}{l}(r_7 r_5 r_3 + r_8 r_6 r_1 + r_9 r_4 r_2) \\ -(r_1 r_5 r_9 + r_6 r_2 r_7 + r_3 r_4 r_8)\end{array}} \qquad (9\text{-}29)$$

Similarly, let $y = N_y/D$, where

$$N_y = \begin{vmatrix} r_7 \, k_3 \, r_g \\ r_4 \, k_2 \, r_6 \\ r_1 \, k_1 \, r_3 \end{vmatrix} = \begin{array}{l} (r_7 k_2 r_3 + r_8 r_6 r_1 + r_9 r_4 k_1) \\ (r_1 k_2 r_9 + r_6 k_1 r_7 + r_3 r_4 k_3) \end{array} \qquad (9\text{-}30)$$

Finally, let $z = N_z/D$, where

$$N_z = \begin{vmatrix} r_7 \, r_8 \, k_3 \\ r_y \, r_5 \, k_2 \\ r_1 \, r_2 \, k_1 \end{vmatrix} = ? \quad \text{(to be supplied by the reader)} \qquad (9\text{-}31)$$

Our method to solve these equations will be straightforward.

1. Store constants r_7, r_8, and r_9 in registers 7, 8, and 9.
2. Store constants r_5, r_6, and r_7 in registers 5, 6, and 7.
3. Store constants r_1, r_2, and r_3 in registers 1, 2, and 3.
4. Using the keyboard as a visual replica of determinant D solve for D and record the result for later use in Eqs. 9-30 and 9-31.
5. Store constants k_3, k_2, and k_1 in registers 7, 4, and 1.
6. To solve for x, repeat the operations of step 4 and divide by D, using the value previously recorded.
7. Reenter constants r_7, r_4, and r_1 in registers 7, 4, and 1. Store k_3, k_2, and k_1 in registers 8, 5, and 2.
8. To solve for y, repeat the operations of step 4 and divide by D.
9. For z, reenter constants k_3, k_2, and k_1 in registers 9, 6, and 3.
10. To solve for z, repeat the operations of step 4 and divide by D.

These instructions for solving three simultaneous linear equations are programed for a pocket calculator with nine memories as shown in example 9-10. Each sequence of calculation is arranged to correspond to the form of Eqs. 9-29 through 9-31 and to mechanize the steps explained above. Example 9-32 solves a specific numerical example, using this general program. These examples should allow you to solve your own set of equations. It is only necessary to store the constants of the new equations and follow the steps shown. To guard against entry or program mistakes, it is important to perform the checks suggested for each solution.

Example 9-10. Set up a program for solving three simultaneous linear equations with a 9-memory calculator.

Sequence (Steps)	Key – Operation	Comment
1 (27)	r_7 STO 7, r_8 STO 8, r_9 STO 9 r_4 STO 4, r_5 STO 5, r_6 STO 6 r_1 STO 1, r_2 STO 2, r_3 STP 3	Store constants for determinant D.
2 (26)	RCL 7 RCL 5 ✕ RCL 3 ✕ RCL 8 RCL 6 ✕ RCL 1 ✕ + RCL 9 RCL 4 ✕ RCL 2 ✕ +	Positive terms of D.
3 (26)	RCL 9 RCL 5 ✕ RCL 1 ✕ RCL 8 RCL 4 ✕ RCL 3 ✕ + RCL 7 RCL 6 ✕ RCL 2 ✕ +	Negative terms of D.
4 (1)	−	Record D.
5 (9)	k_3 STO 7, k_2 STO 4, k_1 STO 1	Store constants for N_x.
6 (53)	Repeat Steps 2, 3, and 4.	$N_x =$
7 (3)	D ENTER −	$x = N_x/d$ (Record.)
8 (18)	r_7 STO 7 r_4 STO 4 r_1 STO 1 k_3 STO 8 k_2 STO 5 r_1 STO 4	Store N_y. Constants.
9 (53)	Repeat steps 2, 3, and 4.	$N_y =$
10 (3)	D ENTER −	$y = N_y/D$ D from step 4
11 (18)	r_8 STO 8, r_5 STO 5, r_2 STO 2 k_3 STO 9, k_2 STO 6, k_1 STO 3	Store N_z constants.
12 (53)	Repeat steps 2, 3, and 4.	$N_z =$
13 (3)	D ENTER −	$z = N_z/D$
	To perform a final check	
14 (12)	r_9 ✕ , RCL 8 (y from 10) ✕ + RCL 7 (x from 7) ✕ +	Should equal k_3.

186

Sequence	Operations	Steps
1	Store nine constants for determinant.	27
2,3,4	Calculate determinant, D.	53
5	Store three constants for n_x.	9
6,7	Calculate N_x, x.	56
8	Store six constants for N_y.	18
9,10	Calculate N_y, y.	56
11	Store six constants for N_2.	18
12,13	Calculate N_z, z.	56
14	Subtotal	293
	Perform check.	12
	Total	305

Following is a numerical example using the program just developed to solve three simultaneous linear equations.

Example 9-11. Solve the following three simultaneous equations.

$$1.5x + 2.0y - 2.0z = 7.2 \qquad (9\text{-}38)$$

$$2.0x + 1.5y + 1.0z = 1.9 \qquad (9\text{-}39)$$

$$-3.0x - 1.5y + 2.0z = 4.4 \qquad (9\text{-}40)$$

Sequence (Steps)	Key—Operation	Comment
1 (27)	1.5 STO 7, 2.0 STO 8, −2.0 STO 9 2.0 STO 4, 1.5 STO 5, 1.0 STO 6 −3.0 STO 1, −1.5 STO 2, +2.0 STO 3	Store constants for determinant D.
2 (26)	RCL 7 RCL 5 × , RCL 3 × RCL 8 RCL 6 × , RCL 1 × + RCL 9 RCL 4 × , RCL 2 × +	Positive terms in D = 4.5.
3 (26)	RCL 9 RCL 5 × , RCL 1 × RCL 8 RCL 4 × , RCL 3 × + RCL 7 RCL 6 × , RCL 2 × +	Negative terms in D = 14.75.
4 (1)	−	Record determinant $D = -10.25$.
5 (9)	−7.2 STO 7, 1.9 STO 4, 4.4 STO 1	Store constants for N_x.

187

Sequence (Steps)	Key—Operation	Comment
6 (53)	Repeat steps 2, 3, and 4.	$N_x = -12.35$
7 (4)	+10.25 [CHS] [ENTER ↑] [÷]	$x = 1.20$
8 (18)	1.5 [STO] 7, 2.0 [STO] 4, −3.0 [STO] 1 −7.2 [STO] 8, 1.9 [STO] 5, 4.4 [STO] 2	Store N_y constants.
9 (53)	Repeat Steps 2, 3, 4.	$N_y = 20.5$
10 (4)	10.25, [CHS] [ENTER ↑] [÷]	$y = -2.00$
11 (18)	2.0 [STO] 8, 1.5 [STO] 5, −1.5 [STO] 2 −7.2 [STO] 9, 1.9 [STO] 6, 4.4 [STO] 5	Store N_z constants.
12 (53)	Repeat steps 2, 3, 4.	$N_z = -25.625$
13 (4)	10.25 [CHS] [ENTER ↑] [÷]	$z = 2.5$
14 (12)	2.0 [×] [RCL] 8, −2.00 [×] [+] [RCL] 7, 1.2 [×] [+]	$-7.2 = k_3$ Check !

Note that $y = -2.0$, from step 10; $x = 1.20$, from step 7.

This program required about 308 steps, including the entry of 27 numbers. It was also necessary to record D and three answers, x, y, and z. The check for k_3 took 12 steps to complete the solution.

This is about as complex a solution for a single problem as one would want to tackle with a manually programed calculator. You should try this program with a different set of equations. Of course, most of the steps required result from the use of a fixed routine to evaluate a 3×3 determinant, as indicated in sequences 2,3,6,9, and 12. Using a programmable calculator, these sequences would reduce to one routine, plus a few commands to initiate and terminate the routine when needed. The actual number of steps in the program would then be reduced significantly.

Alternate Solution—Gauss Reduction Method

It was suggested by Jack Boddy (a coworker) that simultaneous linear equations can be solved by the Gauss reduction method.* Briefly, the reduction process can be summarized as follows: The first term in each equation is reduced to unity by dividing by the leading coefficients. The first equation is then subtracted from the second and third equations to eliminate x, creating two new equations in only two variables, y and z. The process of normalization and subtraction is repeated on these two reduced equations to produce a single equation in z.

This latter equation is solved for and is subsequently substituted back into one reduced equation to solve for y. The last step is to substitute both the y and z values into one of the original equations to solve for x. If desired, all three values may then be substituted into another original equation to check all results. Our solution stores data in eight memory locations in the calculator, including both the original constants and certain intermediate results. The method is perfectly general and can be used for fourth-degree or higher order equations.

Example 9-12. Use a general program to solve three linear simultaneous equations using Gauss reduction method and the HP-45.

$$k_3 = r_7x + r_8y + r_9z \qquad (9\text{-}35)$$
$$k_2 = r_4x + r_5y + r_6z \qquad (9\text{-}36)$$
$$k_1 = r_1x + r_2y + r_3z \qquad (9\text{-}37)$$

r_7 $\boxed{1/x}$ $\boxed{\text{ENTER} \uparrow}$ $\boxed{\text{ENTER} \uparrow}$ $\boxed{\text{ENTER} \uparrow}$	Normalize coefficients in Eq. 9-35.
r_8 $\boxed{\times}$ $\boxed{\text{STO}}$ 1	Store the new
$\boxed{\text{CLx}}$ r_9 $\boxed{\times}$ $\boxed{\text{STO}}$ 2	constants.
$\boxed{\text{CLx}}$ k_3 $\boxed{\times}$ $\boxed{\text{STO}}$ 3	
r_4 $\boxed{1/x}$ $\boxed{\text{ENTER} \uparrow}$ $\boxed{\text{ENTER} \uparrow}$ $\boxed{\text{ENTER} \uparrow}$	Normalize coefficients in Eq. 9-36.
r_5 $\boxed{\times}$ $\boxed{\text{RCL}}$ $\boxed{-}$ 1 $\boxed{\text{STO}}$ 9	
$\boxed{\text{CLx}}$ r_6 $\boxed{\times}$ $\boxed{\text{RCL}}$ $\boxed{-}$ 2 $\boxed{\text{RCL}}$ $\boxed{\div}$ 9 $\boxed{\text{STO}}$ 5	Store the new
$\boxed{\text{CLx}}$ k_2 $\boxed{\times}$ $\boxed{\text{RCL}}$ $\boxed{-}$ 3 $\boxed{\text{RCL}}$ $\boxed{\div}$ 9 $\boxed{\text{STO}}$ 6	constants.
r_1 $\boxed{1/x}$ $\boxed{\text{ENTER} \uparrow}$ $\boxed{\text{ENTER} \uparrow}$ $\boxed{\text{ENTER} \uparrow}$	Normalize coefficients
r_2 $\boxed{\times}$ $\boxed{\text{RCL}}$ $\boxed{-}$ 1 $\boxed{\text{STO}}$ 9	in Eq. 9-37 and

* For further discussion see "Mathematics of Physics and Modern Engineering," by I. S. Sokolnikoff and R. M. Redheffer. McGraw-Hill Book Co., New York, 1958.

| CLr r_3 × RCL − 2 RCL ÷ 9 RCL − 5 STO 8 | Store the new |
| CLr k_1 × RCL − 3 RCL ÷ 9 RCL − 6 | constants. |

| ENTER ↑ RCL ÷ 8 | Answer for z. |

| ENTER ↑ ENTER ↑ RCL × 5 | |
| RCL − 6 CHS | Answer for y. |

RCL × 1 $x \rightleftarrows y$	
RCL × 2 +	
RCL − 3 CHS	Answer for x.

Example 9-13. Solve the following numerical examples.

$$1.5x + 2.0y - 2.0z = -7.2$$
$$\quad (r_7) \quad\;\; (r_8) \quad\;\; (r_9) \quad\;\; (k_3) \qquad\qquad (9\text{-}38)$$
$$2.0x + 1.5y + 1.0z = 1.9 \qquad\qquad (9\text{-}39)$$
$$\quad (r_4) \quad\;\; (r_5) \quad\;\; (r_6) \quad\;\; (k_2)$$
$$-3.0x - 1.5y + 2.0z = 4.4 \qquad\qquad (9\text{-}40)$$
$$\quad (r_1) \quad\;\; (r_2) \quad\;\; (r_3) \quad\;\; (k_1)$$

Key–Operation	Display	Comment
1.5 $1/x$ ENTER ↑ ENTER ↑ ENTER ↑	0.667	Enter
2.0 × STO 1	1.333	Eq. 9-38.
CLr −2.0 × STO 2	−1.333	
CLr −7.2 × STO 3	−4.800	
2.0 $1/x$ ENTER ↑ ENTER ↑ ENTER ↑	0.500	
1.5 × RCL − 1 STO 9	−0.583	Reduced form of
CLr 1.0 × RCL − 2 RCL − 9 STO 5	−3.143	Eq. 9-39.
CLr 1.9 × RCL − 3 RCL − 9 STO 6	−9.857	
−3.0 $1/x$ ENTER ↑ ENTER ↑ ENTER ↑	−0.333	
−1.5 × RCL − 1 STO 9	−0.833	
CLr 2.0 × RCL − 2 RCL − 9 RCL − 5 STO 8	2.342	Reduced form of
CLr 4.4 × RCL − 3 RCL − 9 RCL − 6	5.857	Equation 9-40.
ENTER ↑ RCL − 8	2.50	z
ENTER ↑ ENTER ↑ RCL × 5	−7.857	
RCL − 6 CHS	2.00	y
RCL × 1 $x \rightleftarrows y$	2.50	
RCL × 2 +	−6.00	
RCL − 3 CHS	1.2	x

The solution takes only 116 steps as contrasted to the 293 steps for the determinant method illustrated in examples 9-11 and 9-12. Although the solutions for y and z depend on the solution for x, the savings in labor are very worthwhile. Of course, the reductions in calculation for higher order simultaneous equations are much greater.

It should be recognized that any matrix reduction method can produce inaccurate results if the matrixes are ill conditioned; that is, if the off-diagonal terms are dominant. This would be quite unusual for the 3×3 and 4×4 matrixes under discussion. Furthermore, the buildup of error is unlikely with these scientific calculators, which have accuracies ranging from 7 to 10 figures.

This example shows that a little research for an efficient mathematical solution is well worth the time spent for the more complex problems, even when an advanced scientific calculator is at your disposal. This is especially true when you are manually solving a series of repetitive calculations with different input data for each calculation.

LEAST SQUARES FIT, LINEAR REGRESSION

As a final example, consider the situation where one has a set of data points resulting from a series of measurements, as shown in Fig. 9-1. Let us say that x is a variable that is changed in increments of unity and that y is a resulting measurement. When the data is plotted, it appears to have the shape of a curve with a slowly changing slope. Suppose it is desired to fit the best straight line through this series of points. An accepted procedure is to choose the straight line that minimizes the sum of the squares of the differences from the given set of points.

When one applies mathematical analysis to this problem, a set of linear equations results. If the desired straight line is

$$y = mx + b \tag{9-41}$$

and the given set of data points are x_i and y_i, as typified by example 9-13, then the constants m and b are given by these two linear equations with coefficients that are derived from all the data points.

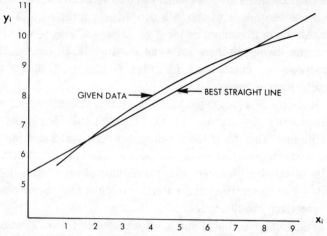

Fig. 9-1. Plot of given data points, x_i and y_i. The least squares program required 97 steps to calculator the constants Σx_i, Σx_i^2, $\Sigma x_i y_i$, and n. An additional 41 steps are required to solve the quadratic equation for the intercept, b, and the slope, m. If only six data points were given, the entire solution would requires only 105 steps. However, if 12 data points were given, the solution would take 171 steps. The labor saving is considerable, especially if the given constants are numbers of several digits, since all constants are stored in memory and manipulated by the STO and RCL keys.

$$\Sigma y_i = bn + m\Sigma x_i \qquad (9\text{-}42)$$
$$\Sigma x_i y_i = b\Sigma x_i + m\Sigma x_i^2 \qquad (9\text{-}43)$$

where

n is the number of data points

Σx_i is the sum of the x_i parameters,

Σy_i is the sum of the y_i parameters,

$\Sigma x_i y_i$ is the sum of the products of the x_i and y_i parameters, and

Σx_i^2 is the sum of the x_i^2 parameters

The HP-45 has an internal program which accepts values of x_i and accumulates Σx_i and Σx_i^2. One merely enters each x_i and presses the $\boxed{\Sigma +}$ key. The same program also sums the y_i entries and counts the number of entries n. It is only necessary to multiply each x_i by the corresponding y_i to find all the constants necessary to solve Eqs. 9-42 and 9-43. The computer program is given in example 9-14 below. It takes an average of 11 steps for each set of data points (x_i, y_i) to derive the constants in the two equations, for a total of 97 steps, including the 18 data entries. It then takes an additional 39 steps to solve the two linear equations for b and m, for a total of 136 program steps. The amount of work to fit a quadratic program through the same set of points would be much greater, involving about 500 program steps.

The best straight line through the given points is found to be

$$y = 5.4028 + 0.5750\, x \tag{9-44}$$

The original set of data points and the least squares straight line is plotted in Fig. 9-1. Note how the straight line intersects the given curve, balancing one large error at either end against a series of small errors for the intervening data points. You might like to check graphically that the sum of these squares is less than for any other straight line drawn through the given points.

Example 9-14. Determine the best straight line to fit the points x_i, y_i, in the set of data shown below.

Given Data Points

x_i	y_i	x_i	y_i
1	5.7	6	9.0
2	6.5	7	9.6
3	7.2	8	10.0
4	7.8	9	10.2
5	8.5		

Steps Required	Key—Operation (HP-45)	Comment
	x_1 ENTER↑ Σ+ . y_1 STO 1 × . STO 4	Enter nine
	x_2 ENTER↑ Σ+ . y_2 STO + 1 + × . STO + 4	x_i points and y_i points.
97	x_8 ENTER↑ Σ+ . y_8 STO + 1 × . STO + 4	Accumulate
	x_9 ENTER↑ Σ+ . y_9 STO + 1 × . STO + 4	x_i in r_7. y_i in r_1. x_i^2 in r_6. $x_i \cdot y_i$ in r_4, and n in r_5.
11	RCL 4 RCL × 7. RCL 1 RCL × 6. −	$N_6 = -2917.50$

193

Steps Required	Key Operation (HP-45)	Comment
11	RCL 7 RCL × 7. RCL 5 RCL × 6. −	$D = 540.00$
2	STO 2	
1	÷ (Record intercept.)	$b = 5.4028$
11	RCL 7 RCL × 1 RCL 5 RCL × 4 −	$N_m = -310.00$
3	RCL ÷ 2 (Record slope.)	$m = 0.5750$

The best straight line for the given data is

$$y = 0.5750x + 5.4028$$

Shown below are the data stored in the various memories.

$$r_5 = 9.0000 = n$$
$$r_7 = 45.0000 = \Sigma x_i$$
$$r_1 = 74.5000 = \Sigma y_i$$
$$r_6 = 285.0000 = \Sigma x_i^2$$
$$r_4 = 407.0000 = \Sigma x_i y_i$$

The calculation of the best straight line constants (m and b) to fit a given set of data points is called *linear regression*. The HP-65 offers a program card for this calculation, and the new Texas Instruments SR-51 has this calculator preprogramed for the user.

Chapter 10

Metric Converters

The system of metric units was created in France and adopted by National Academy of France as far back as 1795. The unit of length is the meter (m), and the unit of mass if the gram (gm). The unit of time is the second which is the same in all systems of measurement. The beauty of the metric system and its derivatives is that all smaller and larger units can be expressed in decimal multiples of the fundamental units. For example, the centimeter (cm) is 10^{-2}m, and the kilometer (km) is 10^3m. Similarly, the milligram is 10^{-3}gm, a microgram is 10^6gm, and a kilogram is 10^3gm.

At the present time, there is a worldwide movement to standardize all scientific, physical, and industrial measurements in terms of the Systeme Internationale (SI) units, which are directly related to metric units. It is expected that international science and industry will conform to these units in the near future. The fundamental, derived, and supplementary units are listed in Table 10-1. Factors for converting to SI units are shown in Table 10-2. Only four significant figures are used for convenience. You will observe that the final units of all physical quantities (e.g., Table 10-2) conform to the units of Table 10-1.

There is no doubt that SI, or metric units, will eventually replace the U.S. customary units, in use since 1893. We will not miss the assorted units of length (inch, foot, yard, furlong, mile) and the equally cumbersome units of mass (dram, ounce, pound, ton). Therefore it is appropriate at this point to consider two new pocket calculators which are preprogramed to facilitate the conversion of customary units to metric units (and to reverse this conversion for those die-hards who cling to the old system). Two typical calculators will be described, the

195

Table 10-1. Systeme' Internationale (SI) Units and Values.
(Reproduced from NASA Document SP-7012.)

Physical Quantity	Name of Unit	Symbol
BASIC UNITS		
Length	meter	m
Mass	kilogram	kg
Time	second	s
Electric current	ampere	A
Temperature	kelvin	K
Luminous intensity	candela	cd
DERIVED UNITS		
Area	square meter	m^2
Volume	cubic meter	m^3
Frequency	hertz	Hz (s^{-1})
Density	kilogram per cubic meter	kg/m^3
Velocity	meter per second	m/s
Ang ar velocity	radian per second	rad/s
Acceleration	meter per second squared	m/s^2
Angular acceleration	radian per second squared	rad/s^2
Force	newton	N $(kg \cdot m/s^2)$
Pressure	newton per sq meter	N/m^2
Kinematic viscosity	sq meter per second	m^2/s
Dynamic viscosity	newton-second per sq meter	$N \cdot s/m^2$
Work, energy, quantity of heat	joule	J $(N \cdot m)$
Power	watt	W (J/s)
Electric charge	coulomb	C $(A \cdot s)$
Voltage, potential difference, electromotive force	volt	V (W/A)
Electric field strength	volt per meter	V/m
Electric resistance	ohm	Ω (V/A)
Electric capacitance	farad	F $(A \cdot s/V)$
Magnetic flux	weber	Wb $(V \cdot s)$
Inductance	henry	H $(V \cdot s/A)$
Magnetic flux density	tesla	T (Wb/m^2)
Magnetic field strength	ampere per meter	A/m
Magnetomontive force	ampere	A
Luminous flux	lumen	lm $(cd \cdot sr)$
Luminance	candela per sq meter	cd/m^2
Illumination	lux	lx (lm/m^2)
Wave number	1 per meter	m^{-1}
Entropy	joule per kelvin	J/K
Specific heat	joule per kilogram kelvin	$J kg^{-1} K^{-1}$
Thermal conductivity	watt per meter kelvin	$W m^{-1} K^{-1}$
Radiant intensity	watt per steradian	W/sr
Activity (of a radioactive source)	1 per second	s^{-1}
SUPPLEMENTARY UNITS		
Plane angle	radian	rad
Solid angle	steradian	sr

Table 10-2. U.S. Customary to SI Conversion Factors.

Quantity	To Convert From	To	Multiply By*
Distance	Astronomical Unit (A.U.)	km	1.496×10^8
Distance	miles	km	1.609
Distance	nautical miles	km	1.852
Distance	foot	m	0.3048
Distance	inch	m	0.02540
Pressure	Atmosphere	newton/m^2	1.013×10^5
Pressure	lb/in.^{2}	newton/m^2	6.895×10^3
Mass	pound	kg	0.4536
Energy	BTU	joule	1.055×10^3
Energy	calorie	joule	4.184
Energy	electron volt	joule	1.602×10^{-19}
Force	pound force	newton	4.448
Force	kilogram force	newton	9.807
Work	foot-pound	joule	1.356
Torque	foot-pound	newton-m	1.356
Torque	inch-pound	newton-m	0.1130
Thermal Conductivity	BTU/ft-hr-day F	W/m-K	0.01728
	cal/cm-S-deg C	W/m-K	4.184
Moment of inertia	slug-ft^2	kg-m^2	1.356
Radiation dose	rad	joule/kg	0.01
Magnetic Induction	gauss	weber/m^2	1×10^{-4}
	gamma	weber/m^2	1×10^{-9}

Table 10-2. Con't.

Quantity	To Convert From	To	Multiply By*
Angle	degree	radian	0.01745
Angle	minute (arc)	radian	2.909×10^{-4}
Angle	second (arc)	radian	4.848×10^{-6}
Power	horsepower	watt	7.457×10^2
Power	ft-lb/sec	watt	1.356

*Only four significant figures needed for ordinary calculations

Rockwell 51R *metric converter* and the Summit *MCC* (metric conversion computer). It is understood that any elementary calculator with an automatic constant capability or a memory can be used to effect these metric conversions. But if you are faced daily with the need to convert a host of customary quantities into their metric equivalents, then you could well use a special-purpose metric converter. If, however, you have to convert only a few quantities in length or weight, you may prefer to commit to memory the one or two conversion factors needed and to use an elementary pocket calculator with memory or automatic constant to perform the conversions.

ROCKWELL 51R METRIC CONVERTER

The general features of the Rockwell 51R are shown in Fig. 10-1. The 51R can be used as both a general-purpose calculator and as a metric converter. Its display, arithmetic controls, memory, and automatic constant capability are similar to the Rockwell 10R described in Chapter 1. In addition, it has an $\boxed{\text{A/O}}$ key for handling fractions, a $\boxed{\text{CONV}}$ key for metric conversion, and an $\boxed{\text{A} \leftrightarrow \text{B}}$ conversion feature for operator-initiated conversions. As a metric converter, it offers 112 conversions that can be obtained directly on the calculator. These conversions are performed by first depressing the *convert* key, $\boxed{\text{CONV}}$. This sets up the operations to convert the number in the display from one set of units to another. The first key touched after depressing $\boxed{\text{CONV}}$ specifies the units being converted. The next key specifies the units you are converting to.

A —USED WITH PROGRAMMABLE CONVERSION
B —USED WITH PROGRAMMABLE CONVERSION
C° —DEGREES CENTIGRADE.
F° —DEGREES FAHRENHEIT.
FEET —FEET
FL OZ —FLUID OUNCES
GAL —GALLONS
GM —GRAMS
INCH —INCHES
K —STORE PROGRAMMABLE CONVERSION CONSTANT
KG —KILOGRAMS
KM —KILOMETERS
LB —POUNDS
LIT —LITERS
M —METERS
M+ —ADD INTO MEMORY
M— —SUBTRACT FROM MEMORY
MC —MEMORY CLEAR
MM —MILLIMETERS
MILE —MILES
MR —MEMORY RECALL
OZ —OUNCES
QT —QUARTS
YARD—YARDS

Fig. 10-1. Rockwell 51R metric converter calculator.

Example 10-1. You want to convert 25 in. into its equivalent in millimeters. Enter 25; depress $\boxed{\text{CONV}}$ (INCH) (MM). The equivalent in millimeters is displayed (635).

The Rockwell 51R can just as easily perform the following conversions:

- Statute or nautical miles ↔ kilometers, meters, or millimeters
- Yards, feet, or inches ↔ kilometers, meters, or millimeters
- Fluid ounces, quarts, or gallons ↔ liters
- Ounces or pounds ↔ grams or kilograms
- Centigrade ↔ Fahrenheit

It not only converts areas and volumes from one system of measurement to another, but also converts measurements within the same system—for example, miles to yards.

The conversion factors used in the Rockwell 51R are listed in Table 10-3.

Nonmenclature Calculator	Table 10-3. Principal Conversion Constants Contained In Metric Converter.
	Units of Mass
(kg)	1 kilogram = 2.2046226 pounds (avop.)
(kg)	1 kilogram = 1000. grams
(lb)	1 pound (avop.) = 16. ounces (avop.)
(oz)	1 ounce (avop.) = 28.349523 grams
	Units of length
(mile)	1 nautical mile (Int.) = 1.1507795 mile (statute)
(mile)	1 mile (statute) = 1.609344 kilometers
(mile)	1 mile (statute) = 1760. yards
(km)	1 kilometer = 1000. meters
(m)	1 meter = 1000. millimeters
(yd)	1 yard = 0.9144 meters
(yd)	1 yard = 3. feet
(ft)	1 foot = 12. inches
(in)	1 inch = 25.4 millimeters
	Units of Volume, Liquid Measure
(gal)	1 gallon (U.K. liquid) = 1.2009503 gallon (U.S. liquid)
(GAL(	1 gallon (U.K. liquid) = 4. quart (U.K. liquid)
(gal)	1 gallon (U.S. liquid) = 3.3306957 quart (U.K. liquid)
(gal)	1 gallon (U.S. liquid) = 4. quart (U.S.liquid)
(qt)	1 quart (U.K.liquid) = 1.1365229 liters
(qt)	1 quart (U.K. liquid) = 40. ounces (U.K. liquid)
(qt)	1 quart (U.S. liquid) = 32. ounces (U.S. liquid)
(lit)	1 liter = 1.0566882 quarts (U.S. liquid)
(fl oz)	1 ounce (U.S. liquid) = 1.0408424 ounces (U.K. liquid)

A more detailed discussion of Rockwell 51R operating keys and features now follows, together with typical applications selected from the manufacturer's operating manual.

SPECIAL FEATURES OF ROCKWELL 51R

During conversion the setting of the US–IMP switch determines whether the liquid measurements fl oz, qt, and gal., are to be interpreted as *U.S. liquid* measurements (units of measure used in the United States, or *Imperial* measurements (units of measure used in England and Canada). The position of this switch may be changed at any time.

The position of the F–2 switch controls the decimal format of answers. With the switch in the F position the final answer will be left in full floating format. With the switch in the 2 position the result is rounded to two decimal places.

The setting of LAND–NAUT switch determines whether the MILE key is to be interpreted as land (statute) miles, or nautical miles. The switch position may be changed at any time.

Special Keys

[C] **Clear Key.** A single depression of [C], when there is no overflow condition, clears the displayed number but does not affect the stored constants or the calculating mode. A double depression of [C] clears any calculating mode and clears the calculator, except for the memories. Touching [C] during an overflow will reset the error condition. The resulting number in the display will be correct, if multiplied by 10^8, and may be used in further calculations.

[A/O] **And Over.** Before using this function, except in chain calculations, depress [C] two times. The depression of this key allows the entry of fractions and mixed numbers. To convert ⅔ to a decimal number, enter 2, depress [A/O], enter 3, and depress [=]. The decimal equivalent (0.67 with decimal switch at 2) will be displayed. For mixed numbers, such as 8¾, enter 8, depress [A/O], enter 3, depress [A/O], enter 4, and depress [=]. The decimal equivalent (8.75) will be displayed.

[M] **Memory Key.** All memory operations are initiated with the depression of this key. Memory 1 is automatically selected when the power is turned on. The depression of the [M] key followed by the number [1] or [2] will select one of the two memories. Touching [M] [2] will select memory 2. Once a memory is selected, subsequent memory operations will apply to that memory until the other memory is selected.

[CONV] **Conversion Key.** This key is used to set up the operation that converts the number in the display from one unit of measure to another. The first key depressed after [CONV] specifies the unit of measure being entered, and the second key specifies the unit of measure to which it is being converted. For example, if you have a number in the display that you want to convert from feet to meters, depress [CONV] FEET M. The equivalent in meters will be displayed. This operation does not affect any other calculations.

Arithmetic With Mixed Numbers

Problem	Keyboard Entry	Result
$3/5 \times 5\,3/4 = 3.45$	3 $\boxed{A/o}$	3.
	5 $\boxed{\times}$	0.6
	5 $\boxed{A/o}$	5.
	3 $\boxed{A/o}$	3.
	4 $\boxed{=}$	3.45
$5/2/3 = 7.5$	5.0 $\boxed{\div}$	5.0
	2 $\boxed{A/o}$	2.
	3 $\boxed{=}$	7.5

* Decimal switch in 2 position.

Operations Using Memory

The two memories are addressed using the $\boxed{M}$ key. To select one of the memories, depress $\boxed{M}$ $\boxed{1}$ or $\boxed{M}$ $\boxed{2}$, followed by one of the memory operating keys. Once a memory is selected, subsequent memory operations will apply to that memory. After depressing $\boxed{M}$, depress $\boxed{MC}$ to clear memory, $\boxed{M+}$ to add into memory, $\boxed{M-}$ to subtract from memory, and $\boxed{MR}$ to recall memory. Memory 1 is automatically selected when the calculator is turned on.

- To clear memory 1, depress $\boxed{M}$ $\boxed{1}$ $\boxed{MC}$; to clear memory 2, depress $\boxed{M}$ $\boxed{2}$ $\boxed{MC}$.

- To add 25 to the selected memory, enter 25, depress $\boxed{M}$ $\boxed{M+}$; 25 will be added to the value already in that memory. The display will not change.

- To subtract from a memory, enter the number to be subtracted and depress $\boxed{M}$ $\boxed{M-}$. The display will not change.

- To display the contents of a memory, depress $\boxed{M}$ $\boxed{MR}$. The contents will be displayed, but the memory is not affected.

Memory And Mixed Calculations

The following example will demonstrate the use of memories

Example 10-2.

$$Calculate \quad x = \frac{782.09/10 - (3.597 \times 18.72)}{142.68/10 - 3.597^2}$$

$$= \frac{10.87}{1.33} = 8.17$$

202

Decimal switch in 2 position

Key			Display	Memory 1	Memory 2
	M	2 , MC	0.		0.
	M	1 , MC	0.	0.	0.
782.09	÷		782.09	0.	0.
10	=		78.21	0.	0.
	M	M+	78.21	78.21	0.
3.597	×		3.597	78.21	0.
18.72	=		67.34	78.21	0.
	M	M	67.34	10.87	0.
142.68	÷		142.68	10.87	0.
10	=		14.27	10.87	0.
	M	2 M+	14.27	10.87	14.27
3.597	×		3.597	10.87	14.27
	=		12.94	10.87	14.27
	M	M−	12.94	10.87	1.33
	M	1 MR	10.87	10.87	1.33
	÷		10.87	10.87	1.33
	M	2 MR	1.33	10.87	1.33
	=		8.17	10.87	1.33

Area Conversion

To convert areas, the sequence used in converting lengths is used twice. Decimal switch is in F position.

Problem	Keyboard Entry	Result
Convert 120 sq. yd. into square meters.	120	120.
	CO NV	120.
	YARD	120.
	(M)	109.728
	CO NV	109.728
	YARD	109.728
	(M)	100.33528

Volume Conversion

To convert volumes, the sequence for converting lengths is used three times. Decimal switch in F position.

Problem	Keyboard Entry	Result
Convert 120 cu yd into cubic meters.	120	120.
	CO NV	120.
	YARD	120.
	(M)	109.728
	CO NV	109.728
	YARD	109.728
	(M)	100.33528
	CO NV	100.33528
	YARD	100.33528
	(M)	91.74658

Typical Volume Calculation

Decimal switch in F position.

Problem	Keyboard Entry	Result
Find the volume in cu ft of a box that is 2 ft. 4⅝ in. by 2½ ft. by 8¹³/₁₆ in.	2 [+]	2.
	4 [A/0]	4.
	5 [A/0]	5.
	8 [CO NV]	4.625
	INCH	
	FEET	0.3854166
	[×]	2.3854166
	2 [A/0]	2.
	1 [A/0]	1.
	2 [×]	5.9635415
	8 [A/0]	8.
	13 [A/0]	13.
	16 [CO NV]	8.8125
	INCH	8.8125
	FEET	0.734375
	[=]	4.3794757 cu. ft.

Temperature Conversion

Decimal switch in F position for the following procedure.

Problem	Keyboard Entry	Result
Convert 0°C. to the equivalent in Fahrenheit degrees.	0	0.
	[CO NV]	0.
	(C°)	0.
	(F°)	32.

Weight Conversion

Problem	Keyboard Entry	Result
Convert 8 oz. to equivalent grams.	8	8.
	[CO NV]	8.
	(OZ)	8.
	(GM)	226.79618

Programing Your Own Conversions

Conversions can also be made to units that do not have a built-in constant by using the programmable conversion function. The conversion factor is set up by entering it and depressing [CONV] ([K→]). This stores the factor in a special memory; it will be maintained until changed or until the calculator is turned off. The conversions utilizing this factor are performed using the A and B keys.

Converting between pounds sterling and U.S. dollars is done as follows. The decimal switch is in the 2 position.

Problem	Keyboard Entry	Result
Assume a conversion factor of one pound-sterling = $2.17.	2.17 $\boxed{\substack{\text{CO}\\\text{NV}}}$ K →	2.17 2.17 The conversion factor is now stored. A = pound sterling B = dollars
Example 1: Convert 174 pounds sterling to dollars.	174 $\boxed{\substack{\text{CO}\\\text{NV}}}$ A, B	174. 377.58 Equivalent in dollars.
Example 2: Convert $420 to pounds sterling.	420 $\boxed{\substack{\text{CO}\\\text{NV}}}$ B, A	420. 193.55 Equivalent in pounds sterling.

THE SUMMIT MCC METRIC CONVERTER

The Summit *MCC* is a smaller and less expensive pocket calculator whose capabilities are illustrated in Fig. 10-2. It, too, can operate as a 5-function arithmetic calculator with memory and as a special metric converter capable of performing 18 customary-to-metric conversions and 18 reverse conversions. As shown in the figure, it has two conversion keys. The $\boxed{\leftrightarrow}$ key is used to perform the customary-to-metric conversions, and the sequence $\boxed{\leftrightarrow}$ $\boxed{\leftarrow}$ is used to perform the reverse conversion. In addition, the MCC has a special squaring (U^2) feature for facilitating area conversions and a special cubing (U^3) feature for volume conversions. This is in contrast to the Rockwell converter, which repeats the length factor once for area conversion and twice for volume conversion.

A more detailed discussion of the operating keys and features follows, together with examples of unit conversions extracted from the manufacturer's operating manual.

$\boxed{\%}$ **Percent.** Executes any previous command and displays the result. If the previous command was a multiply, the result will be automatically divided by 100. If the previous command was a divide, the result will be automatically mutiplied by 100.

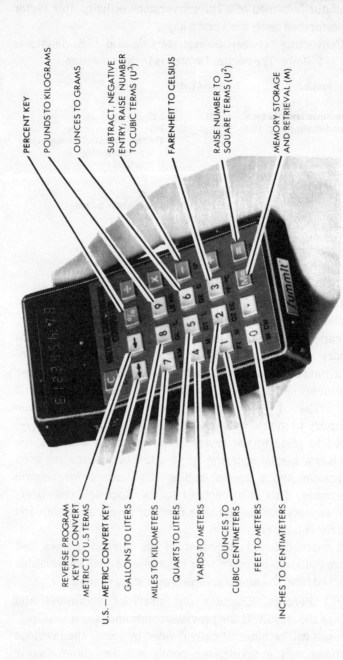

PERCENT KEY

POUNDS TO KILOGRAMS

OUNCES TO GRAMS

SUBTRACT, NEGATIVE ENTRY; RAISE NUMBER TO CUBIC TERMS (U³)

FARENHEIT TO CELSIUS

RAISE NUMBER TO SQUARE TERMS (U²)

MEMORY STORAGE AND RETRIEVAL (M)

REVERSE PROGRAM KEY TO CONVERT METRIC TO U.S TERMS

U.S. – METRIC CONVERT KEY

GALLONS TO LITERS

MILES TO KILOMETERS

QUARTS TO LITERS

YARDS TO METERS

OUNCES TO CUBIC CENTIMETERS

FEET TO METERS

INCHES TO CENTIMETERS

Fig. 10-2. Summit MCC (Metric Conversion Computer).

$\boxed{\text{M} =}$ **Memory Equals.** Normally recalls memory when depressed. It also enters the the display into memory after the $\boxed{=}$ key is pressed.

$\boxed{=}$ **Equals.** Normally executes any previous command and displays the result.

$\boxed{\longleftrightarrow}$**Conversion.** Conditions calculator to convert from customary U.S. to metric measurements.

$\boxed{\longleftarrow}$ **Reverse Conversion.** Conditions calculator to convert from metric to U.S. measurements.

Note: The following keys will be interpreted as conversion keys only during a conversion cycle.

Area Conversion. (U^2) Physically the same as the $\boxed{=}$ key but conditions the calculator to perform the area conversions.

Volume Conversion. (U^3) Physically the same as the $\boxed{+}$ key but conditions the calculator to perform volume conversions.

Conversion Function. Physically the same as the numeric keys. These keys define the units of the conversion, execute the conversion, and display the results. The conversion function for each key is shown just below the key.

SUMMIT MCC CONVERSIONS

The Summit MCC is capable of the following 18 conversions from U.S. metric and vice versa:

Units	Keys
Length	
Inches to centimeters	$\boxed{\longleftrightarrow}$ (INCM)
Feet to meters	$\boxed{\longleftrightarrow}$ (FT M)
Yards to meters	$\boxed{\longleftrightarrow}$ (YD M)
Miles to kilometers	$\boxed{\longleftrightarrow}$ (MI KM)
Area	
Inches^2 to centimeters^2	$\boxed{\longleftrightarrow}$ (U^2)|(IN CM)
Feet^2 to meters^2	$\boxed{\longleftrightarrow}$ (U^2) (FT M)
Yards^2 to meters^2	$\boxed{\longleftrightarrow}$ (U^2) (YD M)
Miles^2 to kilometers^2	$\boxed{\longleftrightarrow}$ (U^2) (MI KM)
Volume	
Inches^3 to centimeters^3	$\boxed{\longleftrightarrow}$ (U^3)|(IN CM)
Feet^3 to meters^3	$\boxed{\longleftrightarrow}$ (U^3) (FT M)
Yards^3 to meters^3	$\boxed{\longleftrightarrow}$ (U^3) (YD M)
Miles^3 to kilometers^3	$\boxed{\longleftrightarrow}$ (U^3) (MI KM)

Units	Keys
Liquid	
Ounces to centimeters^3	[↔] (OZ CC)
Quarts to liters	[↔] (QT L)
Gallons to liters	[↔] (GL L)
Mass	
Pounds to kilograms	[↔] (LB KG)
Ounces to grams	[↔] (OZ G)
Temperature	
°F to °C	[↔] (°F °C)

Note that that the conversion units are put just below the key in exactly the direction in which they will be performed. If you want them to go in the opposite direction, simply push the [←] key. For example, the key [0] converts from inches to centimeters. To convert from inches to centimeters, simply enter the number of inches, push [↔] then push [0]. To convert from centimeters to inches, simply use the same sequence, except push [←] after the [↔] key. Some more simple examples are given later.

Conversion Sequence for Summit MCC

The conversion operation may be initiated at any point in a problem. Where the conversion factors and operations are shown schematically. After the number you want converted is in the display, simply follow the sequence below (refer to the keyboard in Fig. 10-2.) Steps 2 and 3 may not apply to the conversion you are doing. If not, simply leave them out and proceed to the next step. Also, the order of steps 2 and 3 may be reversed if desired. If the wrong key is pushed in step 2 or 3, push the [C] key and start again.

1. Push the [↔] key.
2. Push the (U^2) or the (U^3) key if area or volume conversion is desired. (Parentheses identify operations below a key.)
3. Push the [←] key if metric-to-customary conversion is desired.
4. Push the number key corresponding to the desired conversion units.

SUMMIT MCC CONVERSION EXAMPLES

- How many meters in 100 yd?
  Entry: 1 0 0 ↔ (YD M)   Display: 91.44

- How many yards in 100m?
  Entry: 1 0 0 ↔ ← (YD M)   Display: 109.36132

- How many square miles in 10 km²?
  Entry: 1 0 ← (U²) ← (MI KM)   Display: 3.8610215

- How many cubic centimeters in 5.6 in.
  Entry: 5 • 6 ↔ (U³) (IN CM)   Display: 91.767558

- How much does a 170 lb man weigh in kilograms?
  Entry: 1 7 0 ↔ (LB KG)   Display: 77.112

- How many quarts are in 8 liters?
  Entry: 8 ↔ ← (QT L)   Display: 8.4535319

- If the temperature is 39°C, what is the temperature in Fahrenheit?
  Entry: 3 ⌾ ↔ ← (°F °C)   Display: 102.2

Here is a relatively involved conversion problem: Add the distances 30 mi, 320 mi, 161 km, and 50 mi.

Entry	Display
3 0 +	30.
3 2 0 =	350.
↔ (MI KM)	563.2704
+	563.2704
1 6 1 =	724.2704
↔ ← (MI KM)	450.04076
+	450.04076
5 0 =	500.04076 (mi)
↔ (MI KM)	804.73759 (km)

The answer is approximately 500 mi or 805 km. This same problem can be solved using the memory.

MEMORY—SUMMIT MCC

A single key controls both the storage into and retrieval from memory. The system is very simple: If the = key was pushed immediately prior to the M = key, the number in the display is stored into memory. Any other time the M = key is pushed, the contents of the memory are brought into the display and can be used as an entry.

Example 10-1. The table below illustrates the use of memory in the Summit calculator.

Problem	Key—Operation	Display
Store 2 in memory.	2 $\boxed{=}$ $\boxed{M=}$	2.
Recall 2.	$\boxed{C}$ $\boxed{M=}$	0. 2.
Use the memory as an entry for arithmetic.	$\boxed{C}$ 6 $\boxed{-}$ $\boxed{M=}$ $\boxed{=}$ $\boxed{C}$ 4 $\boxed{\times}$ $\boxed{M=}$ $\boxed{=}$ $\boxed{C}$ 2 $\boxed{+}$ $\boxed{M=}$ $\boxed{=}$	3. 8. 4.
Add 30 mi, 320 mi, 161 km, and 50 mi, using the memory.	30 $\boxed{+}$ 320 $\boxed{=}$ $\boxed{M=}$	30. 350. (in memory)
	$\boxed{C}$ 161 $\boxed{\leftrightarrow}$ $\boxed{\leftarrow}$ $\boxed{+}$ $\boxed{M=}$	100.04076 100.04076 350. (recalled)
	50 $\boxed{=}$	450.04076 500.04076 (mi)
	$\boxed{\leftrightarrow}$ (MI KM)	804.73759 (km)

Note: Pushing the $\boxed{M=}$ immediately after the $\boxed{=}$ replaces the memory with the value in the display. Therefore, I recommend that you use the sequence $\boxed{C}$ $\boxed{M=}$ to recall memory any time there is any question. The memory can be set to zero by turning the calculator off then on, or by the key sequence $\boxed{0}$ $\boxed{=}$ $\boxed{M=}$.

Memory As an Accumulator

Using a simple key sequence, the memory register may be used to accumulate the results of intermediate problems.

2 $\boxed{+}$ 3 $\boxed{=}$ $\boxed{M=}$ (Stores 5 into memory).

3 $\boxed{\times}$ 4 $\boxed{+}$ $\boxed{M=}$ $\boxed{=}$ $\boxed{M=}$ (Stores 17 into memory)

This adds 5 that was in memory to 12 and stores the result back into memory. Note that the first time $\boxed{M=}$ is pushed it recalls the memory and uses it as an entry, and the second time $\boxed{M=}$ is pushed it stores another number back into memory.

Chapter 11

Business Calculators

Thus far we have discussed advanced applications of pocket calculators that are inherently better suited to engineering and scientific problems than commercial problems. Even the special-purpose metric calculators just described are used mostly to convert from one physical system of measurement to another—essentially a scientific application. However, there are at least three pocket calculators especially designed to facilitate calculations in business and finance. These are the Hewlett-Packard HP-80 and HP-70, and the Rockwell 204 *Financier.* Each of these calculators can function as (1) a multipurpose calculator similar to the HP-35 or Rockwell 61SR and (2) as a special-purpose calculator with a variety of preprogramed functions peculiar to business and finance.

Of course, many of the present-value, payment, and interest calculations, which are preprogramed in the business calculators, can be readily solved on any of the scientific calculators which possess an $\boxed{x^y}$, $\boxed{y^y}$ or $\boxed{A^z}$ key.

However, if the great majority of a user's applications are in business and finance, the investment in a special-purpose business calculator may be well worth the price. If only a few calculations are required for personal planning, then any of the more generalized scientific calculators discussed in Chapter 6 will serve the purpose.

Special functions available in business calculators fall into several classes. The broadest category is that of loans and investments, which involve certain common parameters whose values are dependent on the current or expected interest rate. The fundamental relation that governs these quantities is

$$PMT = \frac{P \cdot i}{1 - (1 + i)^{-n}}$$

where PMT = periodic payment; say, monthly
$\quad\quad i$ = periodic interest rate
$\quad\quad P$ = principal amount, or present value
$\quad\quad n$ = total number of periods or payments
Also $F = P(1 + i)^n$ = future value.

Variations of these relations are used to compute data regarding annuities, sinking funds, and mortgages.

Other special functions of interest are the calculation of the time interval between calendar dates, discount and depreciation of notes and capital goods, as well as cash flow and interest amounts of various transactions. Another major application of the business calculator is the calculation of bond transactions and data. These include yield to maturity, bond price, and interest amount.

Other general financial calculations include percentage and net amount, stock and sales trends, and statistical calculations involving mean, variance, and standard deviation of input data such as sales price and quantity of goods. In short, the business calculator runs the gamut from a rather sophisticated mathematical device suitable for hand calculations up to a special-purpose computer dedicated to business transactions. The capabilities listed in Table 11-1 for the Hewlett-Packard HP-80 are typical of this spectrum of business calculator functions.

To illustrate these applications, the Hewlett-Packard HP-80 and HP-70 calculators will be discussed first, followed by the Rockwell 204. You will observe once more that you can trade capability for price, since the HP-70 costs less than the HP-80, and the Rockwell 204 costs less than the HP-70.

HEWLETT-PACKARD HP-80

The HP-80, shown in Fig. 11-1, was the first business calculator to appear on the market. It has the same general

Table 11-1. Financial Functions of HP-80.

Constant storage
Selective roundoff
Percent calculation
Percent difference
Square root
Powers (exponentiation)
Running total (summation)
Mean (arithmetic average)
Standard deviation
Number of days between two dates
Future date, given number of days
Future value of an amount compounded
Present value of an amount compounded
Effective rate of return for compounded amounts
Number of periods for an amount compounded
Future value of an annuity
Present value of an annuity
Effective rate of a sinking fund
Effective rate of a mortgage
Installment of an annuity, given future value
Installment of an annuity, given present value
Number of periods for a sinking fund
Number of periods for a mortage
Add-on to effective annual rate conversion
True equivalent annual rate
Linear regression (trend line) analysis
Sum-of-the-years'-digits depreciation amortization
Rule of 78s finance charge amortization
Discounted cash flow analysis
Accumulated mortgage interest calculation
Remaining principal on a mortgage
Accrued interest (360- and 365-day year)
Discounted notes (360- and 365-day year)
Discounted note yields (360- and 365-day year)
Bond price
Bond yield to maturity

physical appearance and display as the HP-35 or HP-45 and uses the same notation. It also has a gold *function* key, which commands the alternate function printed in gold above the key to be pressed. Keys which have a common application are generally grouped together (see Fig. 11-1). For example, financial keys relating to loans and annuities—such as $\boxed{n}$, $\boxed{i}$, $\boxed{\text{PMT}}$, $\boxed{\text{PV}}$ (present value, or principal), and $\boxed{\text{FV}}$ (future value)—are grouped in the first row. Keys relating to bonds are grouped in alternate functions:

$\boxed{\text{YTM}}$, yield to maturity; $\boxed{\text{INTR}}$, interest; and $\boxed{\text{BOND}}$, bond price. The $\boxed{\text{SAVE} \uparrow}$ key is analogous to the $\boxed{\text{ENTER} \uparrow}$ key in the HP-45. The *compute* function relates to trend line and sum-of-digits calculations, as explained in subsequent examples. Like the HP-45, the HP-80 can select the number of decimals displayed and compute percent change, and mean and standard deviation. The HP-80 also functions as a 200-year calendar; it can compute the number of days between given dates and calculate a date in the future or past which is a given number of days different from the present date.

Figure 11-1, which clarifies the functions of each key, emphasizes the business and financial capabilities of the HP-80. Keys such as $\boxed{\text{STO}}$, $\boxed{\text{RCL}}$, $\boxed{\text{CHS}}$, $\boxed{\sqrt{x}}$, $\boxed{y^x}$, $\boxed{x \gtrless y}$, etc. serve the same purpose as corresponding keys in the HP-35 or HP-45. In general, the HP-80 has the same display and the same physical characteristics as the HP-35 or HP-45.

Calculating Percentage

To avoid confusion relative to percentage problems, the following terms are defined in accordance with those most commonly used by the business community: When finding a fractional part of a given number, the number is called the *base*, the fractional part is called the *rate* or *percent*, and the result is called the *percentage*. When adding the percentage to, or subtracting it from, the base, the result is called the *net amount*.

The HP-80 simplifies the calculation of percentage problems because you don't have to convert percents to their decimal equivalents before using them—just press the $\boxed{\%}$ key after keying in the percent value. Three types of percentage problem are handled:

- Finding percentage of number (base times rate)
- Finding net amount (base plus or minus percentage)
- Finding percent difference between a number and the base (number minus base, divided by base).

Finding Percentage. To find the percentage of a number, enter the base number and press $\boxed{\text{SAVE} \uparrow}$. Then enter the percent and press $\boxed{\%}$. For example, find 14% of $300.

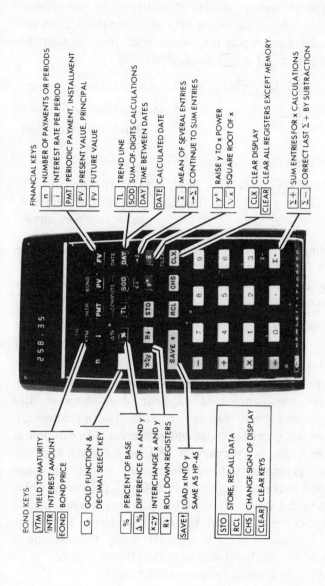

FINANCIAL KEYS

n	NUMBER OF PAYMENTS OR PERIODS
i	INTEREST RATE PER PERIOD
PMT	PERIODIC PAYMENT, INSTALLMENT
PV	PRESENT VALUE, PRINCIPAL
FV	FUTURE VALUE

TL	TREND LINE
SOD	SUM-OF-DIGITS CALCULATIONS
DAY	TIME BETWEEN DATES
DATE	CALCULATED DATE

| x̄ | MEAN OF SEVERAL ENTRIES |
| →Σ | CONTINUE TO SUM ENTRIES |

| yˣ | RAISE y TO x POWER |
| √x | SQUARE ROOT OF x |

| CLX | CLEAR DISPLAY |
| CLEAR | CLEAR ALL REGISTERS EXCEPT MEMORY |

| Σ+ | SUM ENTRIES FOR x CALCULATIONS |
| Σ– | CORRECT LAST Σ + BY SUBTRACTION |

BOND KEYS

YTM	YIELD TO MATURITY
INTR	INTEREST AMOUNT
BOND	BOND PRICE

| G | GOLD FUNCTION & DECIMAL SELECT KEY |

| % | PERCENT OF BASE |
| Δ% | DIFFERENCE OF x AND y |

| x⇄y | INTERCHANGE x AND y |
| R↓ | ROLL DOWN REGISTERS |

| SAVE↑ | LOAD x INTO y SAME AS HP-45 |

STO	STORE, RECALL DATA
RCL	
CHS	CHANGE SIGN OF DISPLAY
CLEAR	CLEAR KEYS

Fig. 11-1. Hewlett-Packard HP-80, programed business calculator. (Same size as HP-35/45.)

215

Entry: 300 [SAVE ↑] 14 [%]   Display $42.00 (percentage)

Finding Net Amount. An additional feature is that after finding the percentage the HP-80 still contains the original base number, from which you may calculate the net amount (such as base price plus tax, or list price less discount) by simply pressing [+] or [−], respectively.

Entry: 300 [SAVE ↑] 14 [%]   Display: $42.00 (percentage)

Entry: [+]   Display: $342.00 (net amount, base plus percentage)

Base *less* percentage is found as follows:

Entry: 300 [SAVE ↑] 14 [%]   Display: $42.00 (percentage)

Entry: [−]   Display: $258.00 (net amount, base less percentage)

Finding Percent Difference Between Any Number and the Base. To find the percent difference between two numbers, enter the base number and press [SAVE ↑]; enter the second number and press Δ%.

Entry: 60 [SAVE ↑] 240 Δ%   Display: 300.00 (240 is 300% greater than 60)

Calculating Time Intervals

Another very useful function involves the [DAY] key. It will determine the number of calendar days between two dates—ranging from January 1, 1900, to December 31, 2099—and will check for range and logic errors. An example of the latter might be February 29, 1973, or February 30 of any year. An erroneous date—whether from a logic or range error—will cause the display to blink. The [DAY] key is used in much the same way as the other function keys, except that the following convention must be observed: Enter the month number; follow it with a decimal point, followed by a 2-numeral day number, followed by the full year number.

May 11, 1973, would be entered as 5.11 1973.

June 3, 1984, would be entered as 6.03 1984.

November 9, 2009, would be entered as 11.09 2009.

Thus, to find the number of days between two dates, simply key in the first date and press [SAVE ↑]; key in the second date and press [DAY]. The answer, shown in days, is ready for other operations or input to another problem. For example, find the exact number of days between December 10, 1974, and March 14, 1976.

Entry: 12.101974 [SAVE] 3.141976 [DAY]   Display: 460.00
                                                         (number of days)

Calculating Future or Past Dates

You can find a future or past date in the range from January 1, 1900, to December 31, 2099, given the number of days, without having to make a calendar search. (You don't need to worry abount whether the year entered is a leap year, as leap year calculations are handled automatically.) The procedure is as follows:

1. If you want the year number to be displayed, set rounding for six decimal places by pressing [G] (gold key) and [6] (number key).
2. Enter the starting date according to the date convention above; press [SAVE ↑].
3. Enter the number of days. (Press [CHS] if you're finding a past date.)
4. Press [G] [DAY].

For example, find maturity date on a 120-day note, issued May 6, 1973.

Entry: [G] 6   Display: 0.000000 (sets decimal)
Entry: 5.06 1973 [SAVE ↑] Display: 9.03 1973
120 [G] Date   (maturity date)

If you want to perform a subsequent date operation on the result in the display, be sure to press [SAVE] first, or you'll get an error. Again, a logic or range error in a date entry will cause the display to blink.

Determining Day of the Week

The day of the week (Monday, Tuesday, etc.) corresponding to future or past dates can be determined as follows:

1. Enter known date and press SAVE ↑.
2. Enter today's date and press DAY SAVE ↑.
3. Enter 7 and press ÷.
4. Enter displayed number (omit decimal portion) and press −.
5. Enter 7 and press × to get day factor.

If known date is in the future, count forward from today by the day factor. For example, if today is Monday and the day factor is 6, the future day would be Sunday. If the known date is in the past, count backwards from today by the day factor.

Suppose today is Monday, January 22, 1973, and you want to find out what day it was when the stock market crashed on October 29, 1929.

Entry: 10.291929 SAVE ↑   Display: 2255.86
1.221973 DAY SAVE ↑ 7 ÷   Display: 6.00 (day factor)
Entry: 2255 − 7 ×

Today is Monday, so count back 6 days to get Tuesday (Black Tuesday, in this case).

Financial Functions

Financial functions are used primarily in investment and loan applications (simple interest, compound interest, annuity, and bond problems). These problems require three known values to get a fourth value. After each value is entered, it is loaded by pressing the applicable key that identifies the value. The fourth value is obtained by pressing the top-row key representing the unknown value. Interest is always an annual rate, unless specified to the contrary.

The key set associated with these functions is shown below (note that SAVE ↑ is not used to load values). The five keys shown below represent 17 functions and replace all the compound interest, discount, bond, and annuity tables commonly in use.

n   i   PMT   PV   FV

Enter values left to right; skip the key that triggers the solution until all values are entered. The meanings of the legends on the special keys are as follows:

n = number of periods (days, months, years, etc.)

i = interest rate per period, expressed as a percent (rather than the decimal equivalent)

PMT = periodic payment or installment portion of an annuity or | sinking fund, or annual coupon rate on bonds

PV = present value or principal; that is, the worth right now

FV = future value after n periods have elapsed

YTM = yield to maturity of a bond

INTR = interest amount

BOND = bond price

When using the top-row financial keys, you may want to store one of the values you are entering for use in subsequent calculations. To do so, just press $\boxed{\text{STO}}$ before (but not *after*—this is an illegal operation) pressing the associated financial key; then proceed with your current financial calculation and recall the stored value, as needed, by pressing $\boxed{\text{RCL}}$.

Interactive Functions

The interactive functions and associated keys are used primarily in applications concerned with constructing and dynamically modifying schedules, charts, and tables; for example:

- Mean and standard deviation, $\boxed{\bar{x}}$ key
- Linear regression (trend line), $\boxed{\text{TL}}$ key
- Sum-of-the-digits amortization, $\boxed{\text{SOD}}$ key
- Interest rebate calculations, $\boxed{\text{INTR}}$

Summation—averaging calculations use the $\boxed{\Sigma+}$ key to sum numbers for use in calculating mean and standard deviations. In addition, the $\boxed{\Sigma+}$ key is used to compute the sum of the squares of all your entries and keeps track of the number of entries you've made. (To see how many entries you've made, simply press $\boxed{x \rightleftarrows y}$. But, before you resume summing, press $\boxed{x \rightleftarrows y}$ again.)

The mean is calculated by pressing $\boxed{\bar{x}}$. The alternate function of this key, $\boxed{\text{G}} \rightarrow \Sigma$, permits you to continue summing, thereby modifying the results of previous mean calculations.

The HP-80 provides an error recovery routine in case incorrect data is entered. To correct your last entry calculation, after pressing $\boxed{\Sigma +}$, reenter the incorrect value and press $\boxed{G}$ $\Sigma -$; you are back where you were before the incorrect entry. Note that a value must be entered prior to each $\boxed{\Sigma +}$ key stroke, or errors will result.

The sum-of-the-digits key, $\boxed{SOD}$, is used to calculate an amortization schedule and related balances for consumer finance charges or depreciation of capital assets.

Amortization on a period-by-period basis, as well as the remaining balance after any given period, can be obtained. Futhermore, you have the option of finding this information at any point in the amortized lifespan and can obtain values for all subsequent periods.

To forecast or estimate trends, you may chart a straight line of best fit through data points across a periodic (daily, weekly, etc.) timespan. This type of analysis is made possible through the $\boxed{TL}$ (trend line) key. The HP-80 calculates the course of a straight trend line by operating on chronologically entered data and then projecting the line to any point.

TYPICAL APPLICATIONS

In the following applications the financial keys are pressed in left to right order to obtain solutions. Some of the applications use interactive and basic keys also. As in ordinary tables, the number of years and interest rate must be converted to reflect the number of compounding periods, if different from those specified. When converting years to periods, multiply the years by the number of compounding periods per year and load the result by pressing $\boxed{n}$. When converting an interest rate to its periodic equivalent, divide the rate by the number of compounding periods per year and load the result by pressing $\boxed{i}$. Then proceed with the calculation.

Future Value of Compounded Amount

This calculation finds the future value of an amount compounded at a certain interest rate over a specified number of periods. Information is entered as follows:

1. Enter number of time periods and press $\boxed{n}$.
2. Enter rate per period and press $\boxed{i}$.
3. Enter principal (present value) and press $\boxed{PV}$.
4. Press $\boxed{FV}$ to obtain the future value.

Example 11-1. What is the future value of $500 invested at 6% for 7 years, if interest is compounded annually?

Key—Operation	Display	Comment
7 $\boxed{n}$ 6 $\boxed{i}$ 500 $\boxed{PV}$ $\boxed{FV}$	$751.82	Value in 7 years.

Example 11-2. What is the future value of the same amount ($500) invested at the same rate (6%) for the same number of years (7), if compounded *quarterly*?

Key—Operation	Display	Comment
7 $\boxed{SAVE}$ 4 $\boxed{\times}$ $\boxed{n}$	28.00	Number of periods (quarters) in 7 years.
6 $\boxed{SAVE}$ 4 $\boxed{\div}$ $\boxed{i}$	1.50	Percent interest rate per quarter.
500 $\boxed{PV}$ $\boxed{FV}$	$758.61	Value in 7 years.

Present Value of Compounded Amount

This calculation finds the present value of a compounded amount when the future value, number of periods, and interest rate are known. Information is entered as follows:

1. Enter number of time periods and press $\boxed{n}$.
2. Enter rate per period and press $\boxed{i}$.
3. Enter future value and press $\boxed{FV}$.
4. Press $\boxed{PV}$ to obtain the present value (principal).

Example 11-3. If you wanted to establish a fund of $15,000 for an extended vacation which you planned to take in 2 years, what would be the investment required now if money is worth 4%, compounded quarterly?

Key—Operation	Display	Comment
2 $\boxed{SAVE}$ 4 $\boxed{\times}$ $\boxed{n}$	8.00	Number of periods (quarters) in 2 years
4 $\boxed{SAVE}$ 4 $\boxed{\div}$ $\boxed{i}$	1.00	Percent interest rate per quarter.
15,000 $\boxed{FV}$ $\boxed{PV}$	$13,852.25	Principal (present value) to be invested.

Number of Periods for Compounded Amount

This calculation finds the number of periods required to amass a given sum at a specified rate on a given investment. Information is entered as follows:

1. Enter rate per period and press $\boxed{i}$.
2. Enter present value and press $\boxed{PV}$.
3. Enter future value and press $\boxed{FV}$.
4. Press $\boxed{n}$ to obtain number of periods.
5. If desired, enter number of periods per year and press $\boxed{\div}$ to convert periods to years.

Example 11-4. You now have $887 in a savings account in your bank, which is paying 5.4%, compounded monthly. How long will it take to reach $1 million?

Key-Operation	Display	Comment
5.4 $\boxed{\text{SAVE}}$ 12 $\boxed{\div}$ $\boxed{i}$ 887 $\boxed{PV}$ 1,000,000 $\boxed{FV}$ $\boxed{n}$	1565.21	Number of months.
12 $\boxed{\div}$	130.43	Number of years.

Although this numerical problem is not realistic, the 10-step solution demonstrates the power of the HP-80 or HP-70. As discussed later, this type of problem requires an iterative routine when using the Rockwell 204. Of course, the number of periods, n, can be easily solved using logarithms, as shown in the example below.

$$n = \frac{\log (FV/P)}{\log(1 + i)}$$

where i is the monthly rate.

In the above example, $FV = 10^6$, $P = 887$, and $i = 0.054/12 = 0.0045$.

$$n = \frac{\log (10^6/887)}{\log (1.0045)} = \frac{\log 1127.40}{\log 1.0045} = \frac{3.0521}{0.00195} = 1565.2 \text{ mo}$$

Future Value of Annuity (Sinking Fund)

This calculation finds the amount to be amassed at the end of a specified number of periods, where the amount of the periodic payment and interest rate per period are known. Information is entered as follows:

1. Enter number of periods and press $\boxed{n}$.
2. Enter interest rate per period and press $\boxed{i}$.
3. Enter amount of periodic payment and press $\boxed{\text{PMT}}$.
4. Press $\boxed{\text{FV}}$ to obtain future value.

Example 11-4. How much money will you have at the end of 5 years if you deposit $250 per month in a savings account, at 6% interest, compounded monthly?

Key—Operation	Display	Comment
12 $\boxed{\text{SAVE}}$ 5 $\boxed{\times}$ $\boxed{n}$	60.00	Number of periods (months) in 5 years.
6 $\boxed{\text{SAVE}}$ 12 $\boxed{\div}$ $\boxed{i}$	0.50	Percent interest rate per month.
250 $\boxed{\text{PMT}}$ $\boxed{\text{FV}}$	$17,442.51	Value in 5 years, compounded monthly.

Payment Amount for Sinking Fund

This calculation finds the periodic payment to be set aside for a sinking fund, when the future value, number of periods, and interest rate per period are known. Enter information as follows:

1. Enter number of periods and press $\boxed{n}$.
2. Enter interest rate per period and press $\boxed{i}$.
3. Enter future value and press $\boxed{\text{FV}}$.
4. Press $\boxed{\text{PMT}}$ to obtain amount of periodic payment for sinking fund.

Example 11-5. Suppose you are planning ahead for your children's education. How much money must be invested each month to amass $10,000 in 10 years, when interest is earned at a rate of 5%, compounded monthly?

Key—Operation	Display	Comment
10 $\boxed{\text{SAVE}}$ 12 $\boxed{\times}$ $\boxed{n}$	120.00	Number of periods (months) in 10 years.
5 $\boxed{\text{SAVE}}$ 12 $\boxed{\div}$ $\boxed{i}$	0.42	Percent monthly interest rate.
10,000 $\boxed{\text{FV}}$ $\boxed{\text{PMT}}$	$64.40	Monthly payment for sinking fund.

Present Value of Annuity

This calculation finds the principal (present value) when the number of periods, interest rate per period, and amount of the periodic payment are known. Information is entered as follows:

1. Enter number of periods and press $\boxed{n}$.
2. Enter interest rate per period and press $\boxed{i}$.

3. Enter amount of periodic payment and press PMT .

4. Press PV to obtain amount of principal (present value).

Example 11-6. If you decide to buy a car for which you plan to pay $80 per month for 36 months, and you are willing to pay 6% annual interest, how much can you afford to pay for the car?

Key—Operation	Display	Comment
36 n 6 SAVE 12 ÷ i 80 PMT PV	$2629.68	Amount you can pay for car.

Bond Price

This calculation finds the exact price of a bond, based on the actual number of days, when the purchase date, maturity date, effective yield-to-maturity rate, and coupon rate are known. Enter the information as follows:

1. Enter the settlement (or purchase) date (1-or 2-numeral month, decimal point, 2-numeral day, and 4-numeral year); press SAVE .

2. Enter maturity rate and press i .

4. Enter annual coupon rate and press PMT .

5. Press G then PV to obtain the price of the bond.

Example 11-7. A bond was purchased January 23, 1973, (coded 1.23 1973), and will mature March 6, 1978, (coded 3.06 1978), and has a coupon rate of 4½% and a yield of 3.22% maturity. What is its price?

Key—Operation	Display	Comment
1.231973 SAVE 3.061978 DAY 3.22 i 4.5 PMT G PV	105.99	Bond price (percentage).

Bond Yield

This calculation finds the yield to maturity (in percent) of a bond, when the purchase date, maturity date, coupon rate, and price (percentage) are known. Information is entered as follows:

1. Enter settlement date (1- or 2-numeral month, decimal point, 2-numeral day, and 4-numeral year); press SAVE .

2. Enter maturity date (according to above convention) and press $\boxed{\text{DAY}}$.
3. Enter annual coupon rate and press $\boxed{\text{PMT}}$.
4. Enter price (present value) of the bond and press $\boxed{\text{PV}}$.
5. Press $\boxed{\text{G}}$, then YTM, to obtain the effective annual yield to maturity.

Example 11-8. What is the yield to maturity of a bond purchased January 23, 1973, at a price of 106, that matures March 6, 1978, and has a coupon rate of 4½%?

Key–Operation	Display	Comment
1.231973 $\boxed{\text{SAVE}}$ 3.061978 $\boxed{\text{DAY}}$ 4.5 $\boxed{\text{PMT}}$ 106 $\boxed{\text{PV}}$ $\boxed{\text{G}}$ $\boxed{i}$ YTM	3.22	Percent effective annual yield to maturity.

Mean and Standard Deviation

This calculation finds the mean (arithmetic average) and standard deviation (measure of dispersion around the mean). Options are provided to enable you to interact with and modify results by adding new data or correcting data entry errors. In addition, the number of entries and sum of the squares can be obtained. Information is entered as follows:

1. Press $\boxed{\text{G}}$ CLx to assure the HP-80 is clear of previous data.
2. Key in values successively until all are entered; press $\boxed{\Sigma+}$ after each entry. To correct an incorrect value after it is loaded, correct by reentering incorrect value, press $\boxed{\text{G}}$ $\Sigma -$, enter correct value, press $\boxed{\Sigma+}$, and continue entering values. The last $\boxed{\Sigma+}$ pressed provides the sum of all entries.
3. Press $\boxed{\bar{x}}$ to obtain mean.
4. Press $\boxed{x \overset{\rightarrow}{\leftarrow} y}$ to obtain standard deviation.

The following option enables you to obtain the sum of squares and sum of entries, as well as the mean and standard deviation:

1. Perform steps 1, 2, and 3 above.
2. Press $\boxed{\text{R}\downarrow}$ to obtain standard deviation.
3. Press $\boxed{\text{R}\downarrow}$ to obtain the sum of squares.
4. Press $\boxed{\text{R}\downarrow}$ to obtain the number of entries.

Sample Case: In a recent survey to determine the average age of the 10 wealthiest people in the U.S., the following ages were obtained:

62 84 47 58 68 60 62 59 71 73

Of the ages given, what is the mean and the standard deviation?

Example 11-9.

Key—Operation	Display	Comment
62 [Σ+] 84 [Σ+] 47 [Σ+] 58 [Σ+]		
60 [Σ+] 62 [Σ+] 59 [Σ+] 71 [Σ+]	644.00	Sum of numbers.
[x̄]	64.40	Mean.
[x⇄y]	10.10	Standard deviation

The same example was solved in Chapter 8, using the HP-45. The only difference is that the HP-80 uses the [x̄] key directly, and the HP-45 uses the gold key followed by the [x̄] key.

Sum-of-the-Year's-Digits Depreciation

This calculation finds the depreciation and remaining depreciable value for each year of an asset's present value (less salvage value) are known.

Example 11-10. A fleet car has a value (less salvage value) of $2100 and a life expectancy of 6 years. Using the sum-of-the-year's-digits method, what is the amount of depreciation, and what is the depreciable value for each of the first 2 years?

Key—Operation	Display	Comment
1 [n] 6 [n] 2100 [PV] [G] [SOD]	$ 600.00	First-year depreciation.
[x⇄y]	$1500.00	Remaining value.
[x⇄y] [SOD]	$ 500.00	Second-year depreciation.
[x⇄y]	$1000.00	Remaining value.

Example 11-11. Using the values from example 11-10, what is the depreciation and depreciable value for years 3 through 6?

Key—Operation	Display	Comment
3 [n] 6 [n] 2100 [PV] [G] [SOD]	$400.00	Year 3 depreciation.
[x⇄y]	$600.00	Remaining value.
[x⇄y] [SOD]	$300.00	Year 4 depreciation.
[x⇄y]	$300.00	Remaining value.

Key—Operation	Display	Comment
x⇄y SOD x⇄y	$200.00 $100.00	Year 5 depreciation. Remaining value.
x⇄y SOD x⇄y	$100.00 $ 0.00	Year 6 depreciation. Remaining value.

Annual Percentage Rate of Interest on Installment Loans

Just as in investment calculations, the following loan application uses the financial (top row) keys, pressed in left-to-right order, for primary entries. In some cases, basic keys, as well as interactive keys, are used. Again, the number of years and interest rates must be converted to reflect the number of compounding periods if different from those stated.

This calculation finds the true annual interest rate of a loan, when the number of periods, amount of each payment, number of installments, and principal are known. The information is entered as follows:

1. Enter number of installments and press n .
2. Enter amount of each installment and press PMT .
3. Enter principal and press PV .
4. Press i to obtain rate of interest per installment.
5. Enter number of installments per year and press × to obtain effective annual rate of interest.

Example 11-12. If you borrow $850 to be repaid in 52 equal weekly installments of $20 each, what is the annual percentage rate of interest?

Key—Operation	Display	Comment
52 n 20 PMT 850 PV i	0.79	Percent weekly interest rate (rounded to two decimal places).
52 x	41.12	Percent annual percentage rate.

This calculation, which takes only nine steps on the HP-80 or HP-70, cannot be solved directly on the Rockwell 204. However, the interest rate is generally known or specified in advance, so that this type of problem occurs infrequently.

Linear Regression Trend Line Analysis

Linear regression techniques are used typically for projecting events based upon an extrapolation from a known trend. The formula uses the constant storage location; therefore, any value stored there will be destroyed when the final key (the one that triggers the result) is pressed. Input data must be evenly spaced and in chronological sequence. Information is entered as follows:

1. Press $\boxed{G}$ CLx to clear machine of existing data.
2. Enter successive values and press $\boxed{TL}$ after each; the entry sequence number is displayed after each entry.
3. After all data is entered (after last $\boxed{TL}$) press $\boxed{G}$ $\boxed{TL}$ to obtain the so-called y-intercept value at point 0, the point at which the trend line intersects the vertical axis (representing given units of quantity).
4. Enter number of time period (any time value) and press $\boxed{n}$.
5. Press $\boxed{TL}$ to obtain trend line value.
6. Repeat step 5 to obtain each successive trend value per time unit, or go back to step 4 to find the values for a unique time position.

Note: *Time position* can be seen at any time by pressing the $\boxed{x \leftrightarrows y}$ key; (be sure to press $\boxed{x \leftrightarrows y}$ again before resuming). The *slope* (change in units of quantity per time period) of the trend line may be found by pressing $\boxed{R\downarrow}$ $\boxed{R\downarrow}$.

Example 11-13. Sales figures for 6-month period are:

Month	Sales
	Thousands of Dollars
1	476
2	589
3	570
4	625
5	619
6	570

Generate a linear trend forecast of the second 6 months' sales level, based on the first 6 months' sales. How many entries are there? Find the theoretical forecast values for the second 6 months.

Key—Operation	Display	Comment
$\boxed{G}$ CLx		
476 $\boxed{TL}$ 589 $\boxed{TL}$ 570 $\boxed{TL}$ 625 $\boxed{TL}$ 619 $\boxed{TL}$		
570 $\boxed{TL}$	6.00	Number of entries.
$\boxed{G}$ $\boxed{TL}$	\$513.33	Value of sales trend line at month.
7 $\boxed{n}$ $\boxed{TL}$	\$636.33	Extrapolated sales at month 7.
$\boxed{TL}$	\$653.90	Extrapolated sales at month 8.

HEWLETT PACKARD HP-70

Hewlett-Packard recently announced a new simplified business calculator, HP-70 (Fig. 11-2). It is modeled after the more powerful HP-80 but is simpler to use and more flexible in operation. It retains the more commonly used features of the HP-80 at a considerably lower price. In particular, it features the preprogramed compound interest keys ($\boxed{n}$, $\boxed{i}$, $\boxed{PMT}$, $\boxed{PV}$, $\boxed{FV}$). In addition, it has available two separate addressable memories, the $\boxed{K}$ and $\boxed{M}$ keys, which can be used to store constants or intermediate results during a calculation. In common other Hewlett-Packard models, it features reverse Polish notation and an operational stack for data manipulation.

The HP-70 is capable of solving most of the common problems in general business, financial management or lending, borrowing, and saving applications. However, it does lack some of the more sophisticated capabilities of the HP-80. These include:

- A 200-year calendar
- Statistical capabilities, including mean, standard deviation and trend line
- A complete set of bond calculations, including solution for yield
- Sum-of-the-year's-digits depreciation
- Rule-of-78 rebate

The instruction manual for the HP-70 shows how problems in the last four categories can be solved using straightforward routines. Refer to the manufacturer's manual for additional information.

ROCKWELL 204

The Rockwell 204 *Financier* can serve as either a general-purpose calculator or as a special-purpose business

Fig. 11-2. Hewlett-Packard HP-70 business calculator.

calculator. As an arithmetic calculator, it behaves like the Rockwell 20R, discussed in Chapter 1. Hence only business-oriented or special applications will be discussed in these sections.

The basic capabilities of the Rockwell 204 are shown in Fig. 11-3. Like the HP-80, it has preprogramed functions for various business and financial applications. These include present- and future-value, interest, loan-payment,

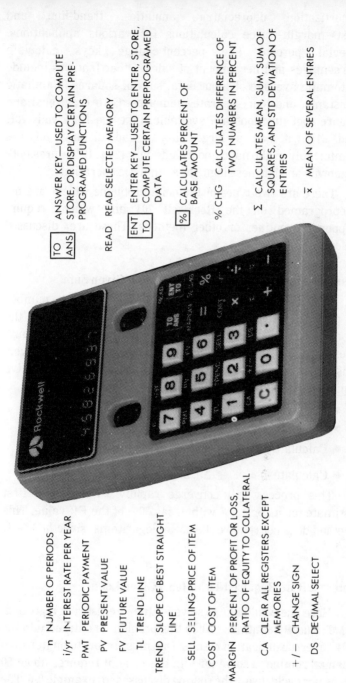

Fig. 11-3. Rockwell 204 Financier pocket calculator.

n NUMBER OF PERIODS

i/yr INTEREST RATE PER YEAR

PMT PERIODIC PAYMENT

PV PRESENT VALUE

FV FUTURE VALUE

TL TREND LINE

TREND SLOPE OF BEST STRAIGHT LINE

SELL SELLING PRICE OF ITEM

COST COST OF ITEM

MARGIN PERCENT OF PROFIT OR LOSS, RATIO OF EQUITY TO COLLATERAL

CA CLEAR ALL REGISTERS EXCEPT MEMORIES

+/− CHANGE SIGN

DS DECIMAL SELECT

TO ANS ANSWER KEY—USED TO COMPUTE STORE, OR DISPLAY CERTAIN PRE-PROGRAMED FUNCTIONS

READ READ SELECTED MEMORY

ENT TO ENTER KEY—USED TO ENTER, STORE, COMPUTE CERTAIN PREPROGRAMED DATA

% CALCULATES PERCENT OF BASE AMOUNT

% CHG CALCULATES DIFFERENCE OF TWO NUMBERS IN PERCENT

Σ CALCULATES MEAN, SUM, SUM OF SQUARES, AND STD DEVIATION OF ENTRIES

x̄ MEAN OF SEVERAL ENTRIES

amortization, depreciation, annuities, trend-line, and cost—margin—price calculations for various applications. Special percent and percent-change keys calculate percentages and net amount of sales. Other features include automatic average of input data, sum of squares, automatic constants, and four separate memories. Both reciprocal and square root functions are available. Like the Rockwell 20R and 61R, it has a large easy-to-read display yet fits comfortably in the hand and weighs only 12 oz. It features both algebraic and business logic for arithmetic operations.

There are two types of financial problems which are not preprogramed on the Rockwell 204 and which require supporting routines or other methods. These are discussed below.

Number of Periods Required To Amass a Given Sum

In such a problem one would like to solve for n, the number of periods, given i, P, and FV. This cannot be done on the Rockwell 204, because the P and FV entries must use the same memory, and different values cannot be entered. However, this problem can be solved on the 204 by using iterative equations as follows:

- Start with an initial estimate for n; say, n_o.
- Calculate $\Delta F = FV - P(1 + i)n_o = FV - F$.
- Calculate $\Delta n = \dfrac{\Delta F}{Fln\,(1 + i)} \simeq \dfrac{\Delta F}{F \cdot ln}$
- Calculate $n_1 = n_o + \Delta n$, and repeat.

This process will converge rapidly with a good first estimate for n_o, or a ΔF within, say 30% of the FV value. This method does not require the use of logarithms, since $ln(1 + i) \simeq i$.

Interest Rate Required To Match a Given Loan

Here one would like to solve for the interest rate i, given n, PMT, and P quantities. When this problem is entered into the 204, an error indication results. One must resort to an iterative manual routine to solve for i. In this case, it requires about 50 steps per cycle, using the routine discussed in example 9-6. The operator gets a good first estimate for i by repeated trials, using the preprogramed functions of the 204, and then makes a final correction with the iteration routine. Fortunately, the interest rate is generally known in advance, so that this type of problem occurs rather seldom.

Addition and Subtraction—Logic Selection

Addition and subtraction may be performed in either business or algebraic logic. The selection is made by placing the switch at the right in the appropriate position. The example $7 + 8 - 9 = 6$ illustrates the two types of logic.

Key—Operation

Business Logic	Algebraic Logic	Display
7 $\boxed{+}$	7	7
8	$\boxed{+}$ 8	8
$\boxed{+}$	$\boxed{-}$	15
9	9	9
$\boxed{-}$	$\boxed{=}$	6

Note that business logic requires that the sign associated with a number be entered after the number. In algebraic logic, number entries are made in the same way an algebra problem would be stated, i.e.: $7 + 8 - 9 = 6$. In business logic, depression of the $\boxed{+}$ or $\boxed{-}$ key performs the operation indicated and displays the answer. In algebraic logic, depression of either of these keys performs the operation indicated by the most recently depressed arithmetic function key and sets up the next operation. Depression of the $\boxed{=}$ key completes the sequence by performing the operation commanded by the last function key depressed.

The logic selection switch affects only addition, subtraction, mixed calculations, repeat and constant multiplication, and automatic markup or discount operations.

Percentage Calculations

Multiplication or division by a percentage is performed by using the $\boxed{\%}$ key in place of the $\boxed{=}$ key. The results of a multiplication are automatically divided by 100, and the results of a division are automatically multiplied by 100. For example, solve $50 \times 30\% = 15$.

Entry: 50 $\boxed{\times}$ 30 $\boxed{\%}$ Display: 15

Or, for another example, solve 32/40% = 80.

Entry: 32 $\boxed{\div}$ 40 $\boxed{\%}$ Display: 80

Automatic Mark up or Discount

An amount can be automatically marked up or discounted a specified percentage.

Example 11-14. Discount an item costing $19.95 by 15% and then add 5% sales tax.

Key—Operation		Display	Comment
Business Logic	**Algebraic Logic**		
19.95	19.95	19.95	
$\boxed{\times}$ 15	$\boxed{-}$ 15	15.	
$\boxed{\%}$	$\boxed{\%}$	2.99	Discount.
$\boxed{-}$	$\boxed{=}$	16.96	Discounted amount.
$\boxed{\times}$ 5	$\boxed{+}$ 5	5.	
$\boxed{\%}$	$\boxed{\%}$	0.85	Tax.
$\boxed{+}$	$\boxed{=}$	17.81	Net price.

Advanced Operations—Rockwell 204

Secondary or alternate function designators are indicated above all keys except $\boxed{\text{TO ANS}}$. The secondary function is made operative by a prior depression of either the $\boxed{\text{ENT TO}}$ or $\boxed{\text{TO ANS}}$ key. For convenience in the following examples the $\boxed{\text{TO ANS}}$ key will be replaced by $\boxed{\text{ANS}}$, and the $\boxed{\text{ENT TO}}$ key will be replaced by $\boxed{\text{ENT}_i}$.

Example 11-15. Round the results of ⅔ to four, then six decimal places.

Key—Operation	Display
2	2.
$\boxed{\div}$ 3	3.
$\boxed{=}$	0.67
$\boxed{\text{ANS}}$ or $\boxed{\text{ENT}}$	0.67
(DS)	0.67
4	0.6667
$\boxed{\text{ANS}}$ or $\boxed{\text{ENT}}$	0.6667
(DS)	0.6667
6	0.666667

Decimal Selection

Unless commanded otherwise, the Rockwell 204 will provide results rounded to two decimal places. To select any other number of decimal places from zero to seven, simply depress either the [ANS] or [ENT] key, then the [DS] (decimal select) key, then the number of decimal places desired. The decimal selection remains set until a change is commanded or the machine is turned off.

Change of Sign

To change the sign of a displayed number, depress either the [ENT] or the [ANS] key, followed by the (+ / −) key.

Square Root

To calculate a square root of a displayed number, depress either the [ENT] or the [ANS] key, followed by the $\sqrt{x}$ key. If the negative indicator is lit, the condition is ignored by the Rockwell 204, and the square root of the absolute value is computed.

Example 11-16. Find the square root of 2 to five decimal places.

Key—Operation	Display	Comment
2	2.	
[ENT] or [ANS]	2.	
($\sqrt{x}$)	1.41	Answer rounded to two
[ENT] or [ANS]	1.41	decimal places.
(DS)	1.41	
5	1.41421	Answer rounded to five decimal places.

Memory Operations

The Rockwell 204 has four memories, designated A, B, N, and I. These memories are accessed through use of financial, margin, or trend line calculation keys, and they are also modified by the Σ key. Four types of operations can be performed on these memories:

Store—Replace the contents of the memory with the displayed number.

Accumulate—Add the displayed number or a function of the displayed number to the contents of the memory.

Read—Cause the contents of the memory to be displayed.

Clear—Store zero in the memory.

The memory access keys are labeled to facilitate their use in financial calculations. However, these keys can be used for any problem requiring temporary storage of a result while other portions of a problem are solved.

Table 11-2. Memory Access Keys.

Memory A		Memory N	
(TREND)	Store or read.	(Limited to whole numbers of four digits or less.)	
(SELL)	Store or read.	(n)	Store or read.
(PMT)	Store or read.	(Σ)	Adds 1 and displays the
(Σ)	Accumulate only.		result.
(CA)	Clear all memories.	(CA)	Clear all memories.

Memory B		Memory I	
(TL)	Store or read.	(i)	Store or read.
(PV)	Store or read.	(i/yr)	Store or read 12i.
(FV)	Store or read.	(CA)	Clear all memories.
(COST)	Store or read.		
(Σ)	Add the square of the		
	displayed number.		
(CA)	Clear all memories.		

To store a displayed number in one of the memories, depress the [ENT] key, followed by the appropriate memory key. To display the contents of a memory, depress the [ENT] and READ keys, followed by the appropriate memory. To accumulate (add) to memory A, depress the [ENT] key, followed by the Σ key.

Example 11-17. Solve $(13 \times 19) + (8 \times 21) + 17^2 = 704$ (accumulating in memory A).

Key–Operation	Display	Comment
[ANS] (CA)	0	Clears all memories.
13	13	
[×] 19	19	
[=]	247	
[ENT] (Σ)	1	
8	8	247 in memory A, 1 in
[×] 21	21	memory N.
[=]	168	
[ENT] (Σ)	2	415 in memory A, 2 in
		memory N.
17	17	
[×] [=]	289	
[ENT] (Σ)	3	704 in memory A, 3 in
		memory N.
[ENT] (READ) (PMT)	704	Displays contents of memory A.

Financial Operations—Rockwell 204

The basic compound interest and annuity (loan amortization or sinking fund) formulas are programed into the

Rockwell 204. This feature makes possible rapid solution of problems involving money invested or borrowed at interest.

The problem variables are entered by depressing the ENT key, followed by the key with the appropriate secondary function designator, where

n = number of periods over which interest is compounded
i = interest rate per period
i/yr = annual interest when n is in months (equals $12i$)
PMT = payment per period (n)
PV = present value
FV = future value

These variables can be entered in any order. After the known variables have been entered, the answer is obtained by depressing the ANS key, followed by the key with the secondary function designator for the unknown variable. This key sequence performs a calculation which depends on the variables entered.

Example 11-18. You borrow $3200 to finance the purchase of a new automobile. The annual percentage rate is 10.8%, and you want to repay the loan in 36 months. What are your monthly payments and last payment?

Key—Operation	Display	Comment
3200 ENT (PV)	3200.	
10.8 ENT (i/yr)	10.8	
36 ENT (n	36.	
ANS PMT)	104.46	Monthly payment (answer).
104.46 ENT (PMT)	104.46	
ANS (i)	560.60	Total interest paid.
ENT (READ) (PV)	0.04	Balance after 36th payment of $104.46.
+ ENT (READ) (PMT)	104.46	
Algebraic =		
Business +	104.50	The last payment would be $104.50.

Example 11-19. You wish to accumulate a $12,000 college fund for your child, who will enter college in 15 years. Your expected annual rate of return is 8%. How much should you invest monthly?

Key—Operation	Display
12000 [ENT] (FV)	12,000.
15	15.
[×] 12	12.
[=]	180.
[ENT] (n)	180.
8 [ENT] (i/yr)	8.
[ANS] (PMT)	34.68

Example 11-20. Under the terms of a life insurance settlement, you are to be paid $50 per month for 20 years, or you may elect to receive a lump sum (commuted value) based on a $3\frac{1}{2}\%$ annual interest rate. What is the amount of the lump sum?

Key—Operation	Display
50 [ENT] (PMT)	50.
20	20.
[×] 12	12.
[=]	240.
[ENT] (n)	240.
3.5 [ENT] (i/yr)	3.5
[ANS] (PV)	8621.34

Example 11-21. Your $25,000, 30-year home mortgage bears interest at a $7\frac{1}{2}\%$ annual rate, and payments are $175 per month. Find the interest portion of the first and second payments and the principal balance after these payments.

Key—Operation	Display	Comment
25,000 [ENT] (PV)	25,000.	
7.5 [ENT] (i/yr)	7.5	
175 [ENT] (PMT)	175.	
1 [ENT] (n)	1.	
[ANS] (i)	156.25	1st month interest.
[ENT] (READ) (PV)	24,981.25	Balance after 1st payment.
[ANS] (i)	156.13	2nd month interest.
[ENT] (READ) (PV)	24,962.38	Balance after 2nd payment.

With $n = 1$, the entire amortization table can be generated in this manner. To generate an annual amortization table, set $n = 12$ and perform the same key sequence.

Margin Operations

The relationship between cost, selling price, and margin is calculated according to the formula

$$\text{margin} = \frac{\text{sell} - \text{cost}}{\text{sell}} \times 100$$

Any of the three variables can be calculated by entering the two known variables (in any order) into the appropriate memory, by depressing the [ENT] key followed by the key with the desired secondary-function designator, then depressing the [ANS] key followed by the secondary-function designator for the unknown variable.

Example 11-22. An item which sells for $11.95 costs the retailer $8.42. What is the margin?

Key—Operation	Display	Comment
11.95 [ENT] (SELL)	11.95	
8.42 [ENT] (COST)	8.42	
[ANS] (MARGIN)	29.54	Answer in percent.

Securities

The securities industry defines margin as the ratio of equity to collateral required to purchase or hold a security. That is,

$$\text{margin} = \frac{\text{equity}}{\text{collateral}} \times 100 = \frac{\text{collateral} - \text{debt}}{\text{collateral}} \times 100$$

For purposes of margin calculation in the securities industry, collateral (stock value) is entered using the (SELL) key, and debt is entered using the (COST) key.

Example 11-23. Federal Reserve Board initial margin requirements are 65%. You own securities with a market value of $8000. How much can be borrowed, using these securities for collateral?

Key—Operation	Display
8000 [ENT] (SELL)	8000.
65 [ENT] (MARGIN)	65.
[ANS] (COST)	2800.

Bond Value Calculation—Compound Discount Method

To determine the price of a bond providing a given yield to maturity, the face value and interest payments must be discounted at the required yield to maturity and summed to determine the present worth.

Example 11-24. A bond which matures in 12 years has a $4\frac{1}{2}\%$ coupon. What price will provide an 8% yield to maturity?

Key—Operation	Display	Comment
4.5 ENT (PMT)	4.5	Annual coupon payment.
12 ENT (n	12.	
8 ENT (i)	8.	
ANS (PV)	33.91	Discounted value of coupon payments.
ENT (PMT)	33.91	33.91 stored into memory A. (Memory A will not be used for the discounted lump sum calculation.)
100 ENT (FV)	100.	Face value of bond entered into memory B.
ANS (PV)	39.71	Discounted value of face amount.
+ ENT (READ) (PMT)	33.91	
Algebraic =		
Business +	73.62	Bond price to yield 8%.

Trend Line Computations

A linear *least square fit* is used by the Rockwell 204 to extrapolate a trend from available data. The extrapolation assumes (1) that the trend is linear (can be approximated by a straight line) and (2) that the straight line which provides the best extrapolation is the one which differs from the available data points in such a way that the sum of the squares of the difference from each of the data points is minimized (see Fig. 11-4). The calculator has been programed to define the line $y = a_0 + a_1 n$.

To clear the memories of prior data, the first data entry must be preceded by depression of the ANS and (CA) keys in succession. Each data point entry is then followed by depression of the ENT and TL keys. Following this key

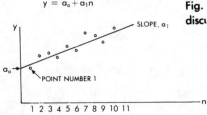

$y = a_0 + a_1 n$

Fig. 11-4. The graph of a trend, discussed in the text.

SLOPE, a_1

a_0

POINT NUMBER 1

1 2 3 4 5 6 7 8 9 10 11

sequence, the number of the data point (n) entered is displayed. Upon completion of data entry, the trend line calculation is performed by the key sequence below.

Key—Operation	Display	Comment
ANS (TL) The following calculations can then be made:	a_0	Intercept.
ANS (TREND)	$y_n + 1$	Extrapolated y for one point beyond the last data point entered.
n ENT (n) ANS (TREND)	y_n	Extrapolated y for any point n.
ENT (READ) (TREND)	a_1	The slope of the line.
ENT (READ) (TL)	a_0	Intercept.

Note: All data points must be equally spaced and begin with point No. 1.

Example 11-25. Sales of an item, which is uninfluenced by seasonal variations, have been 119, 123, 122, 125, 130, 128, 132, and 135 units over the last 8 months.

- What are the projected sales for the ninth month?
- What are the projected sales for the 18th month?
- What is the projected monthly increase in sales (slope of the line)?

Key—Operation	Display	Comment
ANS (CA) 119	0. 119.	Clears all memories. First sale.
ENT (TL) 123	1. 123.	Second sale.
ENT (TL) 122	2. 122.	
ENT (TL) 125	3. 125.	
ENT (TL) 130	4. 130.	
ENT (TL) 128	5. 128.	
ENT (TL) 132	6. 132.	

Key—Operation	Display	Comment
ENT (TL)	7.	
135	135.	Last sale.
ENT (TL)	8.	
ANS (TL)	117.11	The intercept (expected sales in month 0).
ANS (TREND)	136.39	Projected sales for 9th month.
18	18.	
ENT (n)	18.	
ANS (TREND)	155.68	Projected sales for 18th month.
ENT (READ) (TREND)	2.14	Slope (projected monthly increase in sales).

Chapter 12

Programmable
Pocket Calculators

Programmability is the latest advance in the technology for pocket calculators. Simply defined, programmability is the calculator's ability to "learn," "remember," and automatically execute the key stroke sequence required to solve a given class of problems. The value of this feature becomes clearer when we consider that most of us who routinely work with numbers spend a great deal of time doing the same types of calculations over and over again. No matter whether we're preparing flight plans, surveying construction sites, calculating returns on investment, or designing power supplies, we can all identify repetitive, time-consuming problems which diminish our productivity and frustrate our creative capacity.

Although programmable computers and desktop calculators have been available for some time, their expense, complexity, and nonportability have made them inappropriate or impractical for many tasks. The real significance of the programmable pocket calculators is that they overcome these limitations and let almost anyone enjoy the advantages—speed, accuracy, and convenience—of programmability.

This chapter will discuss two types of portable programmable calculators: the Hewlett-Packard HP-65 fully programmable calculator and the manually programmable Monroe 324—326 calculators.

General Description of the HP-65

The HP-65 (Fig. 12-1) is a powerful device that can be used in three ways: as a scientific calculator, to run a prerecorded program, and to run your own program.

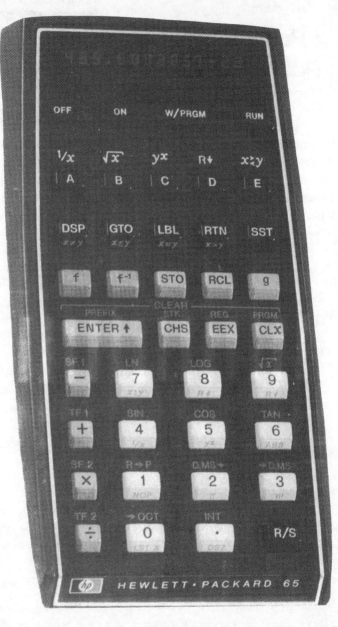

Fig. 12-1. The Hewlett-Packard HP-65 fully programmable scientific calculator.

Scientific Calculations

You control every step of the calculation by pressing keys in the actual order of execution; you enter data, perform functions, store results, control display, etc. by pressing keys. This operation is similar to the operation of the HP-45.

Prerecorded Program

By using prerecorded magnetic cards you can do highly complex calculations with minimal effort or study of the calculator itself. You load a card into the calculator and let the stored program handle the "busy" part of the calculation. Typically, you just key in the data and start the program running. The program stops when it needs more data or when it displays a result.

Running Your Own Programs

To create, record, and execute your own programs, no programing experience is necessary. You can easily define the five top-row keys to calculate functions of your own creation, for use alone or with other programs. Plan your problem in terms of the key strokes needed for calculation and the additional key strokes needed to control the program. Set the mode switch to the W/PRGM position and key sequence into memory. Then record the program for future reentry by merely passing a magnetic card through the calculator. After switching back to RUN, you can execute the stored program.

The main features of the HP-65 are identified in Fig. 12-1. The following sections explain the operations of the special function keys and the programing features of the HP-65.

HP-65 Advanced Scientific Applications

In general, calculations on the HP-65 are done much the same as explained for the HP-45. The calculations are done in an operational stack, and arithmetic operations are done in the same order and combinations.

The HP-65 also has nine addressable memories, which greatly enhances the programing capability of the calculator.

The keyboard operation of the HP-65 differs in that the more special keys are used to select alternate functions. These keys—[f], [f⁻¹], and [g]—are used to extend the capability of a

Table 12-1. Angular Mode Functions.

Keys	Function
g GRD	Set mode to grads.
g RAD	Set mode to radians.
g DEG	Set mode to degrees.

400 grads = 360° = 2π radians
Keys to which angular mode applies:
SIN   COS   TAN   R→P   →DMS

single key to as many as five different functions. For example, pressing the gold f key and the number 9 results in $\sqrt{x}$; pressing the gold f^{-1} key and 9 results in x^2; pressing the blue g key and 9 results in (R↑), which rolls up the values in the operational stack. The 9 key can also be used as the number 9 and, with the STO or RCL key, to address the

Table 12-2. Functions Involving Angles.

Keys	Function
f COS	cos
f^{-1} COS	arc cos
f SIN	sin
f^{-1} SIN	arc sin
f TAN	tan
f^{-1} TAN	arc tan
f R → P	Convert rectangular coordinates (x, y) to polar form (r, θ).
f^{-1} R → P	Convert polar coordinates (r, θ) to rectangular form (x, y).
f → DMS	Convert decimal angle to ddddd.mmss format [1]
f^{-1} → DMS	Convert ddddd.mmss angle to decimal format.
f DMS +	Add x + y in ddddd.mmss format.
f^{-1} DMS +	Subtract x − y in ddddd.mmss format.

[1] ddddd.mmss format: d = degrees, mm = minutes, ss = seconds.

ninth memory register. The combinations of keys and the functions they produce are listed in Tables 12-1 through 12-4. (R↑), which rolls up the values in the operational stack. The 9 key can also be used as the number 9 and, with the STO or RCL key, to address the ninth memory register.

Table 12-3. Conversions of x.

Keys	Function	Input Values	Result
[f] [→OCT]	Convert decimal integer to octal (base 8).	x_{10}, a decimal integer of magnitude less than 1073741824_{10}	x_8 in X
[f⁻¹] [→OCT]	Convert octal integer to decimal (base 10).	x_8, an octal integer *	x_{10} in X
[f] [INT]	Truncate to signed integer.	$\pm$ integer fraction in x	$\pm$ integer.0 in X
[f⁻¹] [INT]	Truncate to signed fraction.	$\pm$ integer fraction in x	$\pm$ 0.fraction in X
[g] [ABS]	Absolute value.	$\pm$ x	If x is negative, change its sign; otherwise, no change.

* As an additional feature, the octal-to-decimal conversion will accept nonoctal arguments containing the digits 8 or 9. A nonoctal number, such as 998, will be interpreted as $(9 \times 8^2) + (9 \times 8) + 8 = 656$.

OTHER EXAMPLES

993_{10} [f] OCT $\longrightarrow$ 1741_8
993_8 [f⁻¹] OCT $\longrightarrow$ 651_{10}
656_8 [f⁻¹] OCT $\longrightarrow$ 430_{10}
656_{10} [f] OCT $\longrightarrow$ 1220_8

RUNNING A PRERECORDED PROGRAM

A built-in magnetic card reader—writer allows a program to be permanently preserved on magnetic cards for future use. By reading such a card, the general-purpose calculator acquires a highly specific capability in a matter of seconds. Some users may wish to use professionally programed cards instead of doing any programing themselves. A set of such cards (called *Standard Pac*) comes with the calculator; special-purpose sets may also be purchased. A card case also is provided with the 19 standard programs, along with a

Table 12-4. Functions of x and the Exponential Function y^x.

Keys	Function	Remarks
[f] LN	Natural logarithm (base e)	Capability same as HP-45 for all functions listed.
[f⁻¹] LN	Natural antilogarithm (e^x)	
[f] LOG	Common logarithm (base 10)	
[f⁻¹] LOG	Common antilogarithm (10^x)	
[f] √x	Square root ($\sqrt{x}$)	
[f⁻¹] √x	Square (x^2)	
[g] 1/x	Reciprocal ($1/x$)	
[g] n!	Integer Factorial (n!) $n! = 1\ 2\ 3...(n-1)\ n$	
[g] y^x	Exponential (y^x)	

Table 12-5. Programs in Hewlett-Packard's Standard Pac.

```
 1. PERSONAL INVESTMENT
 2. MEAN, STANDARD DEVIATION, STANDARD ERROR
 3. GREAT-CIRCLE NAVIGATION
 4. INTEGER BASE CONVERSION
 5. BOYD BODY-SURFACE AREA
 6. PI-NETWORK IMPEDANCE MATCHING
 7. EDM SLOPE REDUCTION (GIVEN ELEVATION)
 8. TEMPERATURE CONVERSION
 9. WEIGHT—MASS CONVERSION
10. VOLUME CONVERSIONS
11. COMPOUND INTEREST
12. LOAN REPAYMENT
13. RECONCILE CHECKING ACCOUNT
14. ITERATIVE SOLUTION OF f(x)
15. QUADRATIC EQUATION
16. AREAS AND SOLUTIONS OF RIGHT TRIANGLE
17. NIMB
18. DIAGNOSTIC I
19. DIAGNOSTIC II
```

head-cleaning card and 20 blank cards for recording programs.

The programs provided vary from general to specialized. Some programs were selected from other sets available through Hewlett-Packard. For example, the pi-network-matching program is from the EE PAC I, and the mean and standard deviation program is from the Stat Pac. The programs in the Standard Pac are shown in Table 12-5.

All of the HP-65's prerecorded programs are described in the instruction book supplied with the calculator. These instructions will be discussed next, followed by several examples of the use of the prerecorded programs to solve problems. This information is presented to aid the reader who is interested in the mechanics of running a program from the user's viewpoint.

HP-65 Prerecorded Programs

All of the HP-65's prerecorded programs are described in the instruction book supplied with the calculator. These instructions will be discussed next, followed by several examples of the use of the prerecorded programs to solve problems.

Format of User Instructions

The user instruction form which accompanies each prerecorded program is a guide to operating the program.

The form is composed of five columns. These are: the instruction step number, instructions and comments concerning the operations to be performed, the input data (and units of data, if applicable), the keys to be pressed, and the output. Data input keys consist of $\boxed{0}$ through $\boxed{9}$ and a decimal point (the numeric keys), $\boxed{\text{EEX}}$ (enter exponent), and $\boxed{\text{CHS}}$ (change sign). The $\boxed{\text{ENTER}}$ key is indicated by a vertical arrow (pointing up). All other key designations are identical to those appearing on the HP-65.

Figure 12-2 illustrates the user instruction form for the *Reconcile Checking Account* program. The steps shown are interpreted as follows:

Step 1. This calls for the entry of the prerecorded magnetic card into the HP-65.

Step 2. This step "initializes" (prepares) the calculator for proper program execution. Pressing the $\boxed{\text{D}}$ key would perform the initialization, in this case, as shown in the instructions.

Step 3. This step stores the statement balance. Press the applicable data input keys, then press $\boxed{\text{A}}$. The statement balance is displayed after program execution ends.

STEP	INSTRUCTIONS	INPUT DATA/UNITS	KEYS		OUTPUT DATA/UNITS
1	Enter program				
2	Initialize		D		0.00
3	Input statement balance	SB	A		SB
4	Repeat 4 for out checks	$C_1 ... C_n$	B		$C_1 ... C_n$
5	Repeat 5 for each outstanding				
	deposit	$D_1 ... D_m$	C		$D_1 ... D_m$
6	Compute final balance		E	A	FB
7	Recall statement balance		R/S		SB
	and/or sum of out checks		E	B	ΣC_i
	and number of checks		R/S		n_c
	and/or sum of out deposit		E	C	ΣD_i
	and number of deposits		R/S		m_D

Fig. 12-2. Instruction form for **Reconcile Checking Account** program. The heavy outline indicates the subroutine that is repeated for each new set of data entries.

Step 4. This step is a repetition instruction, as signified by the bold border enclosing the instructions. To perform step 4, press the applicable data input keys to input the first outstanding-check value. Press [B] to initiate program execution. The check value is still displayed after execution ends. Repeat the procedure for all outstanding checks.

Step 5. This step is also a repetition instruction. Outstanding deposits are the inputs. To perform step 5, press applicable data input keys and press [C]. Repeat the procedure for all outstanding deposits. When all outstanding deposits have been input, go to step 6.

Step 6. This step computes the final balance. Press [E] and then [A] to display the final balance.

Step 7. This step recalls values. Press [R/S] to display bank statement balance. Press [E] and then [B] to compute and display the sum of checks outstanding. Press [R/S] to display the number of checks outstanding. Press [E] and then [C] to compute and display the sum of deposits outstanding. Press [R/S] to display the number of deposits outstanding.

Step 8. This step provides for the inclusion of additional checks and deposits outstanding: For checks, start at step 4; for deposits, start at step 5.

Step 9. This step gives instructions on starting a new case. In this program, go to step 2.

In addition to the general user instruction form, sample problems are provided. These differ from the general user instructions in that they include numeric values instead of variable symbols. Each step number in the sample user instructions corresponds to the step executed in the general instructions.

APPLICATIONS OF PRERECORDED PROGRAMS

Brief descriptions of several preprogramed problems are presented here to enable you to understand how you can use the prerecorded programs. When using standard programs supplied by Hewelett-Packard, the operator functions are limited to the following:

- Entering the program and initializing the execution.
- Entering input data in the proper sequence.

- Recording desired intermediate and final results

The operator of the HP-65 "manages" the calculator. He reads outputs. He does no calculation—that's the job of the machine.

Personal Investment Program

The *Personal Investment Program* was created to allow the user to calculate the growth of a regular monthly savings plan. The program is loaded as shown below.

1. Select the *Personal Investment* card from the card case.
2. Set the W/PRGM—RUN switch to RUN.
3. Insert the card in the lower slot on the right side of the calculator. When the card is partway in, the motor engages and passes the card through the calculator and out the left side. Let it move freely.
4. If the card does not read properly, the display will blink and program memory will be cleared; press $\boxed{\text{RTN}}$ and reinsert the card.
5. Upon completion, insert the card in the upper "window" to identify the top-row keys. You are now ready to use the program.

Example 12-1. Starting on January 1, 1974, you add $100 per month to your savings of $1000 invested at 12% per annum,

Step	Instruction	Input Data—Units	Key	Output Data—Unit
1	Enter *Personal Investment Program*.			
2	Key in start date (January 1974).	1.1974	$\boxed{A}$	0.00
3	Key in present savings ($1000).	1000	$\boxed{\text{ENTER} \uparrow}$	1000.00
4	Key in monthly savings ($100).	100	$\boxed{B}$	1000.00
5	Key in annual interest rate (12).	12	$\boxed{C}$	1000.00
6	Key in future date (September 1975)	9.1975	$\boxed{E}$	3444.11
				Answer

compounded monthly. How much will you have saved on September 1, 1975?

To solve the problem, just follow the instructions given in the standard format below. You read the instructions, line by line, keying in the required input, pressing the indicated keys, and observing the displayed output. The amount saved is displayed after the future date is entered via the $\boxed{E}$ key.

Great-Circle Navigation

This program accepts the coordinates of two points on the globe and calculates the great-circle distance between them, as well as the initial heading.

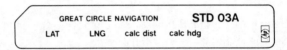

The program inputs are latitude and longitude of the source (lat_s, lng_s), and latitude and longitude of the destination (lat_D, lng_D). (The above are expressed in the notation "degrees *point* minutes"; e.g., 15.30 means 15° 30′.

Northern latitudes are entered as positive values, while southern ones are entered as negative values. Western longitudes are entered as positive values; eastern ones are entered as negative values.

The outputs are great-circle distance (dist) in nautical miles and initial great-circle heading (hdg) in decimal degrees. (You may convert back to degrees, minutes, and seconds by pressing $\boxed{f}$ ($\rightarrow$ DMS).

The applicable formulas are

$$\text{Dist} = \text{arc cos } [\sin(\text{lat}_s) \sin(\text{lat}_D)$$
$$+ \cos(\text{lat}_s) \cos(\text{lat}_D) \cos(\text{lng}_D - \text{lng}_s)] \times 60$$

$$\text{Hdg} = \text{arc cos } \left[\frac{\sin(\text{lat}_D) - \cos(\text{dist}/60) \sin(\text{lat}_s)}{\sin(\text{dist}/60) \cos(\text{lat}_s)} \right]$$

Note: If the sine of ($\text{lng}_s - \text{lng}_D$) is less than 0, then hdg = 360 − hdg.

The general user instructions are shown in Fig. 12-3.

STEP	INSTRUCTIONS	INPUT DATA/UNITS	KEYS		OUTPUT DATA/UNITS
1	Enter program				
2	Initialize		RTN	R/S	0.00
3	Input starting latitude	(deg . min)	A		(dec. deg.)
	and input starting longitude	(deg . min)	B		(dec. deg.)
4	Input destination latitude	(deg . min)	A		(dec. deg.)
	and input destination longitude	(deg . min)	B		(dec. deg.)
5	Calc. Great Circle Dist		C		(naut. miles)
	and/or calc. initial heading		D		(dec. deg.)
6	Go to step 4 to calculate				
	next leg				
7	To reinitialize go to step 2.				

Fig. 12-3. General user instructions for great-circle navigation.

Example 12-2. A navigator wishes to follow great-circle courses from Chicago to St. Louis to New Orleans. Find the great-circle distances and initial courses.

	Latitude	Longitude
Chicago	41° 50′ N	87° 36′ W
St. Louis	38° 38′ N	90° 12′ W
New Orleans	29° 56′ N	90° 04′ W

Note: After entries, the angle in decimal degrees is displayed.
Answers:

$Dist_1 = 225.91$ naut mi, $hdg_1 = 212.66°$

$Dist_2 = 522.04$ naut mi, $hdg_2 = 179.24°$

Step	Instruction	Input Data—Unit	Key	Output Data—Unit
1	Enter program (*Great-Circle Navigation*)			
2	Initialize.		RTN R/S	0.00
3	Input LAT Chicago.	41.50	A	41.83
	Input LNG Chicago.	87.36	B	87.60
4	Input LAT St. Louis.	38.38	A	38.63
	Input LNG St. Louis.	90.12	B	90.20

Step	Instruction	Input Data – Unit	Key	Output Data – Unit
5	Calc. great-circle distance.		C	225.91
	Calc. initial heading.		D	212.66
4	Input LAT New Orleans.	29.56	A	29.93
	Input LNG New Orleans.	90.04	B	90.07
5	Calc. great–circle distance.		C	522.04
	Calc. initial heading.		D	179.24

Loan Repayment Program

Given the term for a direct reduction loan in years, the number of periodic payments per year, and the annual interest rate in percent, this program computes (1) periodic payment amount *if the principal value borrowed is given*, or (2) the principal value *if the periodic payment is given*.

LOAN REPAYMENT			STD 12A	
yrs ♠ per/yr	i%	PV	PMT	CALC(P)

A ½-cent roundoff routine is incorporated, so that the answers are correct to the nearest cent.

The principal value is given by

$$PV = PMT \left[\frac{\left(1 + \dfrac{i}{100n}\right)^{yn} - 1}{\dfrac{i}{100n}\left(1 + \dfrac{i}{100n}\right)^{yn}} \right]$$

where

PV = principal value
PMT = periodic payment
i = annual interest rate in percent
y = number of years
n = number of payment periods per year

Example 12-3. Find the quarterly payment for a 30-year mortgage at 8.75%, with principal amount of $37,500. (Answer: $886.36.)

- What principal value corresponds exactly to the periodic payment calculated? (Answer: $37,499.86.)
- What would the payment be if the interest is 9.25% (Answer: $926.83.)

- At the higher interest, what would the monthly payment be? (Answer: $308.50.)

The answers are found according to the instructions below.

Step	Instruction	Input Data—Unit	Key	Output Data—Units
1	Enter program (*Loan Repayment*).			
2	Input number of years.	30	ENTER ↑	30.00
3	Input payment periods/year.	4	A	120.00
4	Input annual interest.	8.75	B	100.00
5	Input principal value.	37,500	C	37,500.00
6	Calculate payment.		E d	886.36
5	Input payment.		D	886.36
6	Calculate principal value (the difference is due to accumulated ½ cent roundoff)		E C	37,499.86
4	Input new interest.	9.25	B	100.00
6	Calculate payment.		E D	926.83
2	Input number of years.	30	ENTER ↑	
3	Input payment periods/year.	12	A	360.00
6	Calculate payment.		E D	308.50

Iterative Solution of $f(x) = 0$

```
ITERATIVE SOLUTION OF f(x)=0      STD 14A

PARMS    STO x      STO x      f(x)      GO      ⊛
         f(x)+      f(x)−
```

This program performs an iterative solution for the zeros of continuous functions (written in 32 or less program steps) that cross the x axis. To solve a given function, key it in under label D. In addition, provide a value x_1 such that $f(x_1) > 0$, and another value x_2 such that $f(x_2) < 0$. Your function is then used by the iterating routine, "E", to repeatedly evaluate the function, using progressively better approximations. The process continues until a value of x_1 is found such that $f(x_1) < 10^{-6}$ (in which case x_1 is the answer).

The program is especially valuable for solving equations that are not reducible to the form $x = f$ (known values). An example of such an irreducible equation is $ln\ x = ax + b$.

If it is necessary to store the x value so that it can be recalled at several points in the $f(x)$ subroutine, use storage register 5. The parameter a is stored in register 6, b is stored

255

in register 7, and c is stored in register 8. If you do not intend to vary the a, b, and c parameters, it may be convenient to include them as constants in $f(x)$. If this is the case, step 6 of the general user instructions (Fig. 12-4) may be omitted.

Note: If a function crosses the x axis more than once in the interval between x_1 and x_2, this program will find only one of the zero values. Also, if a function crosses the x axis an infinite number of times between x_1 and x_2, the iterative routine may not converge.

The general instructions for solving $f(x) = 0$ using the iterative program are shown below.

GENERAL USER INSTRUCTIONS

STEP	INSTRUCTIONS	INPUT DATA/UNITS	KEYS		OUTPUT DATA/UNITS
1	Enter program				
2	Switch to W/PRGM mode				00 00
3	Single step twice		SST	SST	14
4	Input f(x)				
5	Switch to RUN mode				
6	Input parameters if required by				
	f(x)	c	↑		c
	then	b	↑		b
	then	a	A		c
7	Input x₁ guess	x₁	B		f(x₁)
	If f(x₁) is negative repeat 7 and				
	choose new x₁				
8	Input x₂ guess	x₂	C		f(x₂)
	If f(x₂) is positive repeat 8 and				
	choose new x₂				
9	Compute x		E		x

Fig. 12-4. General user instructions for iterative solution of $f(x) = 0$.

Example 12-4 shows the solution for a specific problem using the above instructions.

Example 12-4. Find the solution to the equation $ln\ x = ax + b$, where $a = -1$ and $b = 3$. First rewrite the equation in the form $(ln\ x) - ax - b = 0$. Now transform the equation into HP-65 code as is shown in step 4 of the instructions below. (Answer: 2.21.)

256

Step	Instruction	Input Data—Unit	Key	Output Data—Unit
1	Enter program (*Iterative Solution of f(x) = 0*).			
2	Switch to w/PRGM mode.			00 00
3	Single-step twice.		SST SST	14
4	Input f(x): (ln|x|) − ax − b = 0.		g	31
			LN	07
			g LST x	35 00
			RCL 6	34 06
			×	71
			−	51
			RCL 7	34 07
			−	51
5	Switch to RUN mode.			
6	Input parameters			
	b	3	ENTER ↑	
	and a.	-1	A	
7	Guess x = 2.	2	B	-0.31
	Answer is not positive.			
	Guess x = 3.	3	B	1.10
8	Guess x = 2.	2	C	-0.31
9	Compute x.		E	2.21

CREATING YOUR OWN PROGRAM

Highly sophisticated calculations can be achieved on the HP-65 by programing sequences of key strokes. Since the calculator is truly programmable—including both branching and testing capability—it is quite possible to set a program to iterate all night. Programs can consist of up to 100 memory locations. In fact, the user can create programs comparable in scope to the recorded programs in the Standard Pac and other Hewlett-Packard program sets.

To create a program, you need to follow these steps:

1. Define the problem.
2. Work out the keying sequence that solves the problem.
3. Add control operations for automatic execution.
4. Key the sequence, including control operations, into program memory.
5. Edit, verify, and record the sequence for later use.
6. Run the sequence, automatically, with your data

To key a program into the machine, you press the successive keys with the switch in the W/PRGM position. Then, by passing an unprotected magnetic card through the lower slot on the right side of the calculator, you can save the program (contents of the 100-step program memory) for future use.

We have seen how the top-row key functions can be defined to a particular use by loading an appropriately prerecorded magnetic card. Using a very simple example, we will now define the $\boxed{A}$ key. We first plan the function, key it into memory, and then test it. If it tests satisfactorily, we will record it on a magnetic card for future use.

Planning the Function

The following key sequence computes x^3 (the cube of whatever value k is in the x register).

T			
Z		k	
Y	k	k	k
X	k	k	k^2 k^3
Key	$\boxed{\text{ENTER} \uparrow}$	$\boxed{\text{ENTER} \uparrow}$	$\boxed{\times}$ $\boxed{\times}$

To make the sequence a function that is callable by the key, we precede the sequence by $\boxed{\text{LBL}}$ $\boxed{A}$ (to identify the function) and conclude the sequence by $\boxed{\text{RTN}}$ (to return control to the keyboard).

Putting the Function in Memory

Set W/PRGM–RUN switch to W/PRGM and press $\boxed{f}$ $\boxed{\text{PRGM}}$ to clear the program memory. Press the keys in the order shown below.

Key	Comment
$\boxed{\text{LBL}}$ $\boxed{A}$	Defines beginning of function $\boxed{A}$.
$\boxed{\text{ENTER} \uparrow}$ $\boxed{\text{ENTER} \uparrow}$ $\boxed{\times}$ $\boxed{\times}$	Calculates x^3.
$\boxed{\text{RTN}}$	Defines the end of function $\boxed{A}$.

The calculator has now "learned" to calculate x^3 when you press $\boxed{A}$ in RUN mode.

Testing the Function

Switch W/PRGM–RUN switch to RUN. Key in a number and press $\boxed{A}$. You should see the cube of the number.

Key	Display	Comment
2 A	8.00	2^3
3 A	27.00	3^3
4 A	64.00	4^3
5 CHS A	125.00	$(-5)^3$

Recording the Function

To record the program; proceed as follows:

1. Select an unprotected magnetic card (edge not cut).
2. Switch to W/PRGM.
3. Pass the card through the lower slot exactly as in loading a program. Provided the card is unprotected, it now contains the program.

In the above example, we left keys B through E undefined. We could have keyed in definitions for them also.

This procedure shows how you can write a program for a simple function and identify it with one of the five user-definable keys. The HP-65 can also be programed without any reference to the top keys. It is easy to create simple functions; and with very little additional effort, you can create functions or other programs of considerable complexity.

Checking the Program

Quite obviously, it is not possible to see the entire program at once; you see one step at a time. Recall that the program memory consists of 100 locations. Above the first location is the top of the memory, which is displayed as [00 00]. Whenever you see this display, you know that the program pointer is at the top.

To see this, turn the calculator off, then on, and switch to W/PRGM. This clears any programs and replaces them with the default programs.

To move the pointer to display the next (first) location, press SST and you will see 23 displayed. Except for the digit keys, the display indicates the row and column of the key that the display represents. Thus, 23 is read as *row 2, column 3*; i.e., LBL. (See Fig. 12-5.)

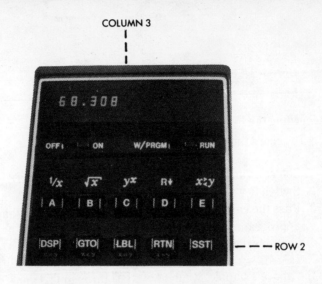

COLUMN 3

----ROW 2

Fig. 12-5. Programing codes LBL = 23.

For ease of recognition, the digit keys 0 through 9 are displayed simply as 00, 01, etc. You can now read the remaining contents of memory.

Key	Display	Comment
	23	represents LBL .
SST	11	represents A .
SST	35	represents g .
SST	04	represents 1/x .
SST	24	represents RTN .

This shows that the first five codes (23, 11, 35, 04, and 24) represent the default function defined for the top-row A key. This function— LBL A g 1/x RTN —does nothing more than compute the reciprocal of x.

In the W/PRGM mode, SST advances the program pointer to the next memory location, displaying the code. Repeated use of the key enables you to review a program and position the pointer for editing.

Note that SST is used also in the RUN mode to execute a program one step at a time. The HP-65 calculator keyboard has control functions built into it which allow the user to control a program he has written to begin and end at predetermined positions, to iterate any number of times, and generally to control the program logic. These functions are used in conjunction with the mathematical function keys to define a complete program and control its execution. The HP-65 has the capability to label steps in the program, to branch to a labeled step, to iterate steps within the program, to jump to the beginning of the program, and to set "flags."

The calculator has two flags (called *flag 1* and *flag 2*) available. A flag is an invisible piece of information with just two possible conditions—on or off. You can set a flag by using the *set flag* operations. These operations can be executed form the keyboard or from a program. The reason for setting a flag is so that a program can later make a decision based on the condition of the flag (using the *test flag* operations).

The HP-65 also allows the programer to edit a program by stepping through the program up to a step which is in error. That single step can then be deleted and replacement step inserted.

When the program is complete and edited, it can be stored on a magnetic card and saved for future use. The capability for permanent storage of programs on magnetic cards is the outstanding advantage of the HP-65.

MONROE[1] 324 PROGRAMMABLE CALCULATOR

The Monroe 324 is a small, programmable calculator which can run on batteries. Although not pocket sized, it is quite small $(5.5 \times 9 \times 2$ in.) and weighs only 3.0 lb. Two independent programs of 80 steps each can be manually entered and automatically executed for each new set of data entered.

This calculator has a full complement of scientific functions, as well as 10 addressable memories. The built-in functional keys are clearly displayed on the face of the calculator (Fig. 12-6). As in many of the other calculators,

---

[1]Earlier models of the 324 and 326 calculators bore the Compucorp label.

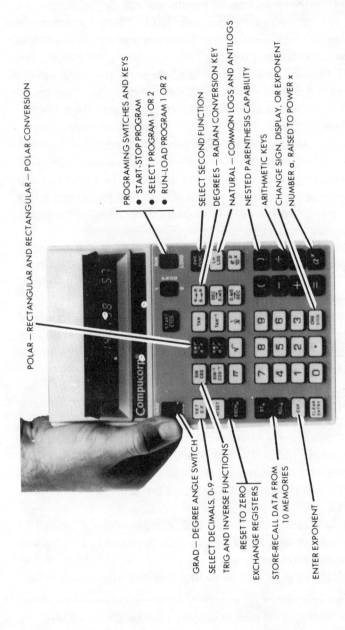

POLAR — RECTANGULAR AND RECTANGULAR — POLAR CONVERSION

PROGRAMING SWITCHES AND KEYS
- START-STOP PROGRAM
- SELECT PROGRAM 1 OR 2
- RUN-LOAD PROGRAM 1 OR 2

SELECT SECOND FUNCTION

DEGREES — RADIAN CONVERSION KEY

NATURAL — COMMON LOGS AND ANTILOGS

NESTED PARENTHESIS CAPABILITY

ARITHMETIC KEYS

CHANGE SIGN, DISPLAY, OR EXPONENT

NUMBER α, RAISED TO POWER x

GRAD — DEGREE ANGLE SWITCH

SELECT DECIMALS, 0-9

TRIG AND INVERSE FUNCTIONS

RESET TO ZERO
EXCHANGE REGISTERS

STORE-RECALL DATA FROM
10 MEMORIES

ENTER EXPONENT

Fig. 12-6. The Monroe 324G programmable calculator.

262

several of the keys perform double calculations. The function given on the top of they key is the primary function and is displayed when the function key is pressed. When the $\boxed{2^{nd}FUNC}$ key is pressed, the function given on the bottom of the key is displayed. Ten storage registers are directly addressable by the user, giving the ability to store many intermediate results in a complicated calculation without writing anything down. Calculations on the Monroe 324G are done in logical arithmetic order. The keyboard also has parenthesis keys $\boxed{(}$ and $\boxed{)}$, which can be nested to permit lengthy chaining of arithmetic calculations.

The Monroe 324G has the capability to store two 80-step programs at the same time. Since the two programs share the same directly addressable storage registers, the two programs can be written to operate consecutively, thus giving the capability, in effect, to create a 160-step program. The two programs must operate independently as two distinct operations, but the second program can use results from the first, obtained from the storage registers without the necessity of the programer reentering any data.

Although the programing capacity and versatility of the Monroe 324 are high, it does not have the powerful storage capability of the Monroe 326, discussed blow. Programs can be retained only by writing each step and keying in the entire program each time it is needed. However, once the program is entered, it can be used repeatedly until the calculator is turned off.

MONROE 326 PROGRAMMABLE CALCULATOR

The 326 scientific calculator, shown in Fig. 12-7, is the next step up in Compucorp's microcomputer line of equipment. Although it can be used as an independent scientific or programmable calculator like the 324, it is intended to work in conjunction with the Monroe 392 tape cassette (Fig. 12-8) which is used to extend its programing capability and memory. The combined price of the Monroe 326 and 392 is about $1395, which is beyond the price range of the pocket calculators discussed in this book; however, the fact that the 326 can accept a plug-in unit to increase its capability is of

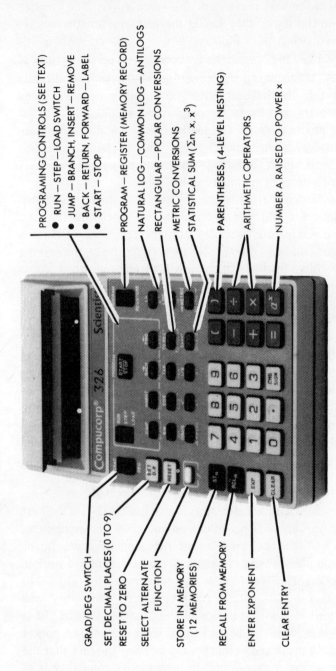

PROGRAMING CONTROLS (SEE TEXT)
● RUN — STEP — LOAD SWITCH
● JUMP — BRANCH, INSERT — REMOVE
● BACK — RETURN, FORWARD — LABEL
● START — STOP

PROGRAM — REGISTER (MEMORY RECORD)

NATURAL LOG — COMMON LOG — ANTILOGS

RECTANGULAR — POLAR CONVERSIONS

METRIC CONVERSIONS

STATISTICAL SUM (Σn, x, x^3)

PARENTHESES, (4-LEVEL NESTING)

ARITHMETIC OPERATORS

NUMBER A RAISED TO POWER x

GRAD/DEG SWITCH

SET DECIMAL PLACES (0 TO 9)

RESET TO ZERO

SELECT ALTERNATE FUNCTION

STORE IN MEMORY (12 MEMORIES)

RECALL FROM MEMORY

ENTER EXPONENT

CLEAR ENTRY

Fig. 12-7. Monroe 326 programmable calculator.

264

Fig. 12-8. Monroe 392 cassette tape drive for use with the 326 calculator.

interest and may indicate the nature of future trends in portable or pocket calculators. After all, the 326 is certainly portable (5 × 9 × 2 in.), weighs only 3.5 lb, and can be operated on rechargeable batteries.

The basic capabilities of the Monroe 326 are indicated in Figure 12-7. However, its chief feature is the dramatic increase in programing capability, which approximates more expensive desk-type computers. By itself, the 326 can be used to store 160 program steps which are available for internal programs, together with 12 addressable memories for additional storage. But additional programs may be loaded into the 392 tape drive and read back into the 326 at a later time under program control. In fact, the tape drive can supply the 326 calculator with 100,000 program steps, or 9,000 data values (or partial combinations), by the use of prerecorded tape cassettes, in 14 blocks of 160 program steps each.

The Monroe 326 also offers an extensive complement of internal scientific functions and metric conversion features, which should satisfy all normal computing demands. For example, it provides a full assortment of trigonometric, logarithmic, exponential, and programing functions, as well as two-way rectangular-to-polar conversion, factorials, statistical mean and standard deviation, sum and store capability, and continuous decimal point selection. It also provides a full set of two-way metric conversion factors, including factors for distance, area, volume, mass, weight, temperature, density, pressure, velocity, acceleration, and other physical quantities. In addition, it also offers 12 addressable storage registers, which should suffice for all applications discussed in this book. It can calculate trigonometric quantities in decimal degrees and grad modes and convert from either mode to radians, or vice versa.

A unique feature is the ability of the 326 to nest parentheses to four levels. This greatly extends the flexibility of the calculator and permits the operator to handle complex formulas and equations. The calculator operates using conventional algebraic logic, as does the 324G, and should pose no learning problems to the new operator.

As shown in Fig. 12-7, the 326 has an attractive, large display, which features 10 significant digits with sign, and a 2-digit exponent with sign. All numbers are carried internally with 13-digit accuracy, regardless of the number of digits displayed. The least significant digit may be rounded if so desired.

Monroe also offers preprogramed software for various mathematical, industrial, and scientific applications. The 326 has the ability to read a magnetic tape input, using the 392 tape drive. In addition, telecommunications with the 326 is available with Monroe's 395 teleprinter-interface peripheral unit.

The following summary indicates the programing and computing capability of the Monroe 326.

Data Memory. All numbers are carried internally with 13-digit accuracy plus to 2-digit exponent. There are 12 data storage registers, which may be recorded on a magnetic tape cassette.

Preprogramed Operations. These include reset, clear entry, set decimal point (zero to nine digits to right of decimal point), exponent (scientific notation), enter and calculate with angles in degrees—minutes—seconds, enter and calculate with angles in decimal degrees or grads, decimal degrees to degrees—minutes—seconds, degrees—minutes—seconds to decimal degrees, square root, square, reciprocal, factorial, statistical summation (number of data items, sum, sum of squares), delete data from summation, mean, standard deviation, sine, arc sine, cosine, arc cosine, tangent, arc tangent, to polar, to rectangular, degrees (or grads) to radians, radians to degrees (or grads), base e logarithm, base e antilogarithm, base 10 logarithm, base 10 antilogarithm, integer, fraction, absolute value, pi, e, and round.

Algebraic Parentheses. Logical parentheses are nested up to four levels.

Two-Way English-to-Metric Conversions. These include degrees Fahrenheit to degrees Celsius, inches to centimeters, inches/second to centimeters/second, inches/second^2 to centimeters/second^2, inches^3 to centimeters^3, feet to meters, miles to kilometers, miles per hour to kilometers per hour, U.S. gallons to liters, U.K. gallons to liters, pounds to kilograms, ounces to grams, pounds/inch^2 to kilograms/centimeter^2 pounds/feet^3 to grams/centimeter^3, degrees to grads.

Programing Operations—Addressing. This provides labeling (symbolic and relocatable addressing) with 13 different labels.

Jumping. There are seven different conditional jumps to labeled addresses:

$$\text{Jump} > 0$$
$$\text{Jump} < 0$$
$$\text{Jump} \geq 0$$
$$\text{Jump} \leq 0$$
$$\text{Jump} = 0$$
$$\text{Jump} \neq 0$$

Jump if keyboard entry has been made

Subroutines. There are seven conditional branches to labeled subroutines, automatic return from subroutine to main program or another subroutine. Subroutines can be nested to six levels.

Additional operation. Identifiers are provided to indicate points where variables are entered or the display of specific calculation results, also start or stop program execution or pause in program execution.

Program Editing. Provides automatic display of memory location, code, and symbol when entering programs from keyboard. Display shows present address and code, plus codes at the previous and next program step, trace feature while stepping through programs enables the operator to observe operations as performed. Backspace and forward keys permit corrections and changes in programs and insert key allows you to add steps in any part of the program at any time. Delete key permits removing steps in any part of the program at any time.

Register Usage. Store and recall of all 12 registers is available. You can exchange an entered number with the number in any of the 12 registers. You can add, subtract, multiply, divide, and raise to a power into and out of data registers. You can also clear all registers, or clear registers 1, 2, and 3 (group registers used in summation operation).

Other Features:

These include the following:

● Self-testing. Hardwired routine automatically tests all the segments of the gas discharge display and all the read-only and random access memory chips.

● **Tape cassette drive**. Manual controls are provided for forward, rewind, record, stop, and eject tape cassette. Manual (or programmable) controls for writing and reading data registers or programs onto or from tape cassette are also provided. The tape cassette drive plugs into and derives power through the Beta 326.

● **Tape cassette medium**. Programs and registers may be stored on either endless or straight line tape. Information is stored in blocks, with 14 blocks on the endless tape and multiple files of 14 blocks each on the straight line tape. Each block can hold up to 12 data registers or 160 program steps.

Chapter 13

Commentary and Preview

Thus far you have seen the state of the art in pocket calculators. However, we can anticipate other breakthroughs just beyond the horizon. Pocket-sized strip-printing calculators are already available, and improvements are in sight. Certainly it is reasonable to expect that miniature plug-in units can be developed which can increase the memory and computing capacity of the scientific pocket calculator at least a hundredfold. In fact, the author visualizes a microminiature computer complex, consisting of a central calculator surrounded by a selected set of memory and function plug-in units and software paks, which can be carried in an attache case. Armed with this portable computer complex, the user may solve or troubleshoot problems in the field, develop software routines for customers on demand, or perform consulting services during the course of a business trip.

Such a development would seem to be more likely than the dramatic appearance on the market of the HP-65—a fully programmable scientific pocket calculator—less than 3 years after the advent of the first commercial pocket calculators.

NEW PRODUCTS

As we go to press, several new products have just been released, and others will be announced shortly. Major characteristics of some recent calculators are summarized in Table 13-1. A brief summary of some leading models is given below.

Table 13-1. Comparison of Recent Scientific Calculators.

	HEWLETT-PACKARD HP-21	NOVUS 4510	NOVUS 4520	ROCKWELL 63R	TEXAS INSTRUMENTS SR-51
BASIC FEATURES					
List price	$125	$70	$100	$100	$225
Rechargeable batteries	Yes	No	No	Yes	Yes
Type of logic	RPN	RPN	RPN	Alg	Alg
Display (digits)	+2	8−	8+2	8+2	10+2
Scientific notation	Yes	No	Yes	Yes	Yes
Addressable memories	1	1	1	1	3
Fix decimal point	Yes	No	No	No	Yes
Degree — radian select	Yes	No	No	Yes	Yes
Register arithmetic	Yes	$\pm, x^2$	No	Yes	Yes
PRIMARY FUNCTIONS					
Trigonometric — inverse	Yes	Yes	Yes	Yes	Yes
Logs, common — natural	Yes	Yes	Yes	Yes	Yes
Antilogs,common—natural	Yes	y^x	Yes	Yes	Yes
Power function (y^x, a^x)	Yes	Yes	Yes	Yes	Yes
Square root $(\sqrt{x})$	Yes	Yes	Yes	Yes	Yes
Squares (x^2)	No	Yes	No	No	Yes
Reciprocal $(1/x)$	Yes	Yes	Yes	Yes	Yes
Degree — radian conversion	No	Yes	No	Yes	Yes
ADVANCED FUNCTIONS					
Hyperbolic functions	No	No	No	No	Yes
Factorials $(x!)$	No	No	No	Yes	Yes
Statistical mean — deviation	No	No	No	No	Yes
Polar — rect conversions	Yes	No	No	No	Yes
Metric conversions	0	0	0	0	13
Linear regression	No	No	No	No	Yes
Sum and store $(\Sigma +)$	No	No	No	Yes	Yes
Permutations	No	No	No	No	Yes
Logical parentheses	†	†	†	Yes	*

* Features algebraic hierarchy instead.
† Features operational stack instead.

Texas Instruments SR-51

This high-powered model represents an advance over TI's existing SR-50. Additional capabilities include two-way polar-to-rectangular conversion; statistical mean, deviation, and variance; 13 metric conversion factors; 3 addressable memories; decimal point selection; and random-number generation. This model has forced a price reduction of the HP-45 to $245, and represents the latest in scientific pocket calculators.

Rockwell 63R

This model is built in the same case size as the Rockwell 61R and sells for only $100. It now features scientific notation, logical parentheses to two levels, factorial functions, and improved display features, including a true minus sign and a MEMORY ON indication. It retains the large blue-green Digitron display.

Hewlett-Packard HP-21

This streamlined model with new features is listed at $125 and will replace the familiar HP-35. It is packaged in a smaller case ($5\frac{1}{8} \times 2\frac{11}{16}$ in.) and provides only 8 significant figures, but offers degree—radian mode selection, common antilog (10^{10}), two-way polar—rectangular conversion, decimal point selection, and complete register arithmetic.

Novus 4510 and Novus 4520

These new scientific calculators, together with the Statistician 6030 and Financier 6020, signal the entry of National Semiconductor into the marketplace. The Novus 4510 sells for $70 and the advanced Novus 4520 sells for $100. Their characteristics are summarized in Table 13-1.

Enterprex International Model 904

Characteristics are not available to us at this time but are believed to be similar to the Novus 4510. Enterprex also offers a Financier Model 2110, which sells for only $80 and has preprogramed functions, including present and future value, payment, interest, and other financial calculations.

Hewlett-Packard HP-55

But perhaps the most significant development so far in 1975 is the new Hewlett-Packard HP-55, a manually programmable scientific calculator with a list price of $395, or about half the price of the HP-55. Although the HP-55 cannot permanently store a program or read a prerecorded program, it offers a combination of scientific function, memory storage, and programing capability which are unmatched in its price range. Some of its capabilities include:

Programing: Looping ("go to") capability, conditional and direct branching, single-step execution or running of a program, relational tests, and 20 addressable memories. There is a total of only 49 key stroke memories or program steps. However, the HP-55 can be programed to solve such problems as four simultaneous linear equations, iterative solutions for $f(x) = 0$, quadratic and cubic equations, and many of the mathematical, statistical, and engineering problems shown in the programs Paks for the HP-35.

Scientific Functions: Prerecorded linear regression of two variables, statistical mean and deviation of one or two variables, summation functions, factorials, degree—radian mode selection and conversion, metric conversions, register arithmetic, deg—min—sec-to-decimal conversion, hours—min—sec arithmetic, and selection of conventional or scientific notation.

Decimal Timer: Accurate to 0.01%, good for 100 hours, with capability for split time measurements which can be stored in 10 addressable memories and displayed in hours, minutes, seconds, and hundredths.

But the end is not in sight. National Semiconductor has recently announced two manually programmable models: the Novus 4515, selling for $140; and the Novus 4525, selling for $170. For these prices, Novus calculators must offer limited scientific function and programing capability. Nevertheless, they could well appeal to the student, the trade-oriented market, or even to the technical professional who cannot afford, or who does not need, the capability of higher priced units.

One thing is certain: The price of both scientific and programmable calculators will keep falling. Creative Strategies, Inc., of San Jose, California predicts in a recent issue of *New Scientist* that other hand-held programmable calculators will appear in 1975—1976 with features similar to the HP-65, but selling for much less. They also indicate that the yearly U.S. market in programmable, desktop dedicated and 4/5 function calculators will top 18 million units and clear $700 million by the end of 1975.

The only sure prediction we can make is that some technical and price breakthroughs will occur by 1976 that we cannot even imagine today.

Appendixes

Chapters 2, 3, and 4 discussed the equations and programs for generating scientific functions on the elementary calculator. The functions included square roots, cube roots, sin x, cos x, tan x, and inverse trigonometric functions, and common and natural logarithms and antilogarithms.

The appendixes summarize these results in handbook fashion by showing a typical program or example for each function, using an elementary calculator with memory.

The examples shown are based on the use of the Rockwell 20R−21R, the DataKing 800, or the Bowmar MX 35-1. However, these routines will apply to any memory-equipped calculator which uses algebraic notation; the programs can be easily modified to produce the desired results.

Appendix A
Square Root Program

The following is an efficient procedure for extracting the square root of any number and can be memorized very easily. Of particular importance is the iteration cycle, or repeating loop, which is in the box in the example below.

Note: The first estimate for the square root should be taken from a square root table to minimize the number of cycles required for high accuracy.

Example A-1. Find $\sqrt{377}$ using a calculator with a memory.

Key—Operation	Display	Comment
377 $\div$ 20 $+$	18.85	First estimate is 20. First check is 18.85.
$\div$ 2 $=$ M $+$	19.425	Second estimate.
377 $\div$ MR $+$	19.407979	Reenter 377. Second check.
$\div$ 2 $=$	19.416489	Third estimate (answer).
M C M $+$	19.416489	Starts next iteration.

It is generally desirable to clear memory before starting this routine by pressing M C .

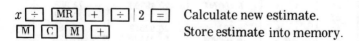

x $\div$ MR $+$ $\div$ 2 $=$ — Calculate new estimate.
M C M $+$ — Store estimate into memory.

Error Analysis

The error in the square root after each cycle of calculation is given by the following formula:

Table A-1. Squares, Square Roots, Cubes, and Cube Roots.

n	n^2	$\sqrt{n}$	$\sqrt{10n}$	n^3
1	1	1.000000	3.162278	1
2	4	1.414214	4.472136	8
3	9	1.732051	5.477226	27
4	16	2.000000	6.324555	64
5	25	2.236068	7.071068	125
6	36	2.449490	7.745967	216
7	49	2.645751	8.366600	343
8	64	2.828427	8.944272	512
9	81	3.000000	9.486833	729
10	100	3.162278	10.00000	1,000
11	121	3.316625	10.48809	1,331
12	144	3.464102	10.95445	1,728
13	169	3.605551	11.40175	2,197
14	196	3.741657	11.83216	2,744
15	225	3.872983	12.24745	3,375
16	256	4.000000	12.64911	4,096
17	289	4.123106	13.03840	4,913
18	324	4.242641	13.41641	5,832
19	361	4.358899	13.78405	6,859
20	400	4.472136	14.14214	8,000
21	441	4.582576	14.49138	9,261
22	484	4.690416	14.83240	10,648
23	529	4.795832	15.16575	12,167
24	576	4.898979	15.49193	13,824
25	625	5.000000	15.81139	15,625
26	676	5.099020	16.12452	17,576
27	729	5.196152	16.43168	19,683
28	784	5.291503	16.73320	21,952
29	841	5.385165	17.02939	24,389
30	900	5.477226	17.32051	27,000
31	961	5.567764	17.60682	29,791
32	1,024	5.656854	17.88854	32,768
33	1,089	5.744563	18.16590	35,937
34	1,156	5.830952	18.43909	39,304
35	1,225	5.916080	18.70829	42,875
36	1,296	6.000000	18.97367	46,656
37	1,369	6.082763	19.23538	50,653
38	1,444	6.164414	19.49359	54,872
39	1,521	6.244998	19.74842	59,319
40	1,600	6.324555	20.00000	64,000
41	1,681	6.403124	20.24846	68,921
42	1,764	6.480741	20.49390	74,088
43	1,849	6.557439	20.73644	79,507
44	1,936	6.633250	20.97618	85,184
45	2,025	6.708204	21.21320	91,125
46	2,116	6.782330	21.44761	97,336
47	2,209	6.855655	21.67948	103,823
48	2,304	6.928203	21.90890	110,592
49	2,401	7.000000	22.13594	117,649
50	2,500	7.071068	22.36068	125,000

n	n^2	$\sqrt{n}$	$\sqrt{10n}$	n^3
50	2,500	7.071068	22.36068	125,000
51	2,601	7.141428	22.58318	132,651
52	2,704	7.211103	22.80351	140,608
53	2,809	7.280110	23.02173	148,877
54	2,916	7.348469	23.23790	157,464
55	3,025	7.416198	23.45208	166,375
56	3,136	7.483315	23.66432	175,616
57	3,249	7.549834	23.87467	185,193
58	3,364	7.615773	24.06319	195,112
59	3,481	7.681146	24.28992	205,379
60	3,600	7.745967	24.49490	216,000
61	3,721	7.810250	24.69818	226,981
62	3,844	7.874008	24.89980	238,328
63	3,969	7.937254	25.09980	250,047
64	4,096	8.000000	25.29822	262,144
65	4,225	8.062258	25.49510	274,625
66	4,356	8.124038	25.69047	287,496
67	4,489	8.185353	25.88436	300,763
68	4,624	8.246211	26.07681	314,432
69	4,761	8.306624	26.26785	328,509
70	4,900	8.366600	26.45751	343,000
71	5,041	8.426150	26.64583	357,911
72	5,184	8.485281	26.83282	373,248
73	5,329	8.544004	27.01851	389,017
74	5,476	8.602325	27.20294	405,224
75	5,625	8.660254	27.38613	421,875
76	5,776	8.717798	27.56810	438,976
77	5,929	8.774964	27.74887	456,533
78	6,084	8.831761	27.92848	474,552
79	6,241	8.888194	28.10694	493,039
80	6,400	8.944272	28.28427	512,000
81	6,561	9.000000	28.46050	531,441
82	6,724	9.055385	28.63564	551,368
83	6,889	9.110434	28.80972	571,787
84	7,056	9.165151	28.98275	592,704
85	7,225	9.219544	29.15476	614,125
86	7,396	9.273618	29.32576	636,056
87	7,569	9.327379	29.49576	658,503
88	7,744	9.380832	29.66479	681,472
89	7,921	9.433981	29.83287	704,969
90	8,100	9.486833	30.00000	729,000
91	8,281	9.539392	30.16621	753,571
92	8,464	9.591663	30.33150	778,688
93	8,649	9.643651	30.49590	804,357
94	8,836	9.695360	30.65942	830,584
95	9,025	9.746794	30.82207	857,375
96	9,216	9.797959	30.98387	884,736
97	9,409	9.848858	31.14482	912,673
98	9,604	9.899495	31.30495	941,192
99	9,801	9.949874	31.46427	970,299
100	10,000	10.00000	31.62278	1,000,000

$$\text{Error} = -\frac{(E_p - E_f)^2}{2 \times E_p}$$

where

$$E_p = \text{previous estimate}$$
$$E_f = \text{final estimate}$$

In example A-1

$$E_p = E_1 = 20 \qquad E_f = E_2 = 19.425$$

The magnitude of the error is approximately

$$\text{Error} = \frac{(20 - 19.425)^2}{2 \times 20} = \frac{0.575^2}{40}$$
$$= 0.0075$$

At the end of the second cycle

$$E_p = E_2 = 19.425 \qquad E_f = E_3 = 19.41689$$

$$\text{Error} = \frac{0.0081^2}{2 \times 19.425} = 1.6 \times 10^{-6}$$

Appendix B
Cube Root Program

Example B1 summarizes the cube root process for any number, and example B-2 shows a numerical example. Although not used here, a good first guess should be taken from a table of cube roots.

Example B-1. General program for $\sqrt[3]{N}$.

Process for $\sqrt[3]{N}$	Comments
Estimate the cube root $(= E_1)$.	First estimate.
Square the estimate (E_1^2).	
Calculate $\dfrac{N}{E_1^2} = C_1$	First check.
Calculate $\dfrac{(2 \times E_1) + C_1}{3} = E_2$	Second estimate.
Calculate E_2^2.	
Calculate $\dfrac{N}{E_2^2} = C_2$.	Second check.
Calculate $\dfrac{(2 \times E_2) + C_2}{3} = E_3$.	Third estimate.

Repeat process until $E_3 = E_2$. or until $\dfrac{E_3 - E_2}{E_3}$ is less than a desired amount.

Example B-2. Find $\sqrt[3]{10}$ using a calculator with a memory.

Key or Operation	Display	Comment
10 $\div$ 2 $\boxed{M}$ + $\div$ 2 $\boxed{M}$ $\boxed{+}$	2.	First estimate E_1.
$\boxed{=}$ $\boxed{M}$ $\boxed{+}$	2.5	First check C_1.
3 $\boxed{M}$ $\boxed{-}$	3	E_2 in memory.
10 $\div$ $\boxed{MR}$ $\div$ $\boxed{MR}$ $\boxed{M}$ $\boxed{+}$	2.1666666	E_2 in display.
$\boxed{=}$ $\boxed{M}$ $\boxed{+}$	2.1301776	Second check C_2.
3 $\boxed{M}$ $\boxed{\div}$	3	E_3 in memory.
10 $\div$ $\boxed{MR}$ $\div$ $\boxed{MR}$ $\boxed{M}$ $\boxed{+}$	2.1545036	E_3 in display.
$\boxed{=}$ $\boxed{M}$ $\boxed{+}$	2.1542968	Third check C_3.
3 $\boxed{M}$ $\boxed{\div}$ $\boxed{MR}$	2.1544346	Final estimate.

The iteration cycle is in the box.

If a better first guess were used, then only one or two cycles would be needed.

ERROR ANALYSIS

The error in the cube root after each cycle of calculation is

$$\text{Error} = -\frac{(E_p - E_f)^2}{E_p}$$

where

$$E_p = \text{previous estimate} \quad E_f = \text{final estimate}$$

In example B-2

$$E_p = E_2 = 2.1666666 \quad E_f = E_3 = 2.1545036$$

The estimate E_3 is too high. Since $E_2 - E_3 = 0.01216$

$$\text{Error} = \frac{0.01216^2}{2 \times 2.1666666} = 3.4 \times 10^{-5}$$

This analysis shows that the last cycle of calculation was really not needed. The error in the final answer is about 2.3×10^{-9}.

Appendix C
Sine Program

General equation:

$$\sin x = \sin x_o + \Delta \cos x_o \qquad \text{(C-1)}$$

where

$$\Delta = \frac{x - x_o}{57.2958} \qquad \text{(C-2)}$$

$$x_o = \text{nearest table value to } x$$

$$\sin x_o \text{ and } \cos x_o = \text{table values}$$

Example C-1. Find $\sin 30.4°$. Let $x_o = 30°$, $x - x_o = 0.4°$. From trigonometric table: $\sin 30° = 0.50000$, $\cos 30° = 0.86603$.

Keyboard Entry	Display	Comments
0.40 ÷ 57.2958 =	0.0069813	Δ in radians
× 0.86603 +	0.0060460	$\cos x_o$
0.500 =	0.5060460	$\sin 30.4°$

The true value of $\sin 30.4°$ is 0.506039; the error is about 0.7×10^{-5}. Note that $x - x_o$ is converted into radians by dividing by 57.2958°/rad.

Example C-2. Find $\sin 44.75°$. Let $x_o = 45°$. From trigonometric table: $\sin 45° = 0.70711$, $\cos 45° = 0.70711$.

Keyboard Entry	Display	Comment
44.75° − 45 ÷	−0.25	$x_o - x_o$ is negative.

Key or Operation	Display	Comment
57.2958 $\times$ 0.70711 $+$	-0.0030853	$-\Delta$ in radians
0.70711 $=$	0.7040246	sin 44.75°

The true value of sin 44.75° is 0.704015; the error is about 1×10^{-5}.

ANGLES GREATER THAN 45°

Example C-3. Find sin x, where x is greater than 45°. Let $\sin x = \cos(90° - x)$. If $x = 67.5°$

$$\sin 67.5° = \cos 22.5° = 0.923880 \qquad \text{(C-3)}$$

(See Example D-1, Appendix D, for cosine routine.)

Table C-1. Trigonometric Functions.

X_o	Sin X_o	Cos X_o	Tan X_o
1	.01745	.99985	.01746
2	.03490	.99939	.03492
3	.05234	.99863	.05241
4	.06976	.99756	.06993
5	.08716	.99619	.08749
6	.10453	.99452	.10510
7	.12187	.99255	.12278
8	.13917	.99027	.14054
9	.15643	.98769	.15838
10	.17365	.98481	.17633
11	.19081	.98163	.19438
12	.20791	.97815	.21256
13	.22495	.97437	.23087
14	.24192	.97030	.24933
15	.25882	.96593	.26795
16	.27564	.96126	.28675
17	.29237	.95630	.30573
18	.30902	.95106	.32492
19	.32557	.94552	.34433
20	.34202	.93969	.36397

X_o	Sin X_o	Cos X_o	Tan X_o
21	.35837	.93358	.38386
22	.37461	.92718	.40403
23	.39073	.92050	.42447
24	.40674	.91355	.44523
25	.42262	.90631	.46631
26	.43837	.89879	.48773
27	.45399	.89101	.50953
28	.46947	.88295	.53171
29	.48481	.87462	.55431
30	.50000	.86603	.57735
31	.51504	.85717	.60086
32	.52992	.84805	.62487
33	.54464	.83867	.64941
34	.55919	.82904	.67451
35	.57358	.81915	.70021
36	.58779	.80902	.72654
37	.60182	.79864	.75355
38	.61566	.78801	.78129
39	.62932	.77715	.80978
40	.64279	.76604	.83910
41	.65606	.75471	.86929
42	.66913	.74314	.90040
43	.68200	.73135	.93252
44	.69466	.71934	.96569
45	.70711	.70711	1.00000

Appendix D
Cosine Program

General equation:

$$\cos x = \cos x_o - \Delta \sin x_o \qquad \text{(D-1)}$$

$$\Delta = \frac{x - x_o}{57.2958}$$

Example D-1. Find $\cos 22.5°$. Let $x_o = 22°$, $x - x_o = 0.5°$. From trigonometric table $\sin 22° = 0.37561$, $\cos 22° = 0.92718$.

Keyboard Entry	Display	Comment
0.50 $\boxed{\div}$ 57.2958 $\boxed{\times}$	0.0087266	Δ in radians
0.37461 $\boxed{=}$	0.003269	$\Delta \sin 22°$
$\boxed{-}$ $\boxed{-}$ $\boxed{+}$ 0.92718 $\boxed{=}$	0.923911	$\cos 22.5°$

The true value is 0.923880; the error is about 3×10^{-5}.

Example D-2. Find $\cos 36.8$. Let $x_o = 37°$, $x - x_o = -0.2$. From trigonometric table $\sin 37° = 0.60182$, $\cos 37° = 0.79864$.

Keyboard Entry	Display	Comment
36.8 $\boxed{-}$ 37 $\boxed{\div}$	$-0.2°$	Δ is negative
57.2958 $\boxed{\times}$ 0.60182 $\boxed{=}$	-0.0021007	$\Delta \sin 37°$
$\boxed{-}$ $\boxed{-}$ $\boxed{+}$ 0.79864 $\boxed{=}$	0.8007407	$\cos 36.8°$

The true value is 0.800731; the error is about 1×10^{-5}.

Example D-3. Find $\cos x$, where x is greater than $45°$. Let

$$\cos x = \sin (90° - x) \qquad \text{(D-2)}$$

If x is $59.6°$

$$\cos 59.6° = \sin 30.4°$$

(Refer to Example C-1, Appendix C, for sine calculations.)

Appendix E
Tangent Program

General Equation:

$$\tan x = \frac{\tan x_o + \Delta}{1 - \Delta \tan x_o}$$

where

$$\Delta = \frac{x - x_o}{57.2958}$$

The general program is given in example E-1, and a specific tangent is calculated in example E-2.

Example E-1. General program for $\tan x$ using memory.

Keyboard Operation	Display	Memory
$\boxed{M}$ $\boxed{C}$ $x°$ $\boxed{-}$ x_o $\boxed{\div}$	$\Delta = x - x_o$	0
57.2958 $\boxed{=}$ $\boxed{M}$ $\boxed{-}$	$+\ \Delta$ in radians	$-\Delta$ in radians
$\boxed{+}$ $\tan x_o$ $\boxed{M}$ $\boxed{\times}$ $\boxed{\div}$	$\tan x_o + \Delta$	$-\Delta \tan x_o$
1 $\boxed{M}$ $\boxed{+}$ $\boxed{\div}$ $\boxed{MR}$ $\boxed{=}$	$\tan x$	$1 - \Delta \tan x_o$

Example E-2. Find $\tan 36.8699°$. From trigonometric table, $x_o = 37°$, $\tan 37° = 0.75355$.

Keyboard Operation	Display	Comment
$\boxed{M}$ $\boxed{C}$ 36.8699 $\boxed{-}$ 37 $\boxed{\div}$	-0.1301	Δ is negative
57.2958 $\boxed{=}$ $\boxed{M}$ $\boxed{-}$	-0.0022706	Δ in radians
$\boxed{+}$ 0.75355 $\boxed{M}$ $\boxed{\times}$ $\boxed{\div}$	0.7512794	$\tan 37° + \Delta$
1 $\boxed{M}$ $\boxed{+}$ $\boxed{\div}$ $\boxed{MR}$ $\boxed{=}$	0.7499961	$\tan 36.8699°$

The true value is 0.750000; the error is about 0.4×10^{-5}. This error would be reduced to almost zero if the correct value of $\tan 37° = 0.753554$ were used.

Example E-3. Find $\tan x$ when $x > 45°$.

Let

$$\tan x = \frac{1}{\tan (90° - x)}$$

If $x = 60$

$$\tan 60° = \frac{1}{\tan 30°}$$

Appendix F
Program for Inverse Sine

General Equation:

$$x = \arcsin y = x_o + K \frac{\sin x - \sin x_o}{\cos x_o}$$

where $K = 57.2958$; and x_o, $\sin x_o$, and $\cos x_o$ are given in the table.

Example F-1. Find arc sin 0.335. From trigonometric table.

$$x_o = 19° \quad \sin 19° = 0.32557 \quad \cos 19° = 0.94552$$

Keyboard Entry	Display	Comment
0.335 $-$ 0.32557 $\times$	0.00943	$\sin x - \sin 19°$
57.2958 $\div$	0.5402993	
0.94552 $+$ 19 $=$	36.869431	arc sin 0.335

The true value for x is 19.5725; the error is about one arc second.

Example F-2. Find arc sin 0.600000. From trigonometric table.

$$x_o = 37° \quad \sin 37° = 00.60182 \quad \cos 37° = 0.79864$$

Keyboard Entry	Display	Comment
0.60 $-$ 0.60182 $\times$	-0.00182	Correction is negative.
57.2958 $\div$	-0.1042783	
0.79864 $+$ 37 $=$	36.869431	$x = $ arc sin 0.600

The true value of $x = $ arc sin 0.600 is 36.8699°; the error is less than 2 arc seconds.

Example 4-3. Find $x = \arcsin y$, where $x > 45°$.
Let

$$x = 90° - \arccos y \qquad \text{(F-2)}$$

Appendix G
Programs for Inverse Functions

INVERSE SINE

General Equation:

$$x = \text{arc cos } y = x_o + K \, \frac{\cos x_o - \cos x}{\sin x_o} \qquad \text{(G-1)}$$

Example G-1. Find arc cos 0.960. Constant $K = 57.2958$. From trigonometric table.

$$x_o = 16° \quad \cos 16° 0.96126 \quad \sin 16° = 0.27564$$

Keyboard Entry	Display	Comment
0.96126 $-$ 0.960 $\times$ 57.2958 $\div$	0.0721927	radians
0.27564 $+$ 16 $=$	16.261909	arc cos 0.96

The true value of arc cos 0.96 is 16.2602°; the error is about 1.7×10^{-3} degrees, or about 6 arc seconds. These errors increase as the angle x falls below 15°. For example, the error for $x = $ arc cos 0.9832549 is over 0.012° for $x = 10.5$°. Therefore, for angles below 15°, Equation G-2 is recommended.

General equation : For angles below 10°, to find $x = $ arc cos y, let

where
$$x = \sqrt[k]{C\left(1 + \frac{C}{129}\right)} \qquad \text{(G-2)}$$

$$C = 2(1 - \cos x) \qquad \text{(G-3)}$$

Although this equation is very accurate, the operator must either use a calculator with a square root function, or else use an accurate square root method.

Example G-2. Find arc cos 0.9832549 using Equation G-2. First calculatoe C.

Keyboard Entry	Display	Comment
1 $-$ 0.98322549 $\times$ 2 $=$	0.0334902	Quantity C.
M C M $+$ $\div$ 12 $+$	0.0027908	C in memory.
1 $\times$ MR $=$ $\sqrt{x}$	0.1832584	Operator find $\sqrt{x}$.
$\times$ 57.2958 $=$	10.499935	Required angle x.

The true value of x is $10.50°$; the error is only 6.5×10^5 degrees. Furthermore, the errors decrease rapidly as x gets smaller.

Example G-3. Find $x =$ arc cos y, where $x > 45°$. Let $x = 90°$ − arc sin y. (See example D-1 or D-2 for arc sin y.)

INVERSE TANGENT

Note: This is an accurate formula for calculation of $x =$ arc tan y which is readily programed on a calculator such as the Rockwell 20R−21R with M+ and M× keys.

General equation:

$$x = x_o + K \frac{\tan x - \tan x_o}{1 + \tan x \tan x_o}$$

Example G-4. Find arc tan 0.475. From trigonometric table

$$x_o = 25°, \ \tan 25° = 0.46631, \ K = 57.2958$$

Keyboard Entry	Display	Comment
0.475 M $+$ $-$ 0.46631	0.46631	$\tan x$ in memory
M $\times$ $\div$	0.00869	$\tan x - \tan 25°$
1 M $+$ $\div$ MR $\times$	0.0071142	correction angle
57.2958 $+$ 25 $=$	25.407613	arc tan 0.475

The true value is $25.4077°$; the error is negligible.

Example G-5. Find $x =$ arc tan y, where $x > 45°$. Let $x = 90°$ arc tan $1/y$, then use the same program as Example G-4.

Appendix H
Programs for Logarithms

LOGARITHMS

Here we summarize all the reference data and programs which allow you to calculate logarithms to an accuracy that generally requires a scientific electronic slide rule. These calculations can be performed to an accuracy of about seven significant figures, using an ordinary electronic calculator with memory, such as the Rockwell 20R−21R.

Table H-1 lists natural logarithms to seven places for numbers N_o under 10. To calculate the natural or common logarithm of a given number N, enter the values of N and N_o into the appropriate example. A typical error is about 1×10^{-8} for natural logs.

Table H-1. Natural Logarithms.

Natural Logarithms			
N_o	Ln N_o	N_o	Ln N_o
1.00	0.0000 000	1.60	0.4700 036
1.05	0.487 902	1.65	0.5007 753
1.10	0.0953 102	1.70	0.5306 283
1.15	0.1397 619	1.75	0.5596 158
1.20	0.1823 216	1.80	0.5877 867
1.25	0.2231 436	1.85	0.6151 856
1.30	0.2623 643	1.90	0.6418 539
1.35	0.3001 046	1.95	0.6678 294
1.40	0.3364 722		
1.45	0.3715 636	2.0	0.6931 472
		2.1	0.7419 373
1.50	0.4054 651	2.2	0.7884 574
1.55	0.4382 549	2.3	0.8329 091

Natural Logarithms			
N_o	$\text{Ln } N_o$	N_o	$\text{Ln } N_o$
2.4	0.0754 687	6.3	1.8405 496
2.5	0.9162 907	6.4	1.8562 980
2.6	0.9555 114	6.5	1.8718 022
2.7	0.9932 518	6.6	1.8870 696
2.8	0.0296 194	6.7	1.9021 075
2.9	1.0647 107	6.8	1.9169 226
3.0	1.0986 123	6.9	1.9315 214
3.1	1.1314 021		
3.2	1.1631 508	7.0	1.9459 101
3.3	1.1939 225	7.1	1.9600 948
3.4	1.2237 754	7.2	1.9740 810
3.5	1.2527 630	7.3	1.9878 743
3.6	1.2809 338	7.4	2.0014 800
3.7	1.3083 328	7.5	2.0149 030
3.8	1.3350 011	7.6	2.0281 482
3.9	1.3609 766	7.7	2.0412 203
4.0	1.3862 944	7.8	2.0541 237
4.1	1.4109 870	7.9	2.0668 628
4.2	1.4350 845		
4.3	1.4586 150	8.0	2.0794 415
4.4	1.4816 045	8.1	2.0918 641
4.5	1.5040 774	8.2	2.1041 342
4.6	1.5260 563	8.3	2.1162 555
4.7	1.5475 625	8.4	2.1282 317
4.8	1.5686 159	8.5	2.1400 662
4.9	1.5892 352	8.6	2.1517 622
		8.7	2.1633 230
5.0	1.6094 379	8.8	2.1747 517
5.1	1.6292 405	8.9	2.1860 513
5.2	1.6486 586		
5.3	1.6677 068	9.0	2.1972 246
5.4	1.6863 990	9.1	2.2082 744
5.5	1.7047 481	9.2	2.2192 035
5.6	1.7227 666	9.3	2.2300 144
5.7	1.7404 662	9.4	2.2407 097
5.8	1.7578 579	9.5	2.2512 918
5.9	1.7749 524	9.6	2.2617 631
6.0	1.7917 595	9.7	2.2721 259
6.1	1.8082 888	9.8	2.2823 824
6.2	1.8245 493	9.9	2.2925 348

NATURAL LOGARITHMS

General equation:

$$\ln N = \frac{\ln N_o + \Delta}{N_o + \Delta/2} \qquad \text{(H-1)}$$

where N_o is the nearest value to N in the table and $\Delta = N - N_o$.

Example H-1. Find $\ln 1.95 = 0.6678294$.

Keyboard Entry	Display	Comments
[M] [C]	0.	Clear memory.
1.97 [−] 1.97 [=]	0.02	$\Delta = N - N_o$
[M] [+] [÷] 2 [+]	0.01	$\Delta/2$
1.95 [=] [M] [M] [÷]	1.96	$N_o + \Delta/2$ in display
		$\Delta/1.96$ in memory.
0.6678294 [+]	0.6678294	$\ln 1.95$
[MR] [=]	0.6780334	$\ln 1.97$

Note: Be sure to clear the memory by pressing [M] and [C] before starting any new problem involving memory.

The correct value of $\ln 1.97 = 0.6780335$; the error is only 1×10^{-7}. The error for $\ln N$ in Equation H-1 is $\Delta^3/12N_o^3$ for all calculations.

Example H-2. Find $\ln 39.5 = \ln 10 + \ln 3.95$. From the table

$$N_o = 3.9 \quad \ln 10 = 2.3025851 \quad \ln 3.9 = 1.3609766$$

The correct value is 3.6763007, the error is about 1 in 18 million.

Keyboard Entry	Display	Comments
[M] [C]	0.0	Clear memory
3.95 [−] 3.9 [=]	0.05	$\Delta = N - n_o$
[M] [+] [÷] 2 [+]	0.025	Δ
3.9 [=] [M] [÷]	3.925	$N_o + \Delta/2$ in display
1.3609766 [+] [MR] [+]	1.3737154	$\ln 3.95$
2.3025851 [=]	3.6763005	$\ln 39.5$

MORE ACCURATE FORMULA

For compound interest problems greater accuracy may be required. Where the interest rate is less than 2½ % per month, use the natural logarithms given below.

$$\ln 1.01 = 0.00995033 \quad \ln 1.02 = 0.01980263$$

The error in $\ln N$ for $\Delta = \pm0.005$ is about 1×10^{-8}.

ERROR ANALYSIS FOR NATURAL LOGARITHMS

General equations:

$$\ln N = \ln (N_o + \Delta)$$

$$= \ln N_o + \cfrac{\Delta}{N_o + \cfrac{\Delta}{2}}$$

where

$$\Delta = N - N_o$$

The error in $\ln N$, E_{ln}, is approximately

$$E_{ln} = \frac{1}{12}\left(\frac{\Delta^3}{N_o}\right)$$

Maximum errors for E_{ln} range from about 1.3×10^{-6} for $\Delta = 0.05$ and $N_o = 2$, to about 1×10^{-8} for $\Delta = 0.05$ and $N_o = 10$. Typical errors for $\Delta = 0.025$ and $N_o = 5$ still average only about 1×10^{-8}.

COMMON LOGARITHMS

Example H-3. Find log 39.5.

General equation: $\log N = 0.4342945 \ln N$

$$\log 39.5 = 0.4342945 \times 3.6763005$$

$$= 1.596597 \qquad\qquad \text{(H-3)}$$

Appendix I
Antilogarithms and
Exponentials

NATURAL ANTILOGS

General equation :

$$N = N_o \left[1 + C \left(1 + \frac{C}{2} \right) \right] \qquad \text{(I-1)}$$

where $C = \ln N - \ln N_o$ and $\ln N_o$ is the nearest value to $\ln N$.
million.

Example I-1. Find $N = e^x$, where $x = \ln \ N = 1.9227877$.
From table H-1 $\ln N_o = 1.9169226$, $N_o = 6.8$.

Keyboard Entry	Display	Comments
1.9227877 [−] 1.9169226 [=]	0.0058651	$C = \ln N - \ln N_o$
[M] [C] [M] [+] [÷] 2 [+] 1 [×]	1.0029325	$1 + \frac{C}{2}$ in display,
		C in memory.
[MR] [+] 1 [×] 6.8 [=]	6.8399989	$N = e^x$

The correct value of N is 6.8399998; the error is about 1 in 6.8
million.

Example I-2. Find $N = e^x$, where $x = 4.1941899$. From the
table $N_o = 6.6$, $\ln 6.6 = 1.8870696$.

Keyboard Entry	Display	Comments
4.1941899 [−] 2.3025851 [=]	1.8916048	$\ln N - \ln 10 = \ln \frac{N d^2}{10}$
[=] 1.8870696 [=]	0.0045352	$C = \ln \frac{N}{10} - \ln 6.6$
[M] [C] [M] [+] [÷] 2 [+] 1 [×]	1.0022676	$1 + \frac{C}{2}$ in display,
		C in memory.
[MR] [+] 1 [×] 6.6 [=]	6.6299996	$\ln \frac{N}{10}$, $N = 66.299996$

The true value is **66.300000**; the error is about 1 in 16.5 million. Note that it was necessary to first subtract $\ln 10 = 2.3025851$ from $\ln N$.

FUTURE VALUE (FV) OF PRESENT AMOUNT COMPOUNDED MONTHLY

General equation:

$$\text{FV} = \text{PV}\left(1 + \frac{i}{12}\right)^{12n} \qquad \text{(I-2)}$$

where $\quad i = $ yearly interest, $n = $ years, PV = present value

Let $\qquad\qquad \ln N = \ln\left(1 + \frac{i}{12}\right)^{12n} \qquad \text{(I-3)}$

Then $\qquad\qquad \ln N \approx \dfrac{in}{1 + \dfrac{i}{24}} \qquad \text{(I-4)}$

$$C = \ln N - \ln N_o \qquad \text{(I-5)}$$

$$N = e^{\ln N} = N_o\left[1 + C\left(1 + \frac{C}{2}\right)\right] \qquad \text{(I-6)}$$

Finally $\qquad\qquad \text{FV} = \text{PV} \times N \qquad \text{(I-7)}$

The general program used to solve Equations I-7 is shown in Example I-3.

MORE ACCURATE FORMULA

For $N_o < 1.03$ or $C < 0.01$, use this equation:

$$N = N_o\left\{1 + C\left[1 + \frac{C}{2}\left(1 + \frac{C}{3}\right)\right]\right\}$$

The error is given by

$$\frac{\Delta N}{N_o} = \frac{C^4}{24}$$

where

$$C = \ln N - \ln N_o$$

Example I-3. Program for future value on Rockwell 20R−21R.

Keyboard Entry	Display	Comments
i [−] 24 [+] 1 [=]	$1 + \frac{i}{24}$	Term in Equation I-4.
[÷] [÷] [×] n [×] i [−]	ln N	See Equation I-4.
ln N_o [=] [M] [C] [M] [+]	C	Equation I-5.
[÷] 2 [+] 1 [×] [MR] [+]	$C(1 + \frac{C}{2})$	Term in Equation I-6.
1 [×] N_o [×]	N	Equation I-6.
PV [=]	FV	Equation I-7.

A specific example of a future value calculation is shown in Example I-4.

Example I-4. Find the future value of \$5,000 invested at 9% compounded monthly for 20 years. Use Equations I-4 to I-7. Let $i = 0.09$, PV = \$5.000, and $n = 20$ years. Clear memory.

Keyboard Entry	Display	Comments
0.09 [÷] 24 [+] 1 [=]	1.00375	Correction term.
[÷] [÷] [×] 20 [×] 0.09 [−]	1.7932752	ln N. Equation H-1.
1.7917595 [=] [M] [+]	0.0015157	$C = \ln N - \ln N_o$, $N_o = 6$
[÷] 2 [+] 1 [×] [MR] [+]	0.0015168	Term in Equation H-3.
1 [×] 6 [×]	6.0091008	One dollar compounded.
5.000 [=]	30045.504	FV. or \$5.000 compounded.

The answer is FV = \$30,046, to the nearest dollar. The correct value is FV = \$30,045.757. In this case the error is about 25 cents over 20 years.

COMMON ANTILOGS

Example I-5. Find 10^x where $x = \log N = 1.5078559$. (N is greater than 10.)

Let
$$\log \frac{N}{10} = \log N - 1.0 = 0.5078559$$
Then
$$\ln \frac{N}{10} = \log \frac{N}{10} \times \ln 10 = 0.5078559 \times 2.3025851$$

Keyboard Entry	Display	Comments
0.5078559 [×] 2.3025851 [−]	1.1693814	$\ln \frac{N}{10}$
1.1631508 [=] [M] [C] [M] [+]	0.0062306	$\ln \frac{N}{10} - \ln 3.2$
[−] 2 [+] 1 [×] [MR] [+]	0.0062500	$C(1 + \frac{C}{2})$
1 [×] 3.2 [=]	3.22	$\frac{N}{10}$
[×] 10 [=]	32.2	$N = 10^x$

The correct value is 32.20000, and the error this time is zero!

Note: To find $N = e^x$ when x is the logarithm of N greater than 10:

- If $x = \ln N$, subtract multiples of ln 10 (2.3025851).
- If $x = \log N$, subtract the characteristic (whole number) of the given log, multiply by 2.3025851, find natural antilog.
- Restore the power of 10 as the last operation.

ERROR ANALYSIS FOR NATRUAL ANTILOGARITHMS

General equations:

$$N = e = \ln N$$

$$= N_o\left[1 + C\left(1 + \frac{C}{2}\right)\right] \tag{I-8}$$

where

$$C = \ln N - \ln N_o$$

The percent error in N is approximately

$$\frac{\Delta}{N_o} = \frac{C^3}{6}, \text{ where } \Delta = N - N_o \tag{I-9}$$

The maximum errors for Δ/N range from 3×10^{-6} for $C = 0.025$ near $N_o = 1$, to about 2×10^{-8} for $C = 0.005$ near $N_o = 10$. A typical error for $C = 0.01$ near $N_o = 5$ is about 2×10^{-7}. These percent errors for Δ/N_o must be multiplied by N_o to get Δ.

Appendix J
Glossary

The following terms and symbols have been used in the text. Calculator keys are identified with a ☐ symbol.

accumulation function—Conditions calculator to sum entries.

algebraic notation—The conventional sequence of arithmetic operations, where the arithmetic operator follows the first number (e.g.: $a \times b = c$, or $a \div b = c$). (See also *reverse Polish notation*.)

antilogarithm $\boxed{e^x}$, $\boxed{10^x}$—The number whose natural or common log is x.

arithmetic functions—The four fundamental operations on numbers or variables: addition $\boxed{+}$, subtraction $\boxed{-}$, multiplication $\boxed{\times}$, and division $\boxed{\div}$.

automatic constants—The ability to multiply and divide a series of numbers by a selected constant without reentering the constant or recalling it from memory.

change sign $\boxed{^+/_-}$, $\boxed{\text{CHS}}$—Changing the algebraic sign of the display from plus to minus, or vice versa.

characteristic—The integer part of a logarithm. If the common log of 20 is 1.30103, then 1 is the characteristic.

clear display $\boxed{\text{CD}}$—Clears the display only, without affecting memory or other working registers. This function is sometimes denoted by $\boxed{\text{CL } x}$ (clear x) or $\boxed{\text{CE}}$ (clear entry).

clear $\boxed{\text{C}}$—Clears all registers except memory.

constant key ⎡K⎤—Selects a constant for multiplication or division by a series of numbers.

constant—Either a known number like 2.5, 0.2, or π, or a quantity symbolized by lower case letters (a,b,c, etc.) which can be considered to be known or fixed in an equation or formula.

centigrade ⎡°C⎤—A measure of temperature in the metric system (also called Celsius).

cube of x ⎡x^3⎤—The result of the operation $x \times x \times x (2^3 = 2 \times 2 \times 2 = 8)$.

cube root of x—The number which gives x when multiplied twice by itself ($2 = \sqrt[3]{8}$).

cubic equation—An equation whose highest term is a constant times x^3, i.e.:

$$E_x\, 2x^3 + 1.5x = 2.5$$

decimal select ⎡DS⎤—Selects the number of decimal places desired in the display. Two decimal places is always one option for decimal select.

display—The visual indication of the numbers entered (or of the result of a calculation or operation). The display is generally located near the top of the calculator.

derivative of f (x)—The rate of change of a function of x. The slope of the function. Written dy/dx.

e—The base for natural logarithms ($e = 2.7182818...$).

error—The difference between the correct value of a quantity and the result of an assumption or calculation.

estimate—A reasonable guess for an unknown value.

exponent—The power to which a base is raised.

exponentiation ⎡x^y⎤, ⎡y^x⎤, ⎡a^x⎤ Raising a given base to a given power. The base must be a positive real number.

extended precision—The ability to calculate answers to more significant figures than can be displayed at the same time. (See Chapter 5.)

floating decimal—The ability of a calculator to correctly position the decimal point in a displayed calculation. (See *underflow* and *overflow*).

factorial n ⌐$n!$⌐—The product of the consecutive integers up to n ($5! = 1 \times 2 \times 3 \times 4 \times 5 = 120$).

Fahrenheit ⌐°F⌐—The measure of temperature in the U.S. customary (or British) system, where water freezes at $32°$ and boils at $212°$.

formula—A compact equation which defines a variable explicitly in terms of other quantities, e.g.: $A = \pi r^2$ (area of a circle).

grads—An angular measure common in Europe. One grad equals $0.90°$.

hyperbolic sine x ⌐HYP⌐ ⌐SIN⌐ — $(e^x - e^{-x})/2$, written *sinh* x.

hyperbolic cosine ⌐HYP⌐ ⌐COS⌐ -- $(e^x + 3^{-x})/2$, written *cosh* x.

hyperbolic tangent ⌐HYP⌐ ⌐TAN⌐ — $(e^x - e^{-x})/(e^x + e^{-x})$, written *tanh* x.

interchange registers ⌐$x \leftrightarrows y$⌐, ⌐$x \leftrightarrow M$⌐—Interchange the contents of the display X register and the Y register ⌐$x \leftrightarrows y$⌐, or interchange the contents of the display and memory ⌐$x \leftrightarrow M$⌐.

kilogram ⌐KG⌐—The fundamental unit of weight in the metric system ($1\,lb = 0.4534\,kg$).

light-emitting diode—A type of display wherein the numerals are formed by semiconductors that emit light when an electric current is applied.

liquid crystal display—A type of display wherein the numerals are formed by electrically activating fluids which scatter light in a frosted-glass effect.

logarithm x $\boxed{ln}$—Natural log of x. The power to the base e corresponding to a number x.

logarithm x $\boxed{log}$—Common log of x. The power to the base 10 corresponding to a number x.

least significant digit—The extreme right digit of a given number; the digit with the least value.

memory $\boxed{M}$—A register whose contents are not changed for a series of calculations; used to store constant.

memory-plus key $\boxed{M+}$—Adds the display to the contents of memory.

memory-minus key $\boxed{M-}$—Subtracts the display from the contents of memory.

memory recall $\boxed{MR}$, $\boxed{RCL}$—Replaces the display by the contents of memory.

mantissa—The decimal part of a common or natural logarithm.

most significant digit—The extreme left digit of a number.

mean $\boxed{\bar{x}}$—The average of a series of values. It is equal to their sum divided by the number of values.

meter $\boxed{m}$, $\boxed{MET}$—The fundamental unit of length in the metric system (1 ft = 0.3048m).

overflow $\boxed{OVF}$—Condition of overloading or overflowing one or more registers in the calculator. Display shows an $\boxed{OVF}$ light or a series of 9s.

percent $\boxed{\%}$—Multiplication by an entered number of percent. The calculator automatically divides the answer by 100.

pi $\boxed{\pi}$—An important constant available in most scientific calculators (π = 3.14159265...).

programmable calculator—A calculator which can accept and automatically execute a prescribed series of calculations (program on command). Data is separately entered by the operator.

power function $\boxed{x^y}$ —(See *exponentiation.*)

radian—The fundamental unit of angular measure. It equals the number of degrees in an angle, times $\pi/180$.

rectangular conversion $\boxed{P \rightarrow R}$, $\boxed{R \rightarrow P}$ —The conversion of polar to rectangular coordinates, or vice versa.

reciprocal $\boxed{1/x}$ —Unity divided by x. The fundamental unit of angular measure. It equals the number of degrees in an angle, times $\pi/180$.

register—A device which stores numbers in the calculator.

reverse-Polish notation (RPN).—The sequence of arithmetic equations wherein the arithmetic operator follows the second number. If the first number is a, and the second number is b, then the operations are: for addition, a $\boxed{\text{ENTER} \uparrow}$ b $\boxed{+}$; for multiplication, a $\boxed{\text{ENTER} \uparrow}$ b $\boxed{\times}$. The answer appears immediately after the $\boxed{+}$ or $\boxed{\times}$ key is pressed. No $\boxed{=}$ key is needed.

roll down $\boxed{R \downarrow}$ —Move the registers down in the stack: Z goes to Y, Y goes to X, and X goes to Z.

roll up $\boxed{R \uparrow}$ —Move the registers up in a stack: X goes to Y, Y goes to Z, and Z goes to X.

scientific notation $\boxed{\text{SCI}}$ —A way of expressing any number with a fixed decimal after the first digit and a power of 10. Available in most scientific calculators.

scientific calculator—A calculator which possesses algebraic, exponential, and trigonometric functions, and a memory. Often called an *electronic slide rule*.

square $\boxed{x^2}$ —The square of the number in the display.

square root $\boxed{\sqrt{x}}$ —A number which gives x when multiplied by itself ($\sqrt{9} = 3$).

standard deviation $\boxed{\sigma}$ —The measure of dispersion about the mean of a series of numbers. (See *mean.*)

summation key $\boxed{\Sigma+}$—A key following a number entry which adds it to a summing register or memory, e.g.: 3 $\boxed{\Sigma+}$ 4 $\boxed{\Sigma+}$ 5 $\boxed{\Sigma+}$, $\boxed{\text{RCL}}$ (display = 12).

sine $\boxed{\sin}$—In a right triangle, the ratio of the side opposite angle x to the hypotenuse (sin x = opposite side/hypotenuse).

cosine $\boxed{\cos}$—In a right triangle, the ratio of the side adjacent to angle x to the hypotenuse (cos x = adjacent side/hypotenuse).

tangent $\boxed{\tan}$—In a right triangle, the ratio of the side opposite angle x to the side adjacent to x(tan x = opposite side/adjacent side).

arc cosine x $\boxed{\text{arc}}$ $\boxed{\cos}$ or $\boxed{\cos^{-1}}$ —The angle whose cosine is x.

arc sine x $\boxed{\text{arc}}$ $\boxed{\sin}$ or $\boxed{\sin^{-1}}$— The angle whose sine is x.

arc tangent x $\boxed{\text{arc}}$ $\boxed{\tan}$ or $\boxed{\tan^{-1}}$ —The angle whose tangent is x.

underflow—Result of calculating a number too small to be displayed by other than zero. Display shows 0s.

variance $\boxed{\sigma^2}$—The square of the standard deviation, σ.

wraparound decimal— The ability to display a result which exceeds the usual number of digits displayed. Requires the operator to multiply the display by 10^8.

302

Index

2 1 8 6 1